METAMORPHIC PETROLOGY

Mineralogical and Field Aspects

Mineralogical and Field Aspects

FRANCIS J. TURNER
Professor of Geology
University of California, Berkeley

McGRAW-HILL BOOK COMPANY
New York   San Francisco   St. Louis   London   Toronto   Sydney

METAMORPHIC PETROLOGY
Mineralogical and Field Aspects

Library of Congress Catalog Card Number: 67-28087

34567890 MAMM *754321*   *65500*

PREFACE

The purpose of this book is to amplify and replace a large section (Chapters 16 to 20, 24) of a previous work, "Metamorphic Petrology," 2d edition (McGraw-Hill, 1960), by this writer and his colleague, J. Verhoogen. Like the previous book it is intended as a general text for advanced students, research workers, and teachers in geology. It embodies a survey of mineralogical aspects of metamorphism, paying more attention to vitally significant field relations than was done before. For this reason emphasis has been placed upon specific regions, with which the writer, at least to some degree, is familiar. A notable exception is metamorphism in Japan. The writer has not yet had the opportunity to visit this country; but Japanese contributions to metamorphic petrology over the past few decades are too important to be omitted.

References, listed collectively at the end of each chapter, are mainly to literature of the last decade, but include also indispensable older classics. For other references the reader is referred to Turner and Verhoogen (1960) and to Fyfe, Turner, and Verhoogen (1958).

A survey of this kind demands a clear statement of the writer's opinions, preferences, criticisms, and prejudices. In no part of the book is this so necessary as in the field of experimental petrology, where opinions of individual workers differ widely and those of the most experienced workers necessarily change, sometimes with disconcerting rapidity. The reader is therefore urged to view critically and cautiously the judgments and conclusions here expressed. All are personal and tentative; many will become discredited or modified—some certainly before this book emerges from the press.

It is assumed that the reader has a reasonable background of chemistry and physics, and especially a feeling for the basic principles of thermodynamics. Calculation in this field has been kept to the simplest possible level. The use of simplifying approximations seems justified in view of the degree of current uncertainty in the basic numerical data. Many readers, of course, especially graduate students of this generation, are more capable by far than is this writer to cope with mathematical treatment of thermodynamic argument at a high level of sophistication. But today's need in petrology is for universal appreciation and application of basic principles relating to free energy, stability, equilibrium, and thermal properties of mineral phases and phase assemblages, and the behavior of water and carbon dioxide at high P and T. Those wishing to pursue the same problems at a higher level are referred to more detailed discussions by J. Verhoogen (Turner and Verhoogen, 1960, pp. 5-49) and by W. S. Fyfe and J. Verhoogen (Fyfe, Turner, and Verhoogen, 1958).

As implied by the title, certain important aspects of metamorphism are not treated in this book. The writer's views regarding the significance of metamorphic textures and fabrics on all scales, and the relation of these to deformation, have been stated elsewhere (Turner and Weiss, 1963). Classic interpretation of metamorphic texture on the microscopic scale, as set out in standard works on petrography, urgently needs revision in the light of modern ideas in solid-state physics and in metallurgy. This is not attempted here, nor is a much-needed, up-to-date discussion of the complex processes of metasomatism as related to metamorphism: a topic on which this writer is not qualified to write with critical insight.

Nearly forty years' work in the field of metamorphic petrology implies indebtedness to many people: teachers, colleagues, students, and others. This cannot be acknowledged individually. But it would be inappropriate to close this preface without expressing gratitude and admiration to three colleagues for the continued stimulus of helpful advice and critical discussion over many years: W. S. Fyfe, L. E. Weiss, and, especially, J. Verhoogen.

Francis J. Turner

To
CLARK KERR
*who, as President of the University of California,
developed and fostered an academic environment
for unfettered pursuit of scholarly activity.*

CONTENTS

1

Metamorphism and
Metamorphic Rocks

DEFINITION AND SCOPE OF METAMORPHISM

Since the days of Charles Lyell (e.g., 1860, pp. 591–593) it has been recognized that in some deeply eroded regions there is a gradual transition from sedimentary rocks to rocks whose mineralogical composition and structure has been imprinted by processes other than those of sedimentation. Such is the transition from shale or mudstone, through slate, to mica schist. Newly crystallized muscovite and chlorite appear at the expense of sedimentary clay minerals; detrital quartz and feldspar recrystallize to a coarse aggregate of quartz, albite, and epidote; and the rock becomes increasingly fissile with the development of a newly imposed planar structure, foliation. Yet even in the fully reconstituted rock, evidence of its sedimentary origin persists in the overall chemical composition, in partially obliterated relics of early structures, notably bedding (e.g., Tobisch, 1965), and even in recognizable fossils (e.g., Bucher, 1953; Boucot and Thompson, 1963). It is usually possible to map lithologically distinct

1

formations of rocks such as quartzite and marble whose sedimentary origin is beyond doubt. Transitions of like nature have also been demonstrated between igneous rocks, especially lavas, and other reconstituted rocks which still retain inherited igneous structures such as amygdales and flow banding.

The term metamorphism has been used for well over a century to cover transformations of this kind; and the products of transformation are the metamorphic rocks. With increasing geological knowledge, it has become possible on the basis of mineralogical and structural criteria alone to recognize rocks as metamorphic, without demonstrating in every case a field transition to nonmetamorphic sedimentary or igneous parent rocks. The inference has never been seriously challenged that metamorphism is the mineralogical and structural response of a rock to imposed conditions of temperature and pressure markedly different from those of its origin.

For convenience of discussion, arbitrary limits have been set to the range of rock transformations that are to be included within the scope of metamorphism. Purely surface changes such as weathering, leaching and cementation by meteoric waters, and the processes of diagenesis operating at depths around 1 km or less, are excluded. But the boundary is artificially drawn; and the student of diagenesis and the petrologist interested in the incipient stages of metamorphism may find themselves studying the same or closely related phenomena. At the opposite end of the scale, another arbitrary limit is customarily drawn between metamorphism, which involves reactions and structural adjustments in solid bodies, and magmatic processes essential to which is participation of a silicate-melt phase. Spanning the corresponding interval are the migmatites. In these are intimately associated a truly metamorphic rock component such as amphibolite and a component of granitic composition that is generally thought once to have been liquid. Just where the line between metamorphic and igneous rocks is to be drawn depends upon the prejudices of the individual geologist; for petrographic criteria of magmatic origin tend to be ambiguous in the case of coarsely crystalline rocks. A crystalline complex in southwest New Zealand was once described as a diorite batholith. Its principal component is a coarse-grained hornblende-plagioclase rock with a foliated structure that can equally well be attributed to flow in the partially liquid or in the solid state. But within the "batholith" are extensive thick beds of marble and of quartz-mica gneiss. So today the complex is generally interpreted as metamorphic, and the principal rock type is termed amphibolite rather than diorite. Again eclogite, a garnet-pyroxene rock of basaltic composition, is generally classified as metamorphic on account of its peculiar mineral composition. From its great density and the data of experimental chemistry eclogite might be expected to form at high pressures such as prevail in the outer mantle. In this environment it might equally well crystallize from basaltic magma or by metamorphism of gabbro.

With such reservations in mind, we have defined metamorphism as the mineralogical and structural adjustment of solid rocks to physical and chemical conditions which have been imposed at depths below the surface zones of weathering and cementation and which differ from the conditions under which the rock in question originated (Turner and Verhoogen, 1960, p. 450). Since all rocks contain water, and the range of metamorphic temperatures must extend to those at which melting begins (perhaps 700 to 800°C), one of the phases participating in metamorphism will be a pore fluid, usually rich in water and in the supercritical state. The quantity of this fluid at a given moment is likely to be small. Apart from that, the reacting phases involved in metamorphism are solid.

Chemical analyses of many metamorphic rocks fall within the compositional limits of common igneous or sedimentary rocks, except for components such as H_2O and CO_2 which enter into the fluid phase and so are relatively mobile and may be expelled or added during metamorphism. It is convenient therefore as a first approximation to treat metamorphic reactions as if the system were closed with respect to all the "nonvolatile" components. This approach, however, is merely for convenience in discussion. Compositional changes, at least within small domains, are the rule rather than the exception. And in some instances the composition of a rock is drastically changed during metamorphism. Such is the case where limestone is converted to garnet-pyroxene rock at granite contacts, or where peridotite is metamorphosed to talc-magnesite schist. Metamorphic transformations of this kind are termed *metasomatic*.

THE METAMORPHIC ROCKS

In a hand specimen or an outcrop, the most striking characteristic which stamps the rock as metamorphic is usually its structure—foliated (schistose or gneissose), lineated, or, in rocks adjacent to igneous contacts, spotted or hornfelsic. Many common metamorphic rocks are defined therefore in terms of structural criteria. Such are the following (Williams, Turner, and Gilbert, 1955, p. 174):

Hornfels. A nonfoliated rock composed of a mosaic of equidimensional grains without preferred orientation (granoblastic or hornfelsic texture). In spotted hornfelses there are porphyroblasts of one or more minerals such as biotite or andalusite.

Slate. A fine-grained rock with perfect planar foliation (slaty cleavage), independent of bedding, resulting from parallel orientation of tabular crystals of mica and chlorite.

Phyllite. A rock resembling slate but somewhat coarser in grain. The cleavage surfaces show a lustrous sheen due to coarsening of mica and chlorite. There may be incipient lamination as recrystallizing quartz and feldspar tend to segregate into thin layers parallel to the cleavage.

Schist. A strongly foliated and commonly lineated rock, coarser than slate and phyllite. Foliation is accentuated by mineral lamination due to segregation of thin layers alternately rich in micaceous minerals and in quartz and feldspar. This lamination, which has been widely mistaken for bedding, is a metamorphic structure due to metamorphic differentiation within what may initially have been homogeneous rock (Turner, 1941; Turner and Verhoogen, 1960, pp. 581–586).

Gneiss. A coarse discontinuously banded quartzo-feldspathic rock with ill-defined or discontinuous foliation.

Granulite (also termed *leptite* or *leptynite*). A plane-foliated non-micaceous rock which may be laminated parallel to the foliation. The term is usually reserved for rocks containing garnet or pyroxene and believed to have crystallized at high metamorphic temperatures.

Mylonite. A fine-grained, flinty-looking, strongly coherent, banded or streaky rock formed by extreme granulation of coarse-grained rocks without notable chemical reconstruction. Eyes or lenses of undestroyed parent rock persist enclosed in the granulated groundmass. A *phyllonite* is a similar rock in which recrystallizing mica or chlorite imparts a silky sheen (as in phyllite) to the foliation surfaces.

Rocks defined, as above, on a structural basis may be classified further on a chemical or mineralogical basis as follows:

1. Pelitic: derivatives of pelitic (aluminous) sediments. Abundance of micas is characteristic.

2. Quartzo-feldspathic: the principal minerals are quartz and feldspar. Here belong metamorphosed sandstones, siliceous tuffs, and granites.

3. Calcareous: derivatives of limestones and dolomites. Typically, calcite or dolomite is abundant; also characteristic are calcium and magnesium silicates such as diopside, tremolite, and grossularite.

4. Basic: derivatives of basic igneous rocks. Characteristic minerals are plagioclase, hornblende, chlorite, and epidote.

5. Magnesian: mainly derivatives of peridotites. Absence of feldspar and abundance of magnesian minerals (antigorite, talc, magnesite, brucite) are characteristic.

6. Ferruginous and manganiferous: derivatives of cherts and other iron-rich sediments. Quartz, iron oxides, manganese garnet, and iron-rich silicates such as grünerite or stilpnomelane are abundant.

Yet other metamorphic rocks are nonfoliated or weakly foliated and are composed of only one or two essential minerals after which they are named accordingly:

Quartzite, composed essentially of recrystallized quartz. Sandstone and chert are common parent rocks.

Marble, composed of calcite, or less commonly dolomite. Most marbles are metamorphosed limestones.

Amphibolite, a dark rock composed of hornblende and plagioclase. Most amphibolites are derivatives of basic igneous rocks; some have formed by metasomatism of calcareous sediments.

Serpentinites and Soapstones. Magnesian rocks composed, respectively, of serpentine and talc, with carbonates, chlorite, and tremolite as possible minor constituents. The parent rocks are peridotites or, more rarely, dolomitic limestones.

CONTACT METAMORPHISM

General Character

Rocks generally show strong local effects of metamorphism in the vicinity of contacts with intrusive igneous bodies. This is contact metamorphism as distinguished from regional metamorphism which occurs over much broader areas not obviously related to bodies of igneous rock. Its characteristic products are hornfelses; but foliated rocks such as spotted slates and schists are widely developed in some instances. The zone of contact metamorphism is termed a *contact aureole*. The effects of contact metamorphism are most obvious where sedimentary rocks, especially shales and limestones, are in contact with large bodies of rock of the granite-granodiorite-tonalite family. It has generally been assumed that the sequence of mineralogical changes observed in a radial traverse across an aureole to the contact represents the response of the parent rock to a thermal gradient imposed by intrusion of hot magma into relatively cold rocks and subsequent outward conductance of heat from the magmatic source. That such a gradient has played an essential part in contact metamorphism is indeed likely. But the simple picture of a "thermal" aureole does not express in full what is perhaps a complex sequence of events both in space and in time.

Many of the classic accounts of contact metamorphism (e.g., Harker and Marr, 1891; Harker, 1904, pp. 144–151; Goldschmidt, 1911; Tilley, 1924*a*) are detailed statements of the mineral assemblages developed in limited exposures or sections of an aureole. Maps showing the complete zonal distinction of such assemblages in any aureole are somewhat rare. This is partly because of variation in lithology of the parent rocks and partly due to imperfect exposures. But the difficulty in mapping an aureole also stems partly from the capricious nature of the metamorphism itself.

Within even one formation the width of an aureole may vary notably; and it is usually uncertain to what extent this represents variation in the attitude of the hidden and perhaps subjacent igneous contact, rather than local fluctuation in the thermal gradient. Finally it must be remembered that many of the most detailed studies of the mineralogy of contact metamorphism are based on material collected, not from complete aureoles, but from isolated masses of metamorphic rocks completely enclosed within igneous plutons.

Since generalization is likely to oversimplify the complex picture of contact metamorphism, we shall refer first to particular well-documented examples.

Illustrative Examples

The Comrie aureole, Scotland. North of Comrie (Perthshire) in the southern Highlands of Scotland, a diorite stock measuring 8 × 1 km in the outcrop cuts a series of slates and fissile grits containing muscovite, chlorite, quartz, albite, and epidote. These rocks represent the earliest stage of regional metamorphism. Around the contact is a contact aureole, averaging 500 to 600 m in width, the mineralogy of which has been discussed in great detail by Tilley (1924*a*). The boundaries of the aureole are not shown on Tilley's map. But three stages of progressive metamorphism can be recognized as the contact is approached in each of several well-exposed sections.

1. The first stage is shown only in the slates. At about 450 m from the contact, spots about 1 mm in diameter appear, in which newly crystallized mica and chlorite are concentrated.

2. The second stage is marked by crystallization of biotite. In the slates this occurs at 270 m from the contact in one section, and at about 420 m in another. The first appearance of biotite in the grits on the other hand is 500 or 600 m from the contact.

3. Within 150 m of the contact the slates have been completely reconstituted to cordierite-bearing hornfelses. Typical assemblages, each of which contains quartz, plagioclase, and orthoclase, are andalusite-cordierite-biotite and cordierite-hypersthene-biotite. Silica-free aluminous hornfelses with corundum or spinel also occur. In the grits the zone of cordierite hornfelses extends to about 260 m from the contact.

The aureole of the Onawa pluton, Maine. The Onawa pluton of Maine described by Philbrick (1936), is an oval body of granodiorite, 70 km² in area, cutting folded Paleozoic slates. Completely surrounding it is a contact aureole averaging over 1000 m in width (Fig. 1-1) and divisible into concentric zones which also vary in width:

7

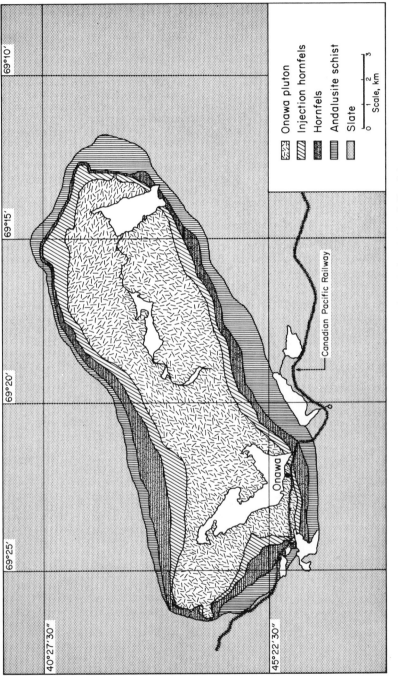

Fig. 1-1. Aureole of Onawa pluton, Maine. (*After S. S. Philbrick.*)

1. An outer transition zone of spotted slates usually 30 to 60 m wide, but locally extending for 1000 m.

2. A zone of andalusite schist in which the typical mineral assemblage is quartz-chlorite-andalusite-biotite-muscovite.

3. A zone of andalusite-biotite hornfelses, all containing quartz and orthoclase, and some with muscovite.

4. An inner zone of injection hornfelses. The rocks are similar to those of zone 3 but locally contain tourmaline, cordierite, or sillimanite. They are intimately veined with small stringers of aplite, in which the most widespread mineral assemblage is quartz-perthite-biotite-muscovite (in some cases with andalusite, sodic plagioclase, or tourmaline).

The Marysville aureole, Montana. One of the earliest documented accounts of a contact aureole is to be found in Barrell's (1907) description and map of the Marysville granodiorite stock in Montana (see also Knopf, 1950). The outcrop of the stock covers 8 km^2. It is late Cretaceous or Paleocene in age and has developed a continuous aureole, 1 to 3 km wide, in the surrounding Precambrian (Beltian) dolomites and shales (Fig. 1–2). In certain places the granodiorite contact dips gently; but locally, as revealed by mining operations, the contact maintains a nearly vertical attitude for several hundred meters. The original cover is estimated to have been thin—perhaps 1 to 2 km.

Within the aureole, shales have been converted to cordierite-biotite-muscovite-hornfels, and dolomitic limestones to marble containing tremolite and diopside. Along the southeast margin of the stock, the limestones have been converted to calc-silicate hornfelses with little or no calcite. Common types consist almost entirely of tremolite or of diopside; other assemblages are diopside-scapolite and diopside-vesuvianite. Clearly, large-scale introduction of SiO_2 and perhaps Al_2O_3, MgO, and FeO, and complete expulsion of CO_2, were involved in this phase of contact metamorphism, which according to Barrell extends only 200 to 300 m from the contact. Beyond this limit, the diopside and tremolite marbles seem to have formed by reaction between carbonates and siliceous impurities present in the parent dolomites.

Contact aureoles of the granitic complex of Donegal, northwest Ireland. The Donegal "granite" complex has been mapped and studied in great detail by Pitcher and Read and their associates. Several of their publications (e.g., Iyengar, Pitcher, and Read, 1954; Akaad, 1956; Pitcher and Sinha, 1958; Pitcher and Read, 1960) discuss the development of contact aureoles in the surrounding rocks. The complex consists of four plutons of Caledonian age successively intruded into Dalradian schists and marbles (Fig. 1-3).

The youngest and most extensive pluton, the Main Donegal Granite,

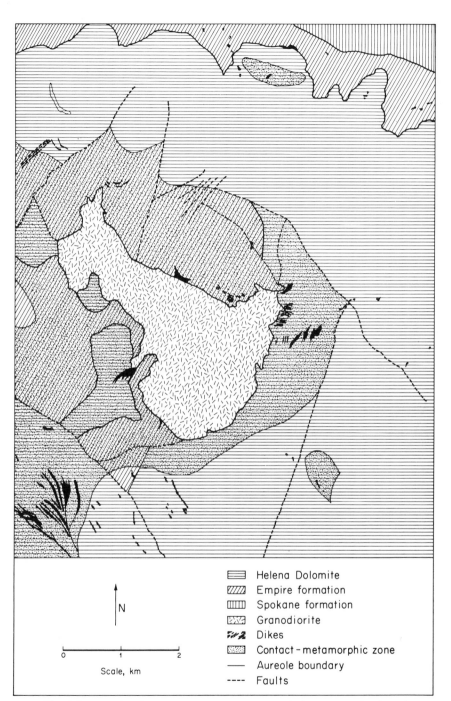

Fig. 1-2. Aureole of Marysville stock, Montana. (*After A. Knopf: adapted from J. Barrell.*)

Legend:
- Helena Dolomite
- Empire formation
- Spokane formation
- Granodiorite
- Dikes
- Contact-metamorphic zone
- Aureole boundary
- Faults

N

Scale, km
0   1   2

9

is an elongate body of biotite granodiorite 350 km^2 in area. The rock itself is strongly foliated and encloses numerous tabular rafts and inclusions of country rock aligned in the direction of flow. The schist envelope shows marked effects of deformation synchronous with intrusion of the grano-diorite. The surrounding aureole (Fig. 1-4) is 1.5 to 2.5 km wide. Since the attitudes of the foliation in both the granodiorite and the country

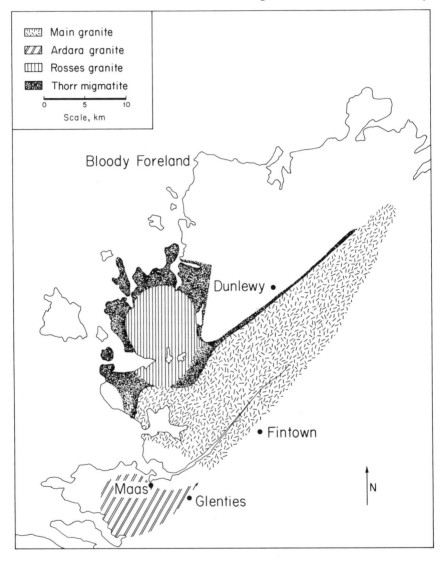

Fig. 1-3. The four plutons of the "Donegal granite," northwestern Ireland. (*After W. S. Pitcher and H. H. Read.*)

rocks are consistently steep, it may be assumed that the contact, too, is steep, so that the outcrop represents a true cross section of the aureole. The mineralogical effects of contact metamorphism are most obvious in the pelitic and calcareous members of the envelope. Beyond the aureole the former are phyllites consisting mainly of quartz, muscovite, and chlorite. In the outer part of the aureole large crystals of muscovite, chlorite and ultimately biotite appear, and in two localities andalusite becomes plentiful. Within about 1 km of the contact, the reconstituted schists contain various combinations of staurolite, garnet, kyanite and sillimanite. It is common for andalusite to be associated with either kyanite or sillimanite, without any indication that one polymorph is replacing the other. Outside the aureole, calcareous members are calc-schists consisting of calcite, quartz, and phlogopite. Within the aureole these pass into tremolite marbles, which in turn are succeeded near the contact by sphene-bearing mica-tremolite-quartz schists, a few of which contain diopside. Rafts of metamorphosed sediments within the granite are of three main types: (1) biotite-muscovite quartzites; (2) pelitic schists

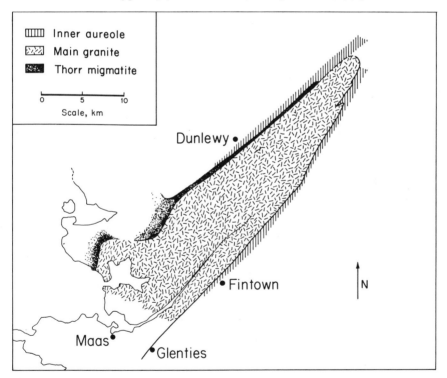

Fig. 1-4. Aureole of main Donegal granite. (*After W. S. Pitcher and H. H. Read.*)

consisting of muscovite, biotite, sillimanite, newly generated feldspar, and quartz; (3) skarns derived from limestone and consisting of some combination of tremolite, clinozoisite, garnet, wollastonite, vesuvianite, talc, and sphene.

The Ardara pluton is the second member of the intrusive sequence. It has a circular outcrop 8 km in diameter and consists of a central body of granodiorite rimmed continuously with a border of hornblende-biotite-granodiorite less than 1 km in width. Contacts with the enveloping schists are sharp and nearly vertical. Along the northern border of the pluton the invaded pelitic schists show effects of contact metamorphism as far as $1\frac{1}{2}$ km from the contact. Beyond the aureole they are highly deformed rocks consisting of quartz, muscovite, and chlorite. The latter is commonly pseudomorphous after biotite and garnet. The aureole itself is concentrically zoned with respect to the arcuate contact (Fig. 1-5):

1. The outer aureole in which biotite has crystallized at the expense of chlorite.

2. The inner aureole, 300 to 550 m wide, in which pelitic rocks have completely recrystallized to hornfelses with aluminum silicates.

   (a) The andalusite zone. Hornfelses are composed mainly of andalusite, biotite, quartz, and plagioclase; some contain garnet or staurolite.

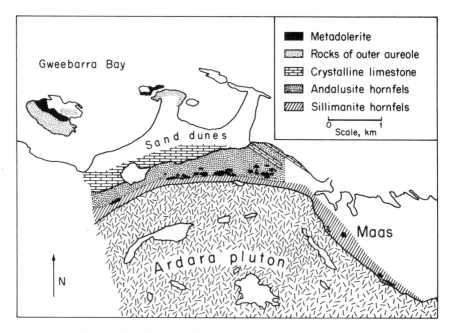

Fig. 1-5. Aureole of Ardara pluton, Donegal. (*After M. K. Akaad.*)

(b) The sillimanite zone, about 140 m in width. The typical assemblage is sillimanite-biotite-quartz-plagioclase-garnet. Staurolite is sporadic. In the outer part of the sillimanite zone, pseudomorphs of sillimanite after andalusite show that andalusite here preceded sillimanite in time. Close to the igneous contact, sillimanite hornfelses contain cordierite.

Throughout the inner aureole late muscovite has developed locally at the expense of aluminum silicates, especially in zones of shearing possibly synchronous with uprise of the central granodiorite magma in the last stages of intrusion. In a very detailed chemical study of pelitic hornfelses and schists within and outside the Ardara aureole, Pitcher and Sinha (1958) showed that the only chemical changes involved in contact metamorphism were general expulsion of water and possibly slight enrichment in alkalis close to the contact. Surprisingly, it would seem that late conversion of aluminum silicates to muscovite involved no influx of magmatically derived potash but was accomplished by chemical reaction in a system closed to all chemical components other than water.

Calc-silicate aureole of the Darwin mine area, California. The Darwin mine area (Hall and MacKevett, 1962) lies in the mountainous desert region west of Death Valley in southeastern California. Except where Pleistocene and recent fans cover the lower slopes and the basin floors, exposures of bedrock are excellent and are supplemented by numerous mine workings extending 300 m below the surface. Mississippian to Permian sedimentary rocks, mostly calcareous, are invaded by irregularly outcropping bodies of quartz monzonite. West of Darwin the main pluton is 10 to 15 km wide. In the mine area itself (longitudinal portion of Fig. 1-6) an outlying mass of quartz monzonite outcrops over an area about 6 km long. Here the Paleozoic sediments show striking effects of contact metamorphism over an area 7 × 2 km around the quartz monzonite outcrop.

The purer limestone beds have been bleached and recrystallized to white marbles. More widely distributed in the Darwin area are impure shaly limestones which have been converted to calc-silicate hornfelses in which the gross bedding is still preserved. Various combinations of diopside, wollastonite, vesuvianite, garnet, calcite, feldspars, quartz, tremolite, and epidote constitute the common mineral assemblages. Forsterite, scapolite, and sphene appear more locally. These rocks (Hall and MacKevett, 1962, p. 47) are believed to have formed by simple recrystallization of impure limestones without significant compositional change other than loss of CO_2. Even a simple change from a carbonate-bearing to a silicate assemblage, such as development of diopside by reaction between dolomite and quartz, must be accompanied by large change of volume—in this case about 35 percent reduction—or by a corresponding increase in porosity.

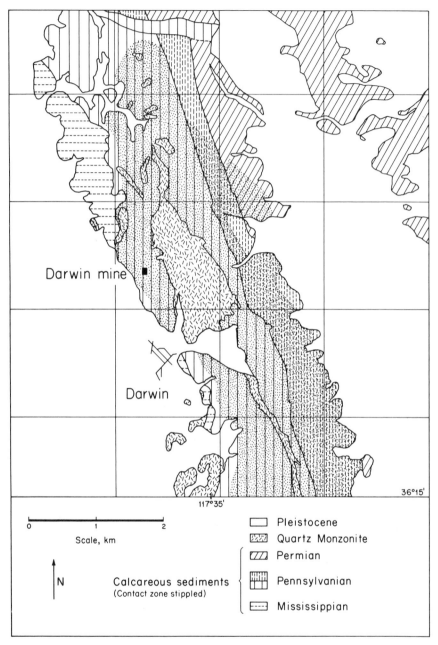

Darwin mine ■

Darwin

36°15'

117°35'

0   1   2
Scale, km

N

☐   Pleistocene
▨   Quartz Monzonite
▨   Permian
▦   Pennsylvanian
⊟   Mississippian

Calcareous sediments
(Contact zone stippled)

Fig. 1-6. Contact metamorphism, Darwin mine region, southeastern California. (*After W. E. Hall and E. M. MacKevett.*)

$$CaMg(CO_3)_2 + 2SiO_2 \rightarrow CaMgSi_2O_6 + 2CO_2$$

Dolomite	Quartz	Diopside
183 g; 63 cm^3	120 g; 41 cm^3	215 g; 67 cm^3

It is possible therefore that even the calc-silicate hornfelses have been affected by introduction of material from a magmatic source. Alternatively, metamorphism must have been accompanied by substantial decrease in volume.

In the vicinity of the igneous contacts, later addition of various oxides, presumably from magmatic fluids, has caused the development of skarns (tactites) at the expense of both calc-silicate hornfels and marble. The former has been converted to assemblages dominated by andradite garnet, vesuvianite, and wollastonite. Most skarns derived from marble are rich in andradite and contain epidote.

The latest mineral changes connected with intrusion of the quartz monzonite are exemplified by ore-bearing pipes and veins in calc-silicate hornfels and skarns in the vicinity of the igneous contacts. To this category belong mineral assemblages dominated by sulfides (mainly galena and sphalerite) or scheelite.

Limited metamorphism adjacent to diabase sill contacts in Tasmania. Thick sills of Jurassic diabase outcrop over much of the island of Tasmania (e.g., Edwards, 1942). At Mt. Wellington, near Hobart, the lower 300 m of what was once an even thicker and very extensive sheet of diabase and the immediately underlying horizontal Triassic sandstones are continuously exposed. Even within a few meters of the contact the sandstones show only minor effects of metamorphism. Elsewhere, where the rocks at the base of the intrusion include shales and limestone, contact metamorphism, exemplified by development of calc-silicates in limestone, although more obvious, is still restricted to within 20 to 30 m from the contacts. Yet the magma at the time of intrusion must have been completely liquid, and therefore at a temperature around 1000°C, for the marginal diabases have a uniformly fine-grained texture.

Contact aureoles of the Bushveld complex, South Africa. The Bushveld complex of South Africa is an immense sheetlike intrusion of stratified basic and ultramafic igneous rocks outcropping over an area of 400 × 150 km. It "has the shape of an elongated basin which has been tilted downward to the east, so that the bottom of the basin is exposed at the west end of the intrusion . . ." (Wilson, 1956, p. 290). The maximum thickness of the sheet is at least 8 km and possibly is considerably more. The underlying rocks are late Precambrian shales, slates, and some quartzites. Within them, a spectacular aureole of great but variable width has developed beneath the floor of the intrusion (Hall, 1914, 1932, pp. 386–

421). Hall records aureole width, measured normal to the bedding, of between 100 and 3,000 m from the observed trace of the contact; but if the intrusion is funnel-shaped in section, with contacts dipping more steeply than the bedding (cf. Wilson, 1956) the true width of the aureole must be less than these figures indicate.

Hall recognizes two zones of progressive metamorphism:

1. In the outer (chiastolite) zone the shales and slates preserve their initial structure, but metamorphic andalusite (chiastolite) is abundant. Rarer metamorphic minerals are chloritoid and cordierite. Local beds of dolomitic limestone contain tremolite or wollastonite.

2. In the inner (hornfels) zone the rocks are mainly pelitic hornfelses containing biotite, cordierite, quartz, andalusite, garnet, and feldspar. Some rocks contain chloritoid.

In some parts of the aureole deformation synchronous with metamorphism has rendered the metamorphic rocks schistose. Here staurolite appears plentifully in the outer zone, and sillimanite accompanies biotite, cordierite, and muscovite in the inner zone.

General Characteristics of Contact Aureoles

Certain generalizations regarding contact aureoles may be drawn from observations made in the field (cf. also Harker, 1932, pp. 20–26).

1. Only maximum limits can be set on the width of most aureoles, measured normal to the surfaces of contact. This is because the contact usually dips gently at the outcrop, and its configuration in depth is rarely known. There are recorded instances, nevertheless, where the aureole must extend at least 1 km, and possibly more, from the nearest plutonic contact.

2. Partly because most large plutons are composed of "granitic" rocks (quartz diorite, granodiorite, quartz monzonite), we tend to associate contact aureoles mentally with "granites." Many of the aureoles of classic geologic literature do indeed exemplify this association. However, the larger sheetlike intrusions of basic rocks (such as the Bushveld complex) are also bordered by extensive contact aureoles, especially in the floor regions. By contrast, metamorphic effects in the floors of porous sediment that underlay many of the massive sheets and sills of diabase tend to be insignificant or else limited to a few meters from the contacts. At contacts with large ultramafic bodies of the alpine type, such as the Dun Mountain intrusion of New Zealand, metamorphism may be restricted to local metasomatism such as albitization or prehnitization. Other ultramafic plutons, such as that of the Lizard in Cornwall, have contact aureoles that are generally interpreted as due to recrystallization at high temperatures (Green, 1964, pp. 181–182).

3. Aureoles in argillaceous rocks may be zoned concentrically with respect to plutonic contacts. A common inward sequence from spotted slates and schists to hornfelses is characterized mineralogically by muscovite and chlorite in the outermost zone, biotite with or without andalusite in the next zone, and biotite, cordierite, and sillimanite close to the contact. The aluminous minerals may on occasion include chloritoid (especially in the outer zones), staurolite, almandine garnet, or even kyanite; but these minerals are much more widely distributed in pelitic rocks that have been affected by regional metamorphism.

4. Aureoles in calcareous rocks tend to show greater mineralogical variation and less regularity. Zoning is usually obscure except on a small or local scale. The nature of the mineral assemblage and the distance from the contact to which it develops, seem to be a function of the chemical composition and the permeability of individual calcareous beds or formations. Near the contact the appearance of special mineral phases may be correlated with introduction, presumably from the intrusive magma, of elements that enter readily into volatile compounds. Such are iron (andradite, hematite), fluorine (humite minerals, fluorite, vesuvianite), boron (axinite, tourmaline), chlorine (scapolite), and others.

5. Some mineral assemblages, usually locally developed, express local sequences of events in time. To this category belong skarns (tactites) and sulfide ores, both common in calcareous rocks near igneous contacts. Late replacement of andalusite and cordierite by micaceous minerals is recorded by pseudomorphs and "sericitized" shear zones in pelitic hornfelses. Pseudomorphs and more ambiguous replacement textures may indicate the encroachment of one zone at the expense of another with passage of time. Such is the case in the Ardara aureole of Donegal, in which pseudomorphs of sillimanite after andalusite occur abundantly where the inner sillimanite zone is encroaching upon the outer zone of andalusite.

Physical Interpretation of Contact Aureoles

For over a century contact metamorphism has been attributed to reactions induced by thermal gradients set up by intrusion of bodies of hot magma into relatively cold rocks. Lyell (1860, p. 593) wrote:

> The precise nature of these altering causes, which may provisionally be termed plutonic, is in a great degree obscure and doubtful; but their reality is no less clear, and we must suppose the influence of heat to be in some way connected with the transmutation, if . . . we concede the igneous origin of granite.

Since we accept the thermal influence as an essential factor in contact metamorphism, we can make further inferences as to the limiting physical conditions in contact aureoles.

Several possible patterns of temperature distribution, in space and in time, in aureoles surrounding plutonic intrusions can be set up and evaluated in the light of simple models proposed by Lovering (1936, 1955) and elaborated by Jaeger (1957, 1959). The temperature at any distance from the contact at any given time depends upon a number of quantities the limits of which are reasonably well known: size and temperature of the magma body; thermal conductivity, density, specific heat, and diffusivity of country rock and solidified magma; initial temperature and water content of country rock; crystallization temperature and latent heat of crystallization of magma; ΔH of metamorphic reactions set up in the aureole.

Other things being equal, the distance from the contact at which a given maximum temperature is reached depends on the thickness of the intrusive body, measured normal to the contact. Large intrusions of hot (e.g., basaltic) magma should have wider aureoles than smaller intrusions of cooler (e.g., granitic) magma. Yet this, of course, is contrary to geologic experience. A most important factor is the role of pore water in a water-saturated country rock. Heat conducted outward from the contact is used in vaporizing pore water or in initiating endothermic metamorphic reactions of dehydration or decarbonation. The result is to chill the contact, the temperature of which never rises to within a few hundred degrees of magmatic temperature, and to limit the width of the high-temperature inner zone of the aureole. Some simple ideal examples, drawn from Jaeger's data, are shown graphically in Figs. 1-7 to 1-9. From these it is obvious that the dimensions of a pluton are the most important influence determining the distance from the contact at which metamorphic temperatures (perhaps 400 to 600°C) can develop. It would seem that temperatures of 400°C or more could be maintained for tens of thousands of years at distances of 500 m from contacts of granitic plutons 1 or 2 km wide, intrusive into dry sediments whose initial temperature was 100°C. At the contact the temperature would remain around 500°C for a similar period of time. Even at the base of a large diabase sill such as that of Tasmania, contact temperatures above and near 600°C might be expected in quartz sandstone, and temperatures could be maintained for several thousand years at 400 to 450°C, at 200 to 300 m below the floor. This last inference conflicts sharply with the relatively insignificant contact effects below even thick diabase sills.

To explain anomalies such as this, we turn to the possible effects of magmatic and pore water. These have been partially examined by Jaeger (1958). The ideal gradients of Fig. 1-9 take into account the water-saturated condition of the invaded sediments, but are based on the simplifying assumptions that all the materials concerned have the same thermal properties and that there is no movement of the vaporized pore water. In such a model, Jaeger finds that vaporization of pore water near the contacts may lower contact temperatures by 100°C. Comparison of Figs. 1-8

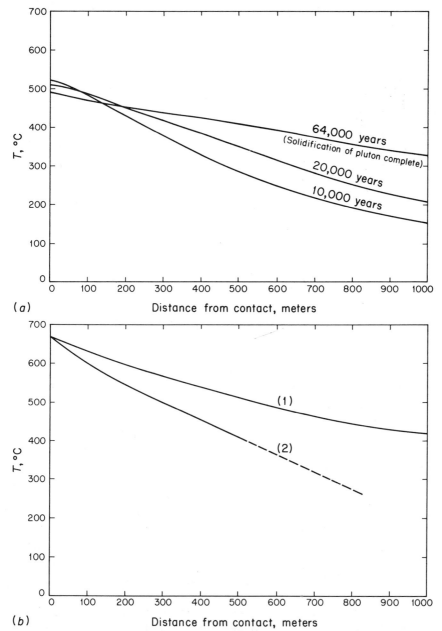

Fig. 1-7. Ideal temperature gradients adjacent to deep "granite" contacts neglecting effects of water. (*a*) Tabular vertical sheet 2000 m thick intruded at 800°C; crystallization range 800 to 600°C; initial temperature of country rock, 100°C. (*From data of J. Jaeger*, 1957, *fig.* 1). (*b*) Maximum temperatures attained in contact zones of tabular vertical sheets (1) 2000, (2) 1000 m thick, intruding shale at 100°C. Temperature of intrusion equals a fixed melting point, 800°C. (*From data of J. Jaeger*, 1959).

19

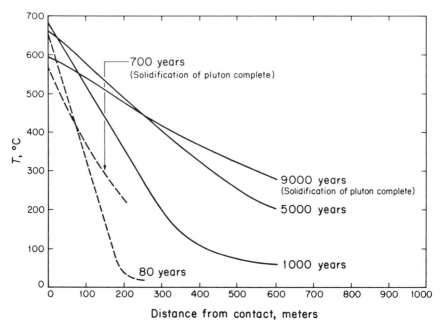

Fig. 1-8. Ideal temperature gradients in floor below diabase sills, neglecting effects of water. (*Constructed from data of J. Jaeger*, 1957, *fig.* 4, *p.* 314.) Intrusion temperature 1050°C; crystallization range in magma, 1050 to 850°C. Full lines refer to sill 700 m thick intruded under 350-m cover; initial temperature of invaded rock, 50°C. Broken lines refer to sill 200 m thick intruded under 100-m cover; initial temperature of intruded rock, 25°C. Times are given in years from data of intrusion.

and 1-9 shows the marked effect of pore water in narrowing the zone at which a given temperature is reached at any time during the cooling history. The geological effect would be to narrow the contact aureole. This general effect of temperature lowering tends to be offset by the higher conductivity and specific heat of water-saturated as compared with dry sediment. But if water escapes readily, and moves through the contact zone toward the surface, the net lowering of contact temperatures where diabase magma at 1100°C is intruded into water-saturated permeable sandstones might still be 100 to 120°C. Intrusive basaltic magma is generally undersaturated in water. Perhaps, then, streaming of water through permeable sediments of the contact zone, and thence into the body of magma itself, could bring about further substantial lowering of temperatures at or near the contact in the earlier stages of intrusion of thick diabase sills into water-saturated sandstones. No quantitative data are available regarding this effect. Granitic magmas, on the other hand, tend to be saturated in water; and it is generally conceded that water is expelled outward through the aureole rocks during the later cooling

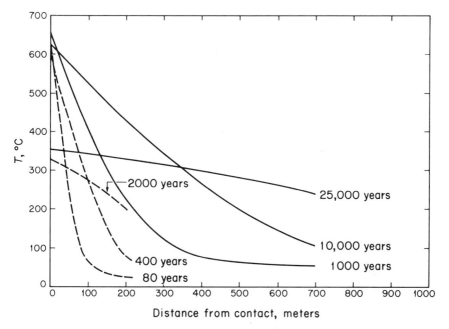

Fig. 1-9. Ideal temperature gradients adjacent to diabase sills intruded into water-saturated sediments (porosity 0.2), at rather shallow depths. (*Constructed from data of J. Jaeger,* 1959, *p.* 51, *fig.* 2.) Intrusion temperature (= melting temperature) of diabase magma, 1050°C. Full lines refer to sill 700 m thick; initial temperature of sediments, 50°C. Broken lines refer to sill 200 m thick; initial temperature of sediments, 25°C. Times are given in years from date of intrusion.

history of most granitic plutons. A quantitative analysis of this effect by Hori (1964) shows that the quantity of heat transferred outward by magmatic waters is significant and that the ultimate width of the resultant aureole may be greatly increased thereby.

In summary, the respective cooling models of Lovering, Jaeger, and Hori suggest the following inferences: Temperatures at contacts with granitic plutons are normally 500 to 550°C; temperatures of 650 to 700°C may be expected at contacts with basic plutons under deep cover. Xenoliths derived from the invaded rocks and completely immersed in magma may attain considerably higher temperatures approximating that of the magma at the time of intrusion. The distance from the contact at which a given temperature is reached, and the interval of time over which the temperature is maintained, are influenced especially by the size of the pluton and outward flow of hot magmatic water. Wide aureoles in which the temperature is held between 400 and 500°C are to be expected near large bodies of granite. Temperatures should be higher at the contact, but aureoles should be narrower in the case of diabase sills, even where these are one or two thousand feet in thickness. But the insignificant effects of metamorphism in the floors of many diabase sills present an anomaly that is not completely explained by Jaeger's model. To explain it we tentatively appeal to the inward flow of pore water from the invaded sediments into the intrusive magma. Another anomaly is the great width of the high-temperature zone indicated by Jaeger's model for intrusive sheets a mile or more in width (cf. Fig. 1-7). It may well be that the narrowness of many aureoles is due to absorption of heat by endothermic reactions of dehydration and decarbonation near the contacts.

The nature of a metamorphic mineral assemblage at a given site in an aureole depends upon the chemical composition of the rock and the physical conditions at the time of crystallization. A glance at Figs. 1-7 and 1-8 is sufficient to show that at any such site temperature is likely to be maintained near its maximum value for thousands of years. It has generally been assumed that this is the "temperature of metamorphism"; but it is also clear that for thousands of years, too, the temperature must slowly drop after the maximum is reached. Metamorphic pressures will be determined by depth. We are inclined to attribute minerals such as almandine, staurolite, and kyanite of some aureoles to unusually high pressures, i.e., great depths, of contact metamorphism. Other physical variables are the partial pressures of principal components of the pore fluids: water, P_{H_2O}, and carbon dioxide P_{CO_2}. It is to large fluctuations of these in the course of contact metamorphism of carbonate rocks that we attribute the characteristic variation, both locally and in time, of mineral assemblages containing silicates of calcium and magnesium.

Intrusion of a hot body of magma into initially cold rocks favors development of a strong temperature gradient. Here the effects of contact metamorphism are likely to be most conspicuous and the role of intrusion in metamorphism most obvious. On the other hand, where bodies of granitic magma develop within, or are intruded into, deep-seated rocks where regional temperatures are several hundred degrees, contact and regional effects may be indistinguishable. It is for this reason that many of the classic accounts of contact metamorphism refer to aureoles that have formed at relatively shallow depths, with correspondingly low pressures, perhaps a few hundred to 2000 bars.

REGIONAL METAMORPHISM

General Character

In the Precambrian shields and in the eroded roots of fold mountains, metamorphic rocks may extend for hundreds or even thousands of square kilometers. Granitic plutons are common in such regions. But they are not invariably present; and even where granitic bodies are extensively developed there is no obvious connection in place and time between intrusion and metamorphism such as we see in a contact aureole. To this kind of metamorphism has been applied the nongenetic term *regional*. Its typical products are foliated rocks such as schists, granulites, and amphibolites.

Foliation is the result of deformation broadly synchronous with metamorphism. Indeed many schists show early foliation folded, disrupted and crossed by later foliations; from this it is inferred that regional metamorphism may be a long-drawn-out process involving repeated episodes of deformation, and indeed of mineral crystallization. While deformation is highly characteristic of regional metamorphism, it is not essential. There are some regions, such as the northern coast of Aberdeenshire in Scotland, where, apart from premetamorphic folding, regionally metamorphic rocks are not conspicuously deformed. Mineralogically and structurally, the rocks of such areas in many respects resemble those of contact aureoles. But their occurrence is on a regional scale not obviously connected with plutonic intrusion. Andesites, deeply buried in the Mesozoic geosyncline of Western Chile, have been almost completely converted to metamorphic mineral assemblages without a trace of internal deformation (B. Levi and J. Corvalán, personal demonstration in the field).

There is great variety in the mineral assemblages of regionally metamorphosed rocks, even among rocks of the same general chemical composition. Thus the metamorphic derivatives of basalt in various situations include chlorite-albite-epidote schist, amphibolite (hornblende-plagioclase), glaucophane-lawsonite-chlorite schist, and pyroxene granulite. Some of the common minerals of the schists are also widely distributed in hornfelses of contact aureoles. These include the micas, pyroxenes, hornblende, epidote, and feldspars. Other minerals that are common in schists are rare or absent in contact hornfelses of corresponding composition. Among these are glaucophane, stilpnomelane, lawsonite, kyanite, almandine, and staurolite. Others again are common in contact aureoles, but rarely found in schists formed by regional metamorphism. Among these are wollastonite, forsterite, vesuvianite, andalusite.

The field character and paragenesis of regionally metamorphosed rocks are subject to wide variation from one province to another, or even within a single province. Yet there are regular patterns in this variation, and these we will now examine by referring to specific well-documented examples.

Dalradian Schists of the Southeastern Highlands of Scotland

The southern geologic limit of the Scottish Highlands is a fault trending NE-SW and known as the *Highland Boundary Fault*. North of it lies a belt of strongly deformed regionally metamorphosed rocks, 50 to

80 km wide, known as the *Dalradian series* (Fig. 1-10). This belt, which also trends NE-SW, is margined along its northwestern border by another series of regionally metamorphosed rocks: the Precambrian metasediments of the *Moinian series*. The Dalradian metamorphics are derivatives of geosynclinal sediments with some interrelated basic volcanic rocks and diabase sills. Their age is still debated. In part at least they appear to be Precambrian; but they possibly include some early Cambrian sediments. The Dalradian series locally is overlain unconformably by nonmetamorphic upper Devonian sandstones. Granitic rocks in the Dalradian terrane are of two kinds. Migmatitic and gneissic granites developed especially in regions of most intense metamorphism are struc-

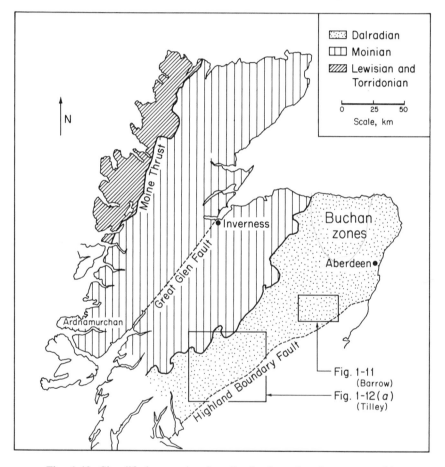

Fig. 1-10. Simplified map showing distribution of main metamorphic Precambrian units, Highlands of Scotland. (*Simplified, after M. R. W. Johnson.*)

turally concordant with the metamorphic rocks. They are known as *Older Granites* and are generally believed to be synchronous with the culmination of metamorphism. They are distinguished from cross-cutting *Newer Granite* plutons that postdate Dalradian metamorphism.

South of Aberdeen, Barrow (1893; 1912) mapped in the Dalradian a sequence of zones of progressive metamorphism (Fig. 1-11) based on mineralogical and textural changes observed in pelitic rocks in passing from slates to coarse-grained sillimanite-garnet-mica schists of approximately the same chemical composition. Each zone is named after an index mineral. The outer limit of any zone is mapped where the corresponding index mineral first appears in the direction of increasing metamorphism. Barrow's (1912) zonal sequences, in order of increasing metamorphism, is as follows:

1. Zone of digested clastic mica, now termed (following Tilley, 1925, p. 102) the *chlorite zone*. The typical pelitic assemblage is quartz-chlorite-muscovite-albite.

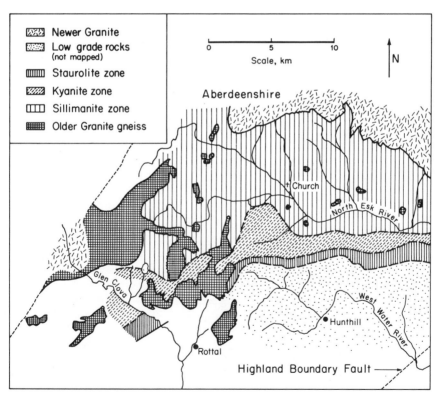

Fig. 1-11. Zones of progressive regional metamorphism, Dalradian of southeast Highlands, Scotland. (*Mapped by G. Barrow, 1893.*)

2. *Zone of biotite*, marked by the appearance of red-brown biotite at the expense of muscovite-chlorite.

3. *Zone of garnet*. The critical assemblage is quartz-muscovite-biotite-almandine (-albite or oligoclase).

4. *Zone of staurolite*: quartz-biotite-muscovite-almandine-staurolite (-oligoclase).

5. *Zone of kyanite*: quartz-biotite-muscovite-oligoclase-almandine-kyanite.

6. *Zone of sillimanite*: quartz-biotite-muscovite-oligoclase-almandine-sillimanite.

Barrow's zones were later extended southwest (Tilley, 1925; Elles and Tilley, 1930) across the full width of the southern Highlands (Fig. 1-12). Zonal boundaries were termed *isograds*, the implication being that each represents a particular grade or degree of metamorphism. Still later, progressive mineralogical changes in basic sills (Wiseman, 1934) and in calcareous sediments (Kennedy, 1949)[1] were correlated with the sequence of metamorphic zones established for pelitic schists. These are summarized in Table 1-1 (alternative addition minerals are listed in parenthesis).

The structure of the Dalradian rocks in the southeastern Highlands is very complex and is the result of several episodes of folding spanning many million years (Sutton, 1960; Johnson, 1963; Fitch, Miller, and Brown 1964). The first recognizable episode was large-scale recumbent folding and development of nappes. The principal foliations and mesoscopic folds

[1]The correlation with calcareous assemblages was established in the Moinian series north and east of Ardnamurchan (Fig. 1–10).

Table 1-1. Correlation of mineral assemblages in zones of progressive metamorphism in Scotland.

Zonal index (pelitic)	Basic rocks	Calcareous rocks
Chlorite	Chlorite-albite-epidote-sphene, (calcite, actinolite)	Quartz-muscovite-biotite-calcite
Biotite		
Almandine		Garnet-zoisite-sodic plagioclase (biotite or hornblende)
Staurolite	Hornblende-plagioclase (epidote, almandine, diopside)	Garnet-anorthite (bytownite)-hornblende
Kyanite		
Sillimanite		Garnet-anorthite (bytownite)-pyroxene

27

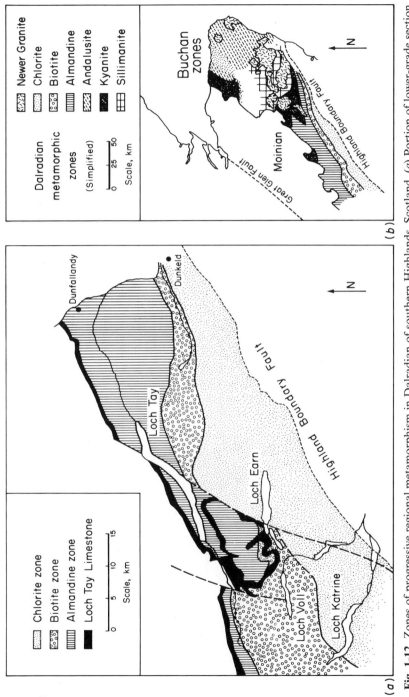

Fig. 1-12. Zones of progressive regional metamorphism in Dalradian of southern Highlands, Scotland. (*a*) Portion of lower-grade section —see Fig. 1-10. (*After C. E. Tilley.*) (*b*) General distribution of zones, simplified. (*After data of W. Q. Kennedy and M. R. W. Johnson.*)

(*a*)

(*b*)

Dunfallandy

Dunkeld

Loch Tay

Loch Earn

Loch Voil

Loch Katrine

Highland Boundary Fault

N

Chlorite zone
Biotite zone
Almandine zone
Loch Tay Limestone

Scale, km
0   5   10   15

Dalradian
metamorphic
zones
(Simplified)

Newer Granite
Chlorite
Biotite
Almandine
Andalusite
Kyanite
Sillimanite

Scale, km
0   25   50

Buchan
zones

Moinian

Highland Boundary Fault

Great Glen Fault

N

represent renewed deformation, accompanied and perhaps outlasted by growth of the minerals which now define the zones of progressive regional metamorphism. This stage is referred to as the *culmination of metamorphism*. It was followed by still later minor deformation and local retrogressive metamorphism: chloritization of biotite and garnet, sericitization of kyanite.

The total stratigraphic thickness of the Dalradian has been obscured by repeated folding, but may have been 10 to 20 km. There is no relation between Barrow's zones and stratigraphic depth. The metamorphic zones, even throughout the whole Dalradian and Moinian terrane between the Highland Border Fault and the Great Glen Fault (Fig. 1-10), cut across the mapped large-scale structures and conform to a simple pattern (Kennedy, 1948; Sutton, 1960; Johnson, 1963). This is a broad arch whose axis plunges southwest, with the grade of metamorphism increasing with tectonic (not stratigraphic) depth. During the culmination of metamorphism, the depth of cover of Barrow's sillimanite zone may have been of the order of 12 km (Johnson, 1963). The northeastern segment of the Dalradian in Banffshire (Fig. 1-10), 60 km or so north of the region mapped by Barrow, was buried much less deeply, perhaps to a depth of only 3 or 4 km (Johnson, 1963, p. 140). Here the sequence of zones of progressive regional metamorphism in pelitic schists, generally referred to today as the *Buchan type* of metamorphism, is not the same as in the southeastern region mapped by Barrow (*Barrovian type*). The highest grades in the Buchan type are marked by mineral assemblages containing andalusite and cordierite as well as staurolite and garnet.

Radiometric dating of Dalradian metamorphic and plutonic rocks has revealed a complex picture, still imperfectly delineated, of metamorphism, plutonic intrusion, and deformation (e.g. Giletti, Moorbath, and Lambert, 1961; Fitch, Miller, and Brown, 1964; Miller and Brown, 1965; Brown, Miller, Soper, and York, 1965). The culmination of regional metamorphism, now expressed by the principal metamorphic mineral assemblages, may well have occurred during Cambrian times (somewhat more than 500 million years ago). Later retrogressive mineralogical changes, mostly of a local nature, are correlated with a late phase of Ordovician deformation (420 million years ago).[1] The postmetamorphic Newer Granites of the Dalradian terrane have been dated at 400 to 410 million years (early Devonian). The whole complex succession of metamorphic, plutonic, and orogenic events, spanning perhaps 100 million years, is correlated with the Caledonian orogeny of northwestern Europe.

[1]In the Precambrian Moine series, northwest of the Dalradian, the culmination of metamorphism has been correlated with this 420-million-year event (Miller and Brown, 1965, p. 132). But in the Moine rocks there are also traces of a much earlier (Precambiran) metamorphic and orogenic episode.

Schists of New Hampshire and Vermont

Zones of progressive regional metamorphism in other parts of the world commonly have a pattern broadly similar to, though differing in detail from, that of the Highlands. Such zones have been mapped in early Paleozoic rocks of New Hampshire and Vermont (e.g., Billings, 1937; Lyons, 1955). Over much of this area, biotite, garnet, and staurolite crowd so closely on one another that separate zones for each cannot be distinguished. Elsewhere, notably near the Vermont-New Hampshire border, a broad chlorite zone is followed by distinct zones of biotite, garnet, staurolite-kyanite, and sillimanite (e.g., White and Billings, 1951; Lyons, 1955). Elsewhere again (Heald, 1950), the zone of sillimanite is subdivided on the basis of the alternative associations sillimanite-muscovite and sillimanite-orthoclase, the latter representing the peak of metamorphism.

The Schists of Otago, New Zealand

In the South Island of New Zealand, quartzo-feldspathic schists outcrop over an area of 30,000 km^2 in the provinces of Otago and Westland, and continue 500 km northeast as a band 15 km wide along the western flank of the Southern Alps (Fig. 1-13). To the east they pass into indurated, partially metamorphosed graywackes of late Paleozoic and Triassic age. To the northwest they terminate abruptly against an immense transcurrent dislocation, the Alpine Fault. Metamorphism and accompanying deformation are generally attributed to a mid-Jurassic or early Cretaceous orogeny.

As in Scotland, several episodes of deformation have been partially deciphered (Wood, 1963; Means, 1963; Grindley, 1963); and these have been related to the evolution of the metamorphic mineral assemblages as follows:

1. Formation of large recumbent folds and nappes and development of axial-plane foliation was accompanied by growth of mineral assemblages typical of the chlorite zone. In schists of the western part of the region porphyroblasts of biotite and garnet grew after cessation of folding.

2. Steeply plunging isoclinal folds with a new axial-plane schistosity were formed during the second and principal episode of deformation. This was followed by the culmination of metamorphic crystallization, which was responsible for the present zonal distribution of metamorphic mineral assemblages.

3. In the last phase of orogeny the schists of Otago were arched gently. Transcurrent movement accompanied by mylonitization began along the Alpine Fault.

In the greatly predominant quartzo-feldspathic schists of southern New Zealand, zones of progressive regional metamorphism (Fig. 1-14)

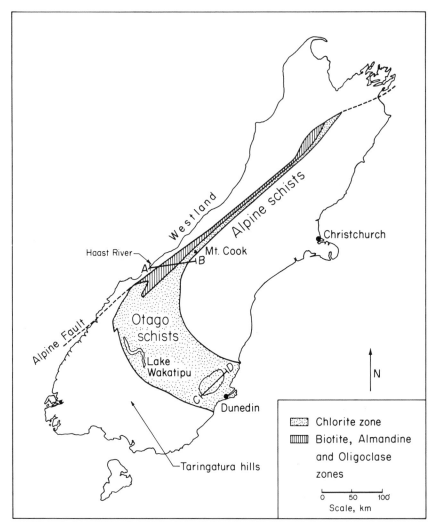

Fig. 1-13. Zones of progressive regional metamorphism in schists of Otago and Southern Alps, New Zealand. (*After J. J. Reed.*) AB, Haast River section; CD, section studied by E. H. Brown.

have been mapped on the basis of the index minerals chlorite, biotite, almandine, and oligoclase (e.g., Turner, 1948, p. 38; Reed, 1958; Mason, 1962; Grindley, 1963). The corresponding critical mineral assemblages in order of increasing metamorphism are:

Quartz-albite-*chlorite*-epidote-muscovite
Quartz-albite-*biotite*-epidote-muscovite
Quartz-albite-biotite-*almandine*-epidote
Quartz-*oligoclase*-biotite-muscovite (-almandine)

The general absence of aluminum silicates and staurolite, and the sporadic distribution of almandine in the more highly metamorphosed rocks, reflect the nonpelitic composition of the parent sediments. As in Scotland, basic igneous rocks have been converted to chlorite-albite-epidote-actinolite schists in the chlorite and biotite zones, and to amphibolites in the oligo-clase zone.

The chlorite zone of Otago is very extensive compared with that in Scotland or in New England.[1] In eastern Otago a zone transitional be-tween those of chlorite and biotite contains rocks with coexisting musco-vite, chlorite and biotite (Robinson, 1959; Brown, 1966). Biotite also is said to occur sporadically in many parts of the chlorite zone of Otago,[2] so that there is a possibility that the present chlorite-zone mineral assemblages over much of Otago developed during the second deformational stage from rocks which had originally reached the biotite stage of metamorphism following the first episode of deformation (Means, 1963). It is more probable, on the other hand, that the present distribution of schists, with and without biotite, throughout the broad chlorite zone represents local slight variations in physical conditions (e.g., temperature) during a single episode of metamorphic crystallization.

On the basis of textural evolution reflecting increasing intensity of deformation, it is possible to map four mutually gradational subzones of the chlorite zone (Hutton and Turner, 1936; Turner, 1948, p. 38; Grindley, 1963, pp. 894, 895):

Chlorite 1: Graywackes retain their initial texture except for slight cataclasis of quartz and feldspar grains and reconstitution of the clay matrix to a fine aggregate of micaceous and chlorite minerals. On the mesoscopic scale graywackes are commonly veined irregularly with quartz and calcite. In pelitic rocks slaty cleavage begins to appear.

Chlorite 2: Quartz and feldspar become extensively granulated and recrystallized, and the mica-chlorite matrix coarsens. The rocks are now foliated metagraywackes or *semischists.*

Chlorite 3: Metagraywackes have been converted to completely recrystallized fine-grained well-foliated schists. A few undestroyed quartz and feldspar grains still persist. Some rocks show incipient segregation of quartz and albite into thin lenticles and laminae parallel to the principal foliation. In some rocks strain-slip cleavage crossing the foliation gives rise to mesoscopic lineation.

Chlorite 4: Derivatives of graywacke are fully reconstituted coarse-grained foliated and lineated schists with segregation laminae of quartz

---

[1] Very extensive regions of chlorite-zone metamorphism are, however, known in other countries. An example is the Brisbane schist belt of southern Queensland, Australia.

[2] Much of this "biotite" is highly birefringent vermiculite formed from chlorite by absorption of iron during weathering (Brown, 1966).

and albite a few millimeters thick parallel to the early shear foliation. On the microscopic scale no trace of the original sedimentary textures remains.

In the northern part of the Alpine schist belt, subzone 3 of the chlorite zone is followed directly by the biotite zone in which schists for the first time develop segregation lamination (Reed, 1958). As might be expected, the stages of deformation and crystallization on which the

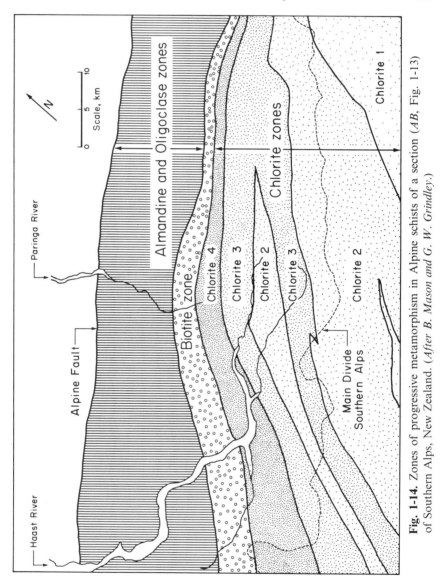

Fig. 1-14. Zones of progressive metamorphism in Alpine schists of a section (*AB*, Fig. 1-13) of Southern Alps, New Zealand. (*After B. Mason and G. W. Grindley.*)

subzones are based are to some degree independent of the physical conditions, presumably a temperature-pressure gradient, that control the nature of the metamorphic mineral assemblage.

In subzones 1 and 2 of the chlorite zone and in the graywackes beyond, which are generally classified as nonmetamorphic, it is possible to trace a sequence of mineralogical changes that mark the transition from diagenesis to metamorphism (e.g., Coombs, 1960; Brothers, 1956). On the basis of the distinctive mineralogy of irregular joint fillings and the reconstituted clay matrix of the rocks themselves, Coombs has drawn zones extending beyond the zone of chlorite (Fig. 1-15). In order of increasing mineralogical reconstitution, which can be shown from mapping to be at least in part a function of depth, the following zones may be recognized:

1. Zeolitic zone. Zeolites, especially heulandite and laumontite, appear as diagenetic products in graywackes and may be the main constituents of rocks originally rich in volcanic debris.

2. Prehnite-pumpellyite zone. Prehnite is an abundant constituent of joint fillings in metagraywackes of subzone Chl. 1, and pumpellyite is widespread in many metagraywackes and "semischists" of subzones 1 and 2. A typical Chl. 2 assemblage is quartz-albite-pumpellyite-chlorite-

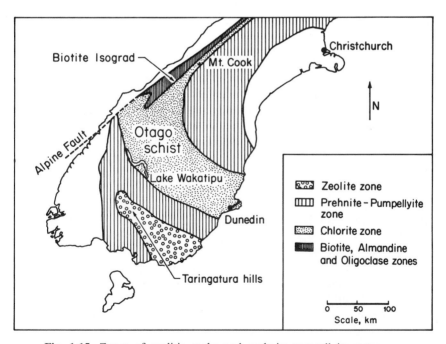

Fig. 1-15. Zones of zeolitic rocks and prehnite-pumpellyite-metagraywackes, southern New Zealand. (*After D. S. Coombs.*)

sphene. Epidote is much less widespread at this stage, but with passage into subzone 3 it becomes dominant, and pumpellyite is no longer characteristic.

As in Scotland, the pattern of metamorphic zones in New Zealand is very simple compared with the structure of the metamorphic rocks on the macroscopic scale. In one important respect, regional metamorphism in New Zealand differs sharply from that in Scotland or New England. There are no associated bodies of granitic rocks. At one time metamorphism in Otago was supposed to be connected with a subjacent granitic batholith. But the only supposed evidence for the existence of such a mass is the metamorphism itself and the rather widespread occurrence of auriferous and scheelite-bearing veins in the metamorphic terrane. Considering the great extent of metamorphic rocks and the high relief (1000 to 3000 m) of the country in which they outcrop, it would be remarkable indeed if a subjacent granitic batholith were nowhere exposed at the surface.

The Sanbagawa Schists of Japan

The islands of Sikoku and Honsyu in Japan are traversed longitudinally by a belt of low-grade schists 800 km long and up to 30 km in width, known as the *Sanbagawa schists* (Fig. 1-16). These are believed to be Paleozoic geosynclinal sediments and intercalated basic igneous rocks that were metamorphosed, according to radiometric dating, in Cretaceous times (Miyashiro, 1961, p. 287; Banno, 1964, p. 220).

The Sanbagawa schists have been studied intensively by Banno (1964) over an area of 300 km^2 in the Bessi mining district of Sikoku. Here their northern boundary is a major dislocation called the *Median Line*, which brings the schists into contact with nonmetamorphic late Mesozoic sediments. Southward, they merge into incompletely metamorphosed sediments of the Titibu group. Banno has mapped five zones, A to E in order of increasing grade, of progressive regional metamorphism (Fig. 1-17), based on mineral assemblages in pelitic and basic schists. In pelitic rocks the characteristic mineral assemblage quartz-muscovite-chlorite-albite-epidote of zones A to C gives way, via a transitional assemblage in zone D, to quartz-muscovite-biotite-almandine-oligoclase in zone E. Garnet first appears in zone C; but here and as far as the middle of zone D it is a variety rich in manganese. The pelitic assemblage of zone D resembles that typical of the transitional zone (between chlorite and biotite) in eastern Otago, New Zealand (p. 31). In derivatives of basic rocks, the low-grade assemblage albite-chlorite-epidote-actinolite is accompanied by pumpellyite and glaucophane[1] in zone A, and by glaucophane alone in zone B. Hornblende is present in zones C to E, and oligoclase appears while

[1]Lawsonite has also been recorded.

chlorite diminishes in zone E. The succession of zones is reminiscent of that in the Dalradian or in southern New Zealand, except for the presence of glaucophane and lawsonite at the lowest grades of metamorphism. The Sanbagawa schists of Sikoku are cut by ultramafic intrusives. The largest of these, at Bessi, contains lenses of eclogite and is enclosed within schists of relatively high grade (zones D and E).

In the Kanto Mountains of Honsyu, 500 km northwest of the region just described, the Sanbagawa schist belt has been studied especially by Seki (1958, 1960). Here the metamorphic picture has much in common with that of zones A and B of the Bessi district, but is developed in greater detail. Incompletely metamorphic rocks pass with increasing grade into a zone of glaucophane schists and pumpellyite-bearing schists, which in

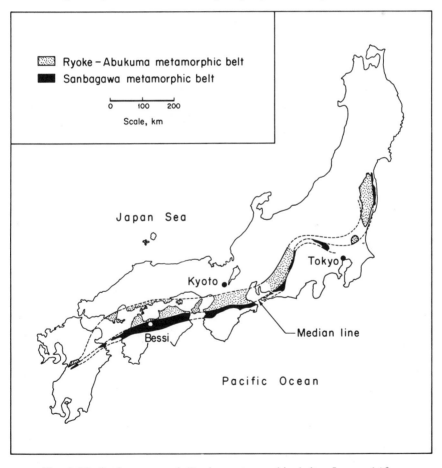

Ryoke – Abukuma metamorphic belt
Sanbagawa metamorphic belt

0   100   200
Scale, km

Japan Sea

Tokyo

Kyoto

Median line

Bessi

Pacific Ocean

Fig. 1-16. Sanbagawa and Ryoke metamorphic belts, Japan. (*After A. Miyashiro.*)

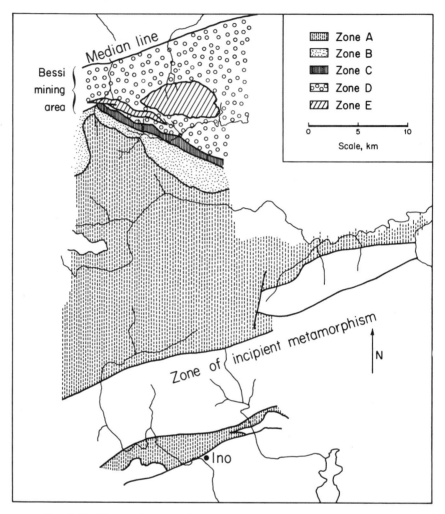

Fig. 1-17. Zones of progressive regional metamorphism in vicinity of Bessi mine, Japan. (*After S. Banno.*)

turn passes into a zone of pelitic schists and greenschists containing quartz, albite, muscovite, chlorite, epidote, and often stilpnomelane, manganiferous garnet or actinolite. These rocks lack pumpellyite or glaucophane. Their mineralogy duplicates that of the chlorite zone (Chl. 3 and Chl. 4) of southern New Zealand. Lawsonite and jadeite are characteristic of, and confined to, the middle portion of the zone of glaucophane schists. They are mutually associated with various combinations of quartz, albite, glaucophane, pumpellyite, chlorite, muscovite and epidote.

Throughout most of its length, the Sanbagawa schist belt is in faulted contact, along its northern border, with another metamorphic belt of totally different character: the *Ryoke belt* (Suwa, 1961). Associated plutonic rocks are granitic. Four zones of progressive metamorphism are recognized in the Ryoke belt. Pelitic and basic assemblages in order of increasing grade are as follows:

1. Pelitic: Quartz-albite-chlorite-muscovite (-biotite).
   Basic: Albite-epidote-actinolite-chlorite (-calcite).
2. Pelitic: Quartz-oligoclase-biotite-muscovite.
   Basic: Andesine-hornblende (-epidote-sphene).
3. Pelitic: Quartz-andesine-biotite-muscovite (-cordierite or -andalusite or almandine).
   Basic: Labradorite-hornblende-diopside.
4. Pelitic: Quartz-andesine-orthoclase-biotite-sillimanite (-almandine or cordierite).
   Basic: Bytownite-hornblende-diopside (-cummingtonite or hypersthene).

In calcareous rocks actinolite is characteristic in zone 1; hornblende-diopside-grossularite in zones 2 and 3; wollastonite-diopside-grossularite in zone 4.

Metamorphism in the Ryoke and in Sanbagawa belts, although approximately synchronous, was evidently effected under very different physical conditions.

Gneisses of the Northwest Adirondacks, New York State

Intimate association of metamorphic rocks and gneissic granite is characteristic of the Archaean the world over. A detailed account of field and chemical aspects of metamorphism of this type in a section of the Adirondack Mountains has been given by Engel and Engel (1958; 1960). Here the rocks that most closely retain their original chemical identity are quartzo-feldspathic gneisses derived from graywackes, with less abundant marbles and some amphibolites. On the mesoscopic scale the metasedimentary gneisses, which themselves contain little or no potash feldspar, are everywhere streaked to some degree with granite. On the macroscopic scale (Fig. 1-18), such rocks occur in elongate areas of a few square kilometers interfingering with similar areas of microcline-rich granite gneiss. Between the two are transitional zones of migmatite: gneisses of sedimentary origin, intimately layered with thin seams of granite or studded with microcline porphyroblasts on the mesoscopic scale.

Along a 50-km traverse, a single zonal boundary has been mapped on the basis of the mineral assemblages in the nongranitized metasedimentary gneiss (Fig. 1-19). To the west, representing the lower grade of metamorphism, the characteristic assemblage is quartz-biotite-oligoclase-muscovite. Hornblende-andesine is the assemblage in interlayered amphibolites. To the east of the isograd, the gneiss is composed of quartz-andesine-biotite-garnet, and in associated amphibolites the assemblage is andesine-hornblende-diopside-hypersthene. Although only one isograd has been drawn, increasing grade of metamorphism along the whole section can be traced by regular chemical changes in the principal minerals: that is, TiO_2/MnO changes from 16 to 520 in biotites, and from 0.003 to 0.06 in garnets; in both minerals the ratio Mg/Fe varies systematically along the metamorphic gradient. The range of temperature involved has been estimated from mineralogical data, such as Mg/Ca ratios in dolomite and Na/K ratios in muscovite, as 500 to 600°C; but these values are subject to considerable uncertainty.

With increase in grade of metamorphism, the metasedimentary gneiss becomes somewhat "basified" by depletion in K and Si and complementary enrichment in Al, Fe, Mg, and Ca. The liberated K and Si are partly retained in newly developed granitic veins in migmatite. Parts of the gneiss, on the other hand, are granitized by "several processes, especially mechanical injection of magma, permeation, and replacement of the gneiss by magma, by fluids from magma, or by ichors and ions" (Engel and Engel, 1958, pp. 1411–1412). In the eastern area of maximum metamorphic grade, granitic rock "clearly of igneous origin" is abundant in the gneiss complex. The picture presented by Engel and Engel is one in which high-temperature metamorphism involves the beginning of differential fusion, and is associated in time and in place with large-scale intrusion of granitic magma, probably itself the result of fusion of crustal rocks at no great distance from the site under consideration.

A General Model of Regional Metamorphism

It is now recognized that regional metamorphism is a progressive process. Typically in a given terrane it is possible to trace in the field a progression of mineral assemblages in rocks of the same general composition, and on this basis to map metamorphic zones bounded by isograds. The existence of low-grade zones, in which the texture and mineral assemblage of the parent rock are partially preserved, often shows unequivocally which is the direction of increasing metamorphic grade. The knowledge so obtained can be applied confidently to determine the direction in which the grade of metamorphism increases in other regions where the textures and mineral assemblages of the parent rocks have been completely obliterated. Although the sequence of mineralogical changes may be striking, significant progressive chemical variation other than loss of water or carbon dioxide has not been demonstrated, except where metamorphism overlaps the temperature range of partial fusion.

Fig. 1-18. Distribution of Precambrian gneiss, granite-gneiss and migmatite, Emeryville area, New York State. *(After A. E. J. and C. G. Engel.)*

39

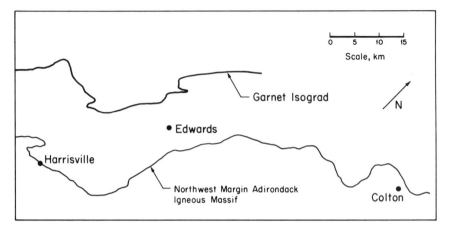

Fig. 1-19. Simplified map of Precambrian metamorphic and migmatitic terrane, northwest Adirondacks, New York State, showing the garnet isograd. (*After A. E. J. and C. G. Engel.*)

The mapped zonal sequences have long been interpreted as expressing gradients in physical conditions of metamorphism. Some writers have equated grade with temperature alone; e.g., Kennedy (1948, p. 231) referred to isograds as representing the traces or outcrops of isothermal surfaces. But Tilley (1924b, pp. 168–170), in a classic discussion relating to metamorphic grade and allied topics, defined an isograd as the line joining points of similar pressure-temperature values. Earlier, Harker (1919, p. lxxix) had referred to the zonal boundaries as "at once isothermals and isodynamics." It is indeed obvious that pressure conditions, as well as temperature, must influence the course of metamorphic reactions involving phases of different density, especially when one of these is a fluid. In any particular region, increasing grade implies increasing temperature of metamorphism, and in most geologic situations pressure is likely to increase rather than to decrease with temperature. However, although indeed it is likely, it cannot be stated with certainty that the high-grade biotite-muscovite schists of the Dalradian in Scotland were necessarily formed at a higher temperature than the low-grade chemically equivalent muscovite-chlorite schists of New Zealand. Each of the critical mineral assemblages on which the zones are based probably forms over a considerable range of both temperature and pressure.

The general similarity in the sequence of zones defined for pelitic schists in widely separate areas such as the southern Scottish Highlands, New Hampshire-Vermont, and Pennsylvania (McKinstry, 1949) implies that the respective metamorphic temperature-pressure gradients were similar. Every gradient is unique; so that the observed minor mineralogical

differences between the three regions are no greater than might be antici-
pated. Elsewhere totally different zonal sequences indicate correspondingly
diverse temperature-pressure gradients (cf. Miyashiro, 1961). One such is
exemplified in the sector of the northern Adirondacks described by Engel
and Engel. This perhaps expresses a type of metamorphic gradient generally
common in Archaean metamorphism. It is marked by a flat temperature
gradient in an environment of incipient fusion. Equally different, but in
another sense, is the zonal sequence described by Zwart (1963) in the central
Pyrenees. Here the zonal indices, in order of increasing grade, are biotite,
staurolite-andalusite-cordierite, andalusite-cordierite, and sillimanite-cor-
dierite. As in the case of the mineralogically similar metamorphic rocks
of the Banffshire Dalradian, the cover at the time of metamorphism is
estimated to have been thin—only a few thousand meters. Assuming that
metamorphic minerals such as biotite and cordierite form only at temperatures greater than 400 to 500°C, temperature-pressure gradients in the
Pyrenees may have been around 150°C/km: about 5 to 10 times the value
generally attributed to "normal" geothermal gradients. A reasonable value
for the gradient reflected in Barrow's classic zones would be less than
that in the Pyrenees, but probably considerably greater than conventionally
accepted normal gradients. Heat flow in sectors of the crust where regional
metamorphism is in progress clearly can be stepped up to values much
higher than normal.

It has been customary to consider temperature-pressure gradients of regional metamorphism as they may have existed over a short time interval—
the "time of metamorphism." However, largely from studies of metamorphic crystallization in relation to evolution of structure,[1] it has become
obvious that, in any given terrane, temperatures and pressures conducive to
metamorphism must have been maintained for millions rather than
thousands of years. At any particular site, temperatures and pressures must
have risen and fallen in each metamorphic cycle; and there is evidence that
repeated cycles are the rule rather than the exception. In spite of such
changes and fluctuations in metamorphic gradients it is usually possible to
recognize in a regular zonal progression the "frozen in" expression of a
single gradient. It is to this gradient that we refer when speaking of the
culmination of metamorphism. Superposed on the progressive sequence
of mineral assemblages, there are almost invariably traces of partial reaction in response to the falling temperature gradient that must have been
maintained for long intervals after the climax has been reached. There are
even regions where the zonal sequence now preserved has been attributed
to different degrees of retrogressive reaction in response to waning tem-

---

[1] A classic essay on the time relations of deformation, crystallization, and granite
emplacement is H. H. Read's (1949) "A contemplation of time in plutonism."

peratures. This is the interpretation placed by Wyckoff (1952, p. 25) upon metamorphic zones developed in the Wissahickon schist near Philadelphia:

> The most intense metamorphism took place, not at the time of highest temperatures, but during a period of declining temperatures, when mineral changes were facilitated by copious hydrothermal solutions and strong regional deformation. The decipherable history is therefore largely one of retrograde metamorphism.

One of the most provocative questions relating to regional metamorphism is this: considering the great length of time available, why are not all regionally metamorphic rocks reduced to the mineral assemblages characteristic of the chlorite zone? To this question we shall return later.

Another important question concerns the relation of granitic magma to regional metamorphism. Granite intrusions are not invariably associated with regional metamorphism, even of high grade. But the association of granitic magma with high-grade metamorphism is widespread, and in the Archaean terranes perhaps universal. To recognize the association is more important than to decide whether uprise of magma on a regional scale is the primary cause of the metamorphic gradient, or whether differential fusion of crustal rocks, with granitic magma as the product of fusion, is the culmination of the metamorphic process. In either case we are left with the still unsolved problem of the means by which, from time to time in different parts of the crust, heat becomes concentrated to the point where it constitutes the driving force of orogeny, generation of magma, and regional metamorphism.

REFERENCES

Akaad, M. K.: The northern aureole of the Ardara pluton of County Donegal, *Geol. Mag.*, vol. 93, pp. 377–398, 1956.

Banno, S.: Petrologic studies on the Sanbagawa crystalline schists in the Bessi-Ino district, Sikoku, Japan, *Univ. Tokyo Fac. Sci. J.*, sec. 2, vol. 15, pp. 203–319, 1964.

Barrell, J.: Geology of the Marysville mining district, Montana, *U.S. Geol. Surv. Profess. Papers*, no. 57, 1907.

Barrow, G.: On an intrusion of biotite-muscovite gneiss in the south-east Highlands of Scotland and its accompanying metamorphism. *Geol. Soc. London Quart. J.*, vol. 49, pp. 330–358, 1893.

Billings, M. P.: Regional metamorphism of the Littleton-Moosilauke area, New Hampshire, *Bull. Geol. Soc. Am.*, vol. 48, pp. 463–566, 1937.

Boucot, A. J., and J. B. Thompson: Metamorphosed Silurian brachiopods from New Hampshire, *Bull. Geol. Soc. Am.*, vol. 74, pp. 1313–1334, 1963.

Brothers, R. N.: The structure and petrography of graywackes near Auckland, New Zealand, *Trans. Roy. Soc. New Zealand*, vol. 83, pp. 465–482, 1956.

Brown, E. H.: The greenschist facies in part of eastern Otago, New Zealand, *Contrib. Mineral. Petrol.*, vol. 4, pp. 259–292, 1967.

Brown, P. E., J. A. Miller, N. J. Soper, and D. York: Potassium-argon age pattern of the British Caledonides, *Proc. Yorkshire Geol. Soc.*, vol. 3, pp. 103–138, 1965.

Bucher, W. H.: Fossils in metamorphic rocks; a review, *Bull. Geol. Soc. Am.*, vol. 64, pp. 275–300, 1953.

Coombs, D. S.: Lower grade mineral facies in New Zealand, *Rept. Intern. Geol. Cong., 21st Session, Norden*, 1960, vol. 13, pp. 339–351, 1960.

Edwards, A. B.: Differentiation of the dolerites of Tasmania, *J. Geol.*, vol. 50, pp. 451–480, 1942.

Elles, G. L., and Tilley, C. E.: Metamorphism in relation to structure in the Scottish Highlands, *Trans. Roy. Soc. Edinburgh*, vol. 56, pt. 3, pp. 621–646, 1930.

Engel, A. E. J., and C. E. Engel: Progressive metamorphism and granitization of the major paragneiss, northwest Adirondack Mountains, New York: Part I, *Bull. Geol. Soc. Am.*, vol. 69, pp. 1369–1414, 1958; Part II, *Bull. Geol. Soc. Am.*, vol. 71, pp. 1–58, 1960.

Fitch, F. J., J. A. Miller, and P. E. Brown: Age of Caledonian orogeny and metamorphism in Britain, *Nature*, vol. 203, pp. 275–278, 1964.

Giletti, B. J., S. Moorbath, and R. S. Lambert: A geochronological study of the metamorphic complexes of the Scottish Highlands, *Geol. Soc. London Quart. J.*, vol. 117, pp. 233–272, 1961.

Goldschmidt, V. M.: Die Kontaktmetamorphose im Kristianiagebiet, *Kristiania Vidensk. Skr., I, Math-Naturv. Kl. 11*, 1911.

Green, D. H.: The petrogenesis of the high-temperature peridotite intrusion in the Lizard area of Cornwall, *J. Petrol.*, vol. 5, pp. 134–188, 1964.

Grindley, G. W.: Structure of the alpine schists of South Westland, Southern Alps, New Zealand, *New Zealand J. Geol. and Geophys.*, vol. 6, pp. 872–930, 1963.

Hall, A. L.: The Bushveld complex as a metamorphic province, *Geol. Soc. South Africa Trans.*, vol. 17, pp. xxii–xxxvii, 1915.

———: The Bushveld igneous complex of central Transvaal, *Geol. Surv. South Africa, Mem.*, no. 28, 1932.

Hall, W. E., and E. M. MacKevett: Geology and ore deposits of the Darwin Quadrangle, Inyo County, California, *U.S. Geol. Surv. Profess. Papers*, no. 368, 1962.

Harker, A.: The Tertiary igneous rocks of Skye, *Mem. Geol. Surv. United Kingdom*, 1904.

———: Anniversary address of the president, *Geol. Soc. London Proc.*, pp. li–lxxx, 1919.

———: "Metamorphism," Methuen, London, 1932.

———, and J. E. Marr: The Shap granite and the associated igneous and metamorphic rocks, *Geol. Soc. London Quart. J.*, vol. 47, pp. 266–328, 1891.

Heald, M. T.: Structure and petrology of the Lovewell Mountain Quadrangle, New Hampshire, *Bull. Geol. Soc. Am.*, vol. 61, pp. 43–89, 1950.

Hori, F.: On the role of water in heat transfer from a cooling magma, *Coll. Gen. Educ., Univ. Tokyo, Sci. Paper*, vol. 14, pp. 121–127, 1964.

Hutton, C. O., and F. J. Turner: Metamorphic zones in north-west Otago, *Trans. Roy. Soc. New Zealand*, vol. 65, pp. 405–406, 1936.

Iyengar, S. V. P., W. S. Pitcher, and H. H. Read: The plutonic history of the Maas area, Co. Donegal, *Geol. Soc. London Quart. J.*, vol. 110, pp. 203–239, 1954.

Jaeger, J. C.: The temperature in the neighborhood of a cooling intrusive sheet, *Am. J. Sci.*, vol. 255, pp. 306–318, 1957.

——: Temperatures outside a cooling intrusive sheet, *Am. J. Sci.*, vol. 257, pp. 44–54, 1959.

Johnson, M. R. W.: Some time relations of movement and metamorphism in the Scottish Highlands, *Geol. Mijnbouw*, 42, pp. 121–142, 1963.

Kennedy, W. Q.: On the significance of thermal structure in the Scottish Highlands, *Geol. Mag.*, vol. 85, pp. 229–234, 1948.

——: Zones of progressive regional metamorphism in the Moine schists of the western Highlands of Scotland, *Geol. Mag.*, vol. 86, pp. 43–56, 1949.

Knopf, A.: The Marysville granodiorite stock, Montana, *Am. J. Sci.*, vol. 35, pp. 834–844, 1950.

Lovering, T. S.: Heat conduction in dissimilar rocks and the use of thermal models, *Bull. Geol. Soc. Am.*, vol. 47, pp. 87–100, 1936.

——: Temperatures near and in intrusions, *Econ. Geol.*, 50th anniversary vol., pp. 249–281, 1958.

Lyell, C.: "Manual of Elementary Geology," 6th edition, Appleton, New York, 1860.

Lyons, J. B.: Geology of the Hanover quadrangle, New Hampshire-Vermont, *Bull. Geol. Soc. Am.*, vol. 66, pp. 105–146, 1955.

Mason, B.: Metamorphism in the Southern Alps of New Zealand, *Am. Museum Nat. Hist. Bull.*, vol. 123, pp. 217–247, 1962.

McKinstry, H. E.: Mineral isograds in southeastern Pennsylvania, *Am. Mineralogist*, vol. 34, pp. 874–892, 1949.

Means, W. D.: Mesoscopic structures and multiple deformation in the Otago schists, *New Zealand J. Geol. Geophys.*, vol. 6, pp. 801–816, 1963.

Miller, J. A., and P. E. Brown: Potassium-argon age studies in Scotland, *Geol. Mag.*, vol. 102, pp. 106–134, 1965.

Miyashiro, A.: Evolution of metamorphic belts, *J. Petrol.*, vol. 2, pp. 277–311, 1961.

Nash, D. B.: Contact metamorphism at Birch Creek, Blanco Mountain Quadrangle, California, University of California, Berkeley, master's thesis, 1962.

Philbrick, S. S.: The contact metamorphism of the Onawa pluton, Piscataquis County, Maine, *Am. J. Sci.*, vol. 31, pp. 1–40, 1936.

Pitcher, W. S., and H. H. Read: The aureole of the main Donegal granite, *Geol. Soc. London Quart J.*, vol. 116, pp. 1–36, 1960.

——, and R. S. Sinha: The petrochemistry of the Ardara aureole, *Geol. Soc. London Quart J.*, vol. 113, pp. 393–408, 1958.

Read, H. H.: A contemplation of time in plutonism, *Geol. Soc. London Quart. J.*, vol. 105, pp. 101–156, 1949.

Reed, J. J.: Regional metamorphism in south-east Nelson, *New Zealand Geol. Surv. Bull.* no. 60, 1958.

Robinson, P.: Progressive metamorphism in the Otago schist, east Otago, New Zealand, *Bull. Geol. Soc. Am.*, vol. 70, p. 1662, 1959.

Seki, Y.: Glaucophanitic regional metamorphism in the Kanto Mountains, central Japan, *Jap. J. Geol. Geography, Trans.*, vol. 29, pp. 705–715, 1960.

Sutton, J.: Some structural problems in the Scottish Highlands, *Rept. Intern. Geol. Cong., 21st Session, Norden*, 1960, vol. 18, pp. 371–383, 1960.

Suwa, K.: Petrological and geological studies on the Ryoke metamorphic belt, *J. Earth Sci., Nagoya University*, vol. 9, pp. 274–303, 1961.

Tilley, C. E.: Contact metamorphism in the Comrie area of the Perthshire Highlands, *Geol. Soc. London Quart. J.*, vol. 80, pp. 22–71, 1924(a).

————: The facies classification of metamorphic rocks, *Geol. Mag.*, vol. 61, pp. 167–171, 1924(b).

————: Metamorphic zones in the southern Highlands of Scotland, *Geol. Soc. London Quart. J.*, vol. 81, pp. 100–112, 1925.

Tobisch, O. T.: Observations on primary deformed sedimentary structures in some metamorphic rocks from Scotland, *Jour. Sediment. Petrol.*, vol. 35, pp. 415–419, 1965.

Turner, F. J.: Mineralogical and structural evolution of the metamorphic rocks, *Geol. Soc. Am. Mem.*, no. 30, 1948.

————, and J. Verhoogen: "Igneous and Metamorphic Petrology," McGraw-Hill, New York, 1960.

White, W. S., and M. P. Billings: Geology of the Woodsville Quadrangle, Vermont-New Hampshire, *Bull. Geol. Soc. Am.*, vol. 62, pp. 647–696, 1951.

Williams, H., F. J. Turner, and C. M. Gilbert: "Petrography," Freeman, San Francisco, 1955.

Wilson, H. D.: Structure of lopoliths, *Bull. Geol. Soc. Am.*, vol. 67, pp. 289–300, 1956.

Wood, B. L.: Structure of the Otago schists, *New Zealand J. Geol. Geophys.*, vol. 6, pp. 641–680, 1963.

Wyckoff, D.: Metamorphic facies in the Wissahickon schist near Philadelphia, Pennsylvania, *Bull. Geol. Soc. Am.*, vol. 63, pp. 25–58, 1952.

Zwart, H. J.: On the determination of polymetamorphic mineral associations and its application to the Bosost area (central Pyrenees), *Geol. Rundschau*, vol. 52, pp. 38–65, 1963.

General Significance
of Metamorphic
Mineral Assemblages:
Metamorphic Facies

HISTORICAL BACKGROUND—NINETEENTH
CENTURY CONCEPTS

Lyell, in developing his concept of metamorphism, attributed the accompanying mineralogical and structural changes to elevated temperatures acting at depth or in proximity to granitic intrusions. He recognized the essential roles of time and of aqueous fluids in metamorphic processes, and he visualized granitic magma as a product of rock fusion in the culmination of metamorphism. With reference to the genesis of schist from mudstones and of marble from limestone he wrote (Lyell, 1847, p. 171):

> The transmutation has been effected apparently by the influence of subterranean heat, acting under great pressure, or by chemical and electrical causes operating in a manner not yet understood, and which have been termed *Plutonic* action . . . . To this plutonic action the fusion of granite itself in the bowels of the earth, as well as the super-inducement of the metamorphic texture into sedimentary strata, must be attributed; . . .

It is to G. H. Williams in particular that we owe the more sophisticated notion of metamorphism as the response of a rock to imposed progressively changing conditions of temperature and pressure, under the influence of which the metamorphic mineral assemblage tends to a state of internal equilibrium in the thermodynamic sense. Commenting on the small number of chemical components (MgO, SiO_2, etc.) that enter into the comparatively large number of known metamorphic mineral assemblages, Williams (1890, p. 39)[1] wrote:

> It seems to be oftentimes more a matter of external condition rather than of chemical composition, which determines what particular mineral is formed; and the equipoise between the existence of a certain silicate and the external conditions is often so delicate that a mere change in the latter alone is sufficient to destroy the mineral as such and to cause it to change to some other modification or compound. . . . Rocks whose component minerals are so delicately balanced to accord with the particular set of conditions under which they were formed [the reference is to igneous rocks] must be peculiarly subject to alteration when these conditions are changed; . . .

Meanwhile Sederholm (1891), in an account of the Archaean migmatites of Finland, recognized the profound differences in style of metamorphism, structural as well as mineralogical, between Archaean gneisses of Finland and the schists of younger eroded fold-mountain systems in the Harz and Taunus (Sederholm, 1891, p. 140).

> The . . . uniform type of transformation with in the main thoroughly crystalline reconstitution occurs predominantly in Archaean rocks whose layers have a nearly vertical attitude, and which accordingly were once exposed to the activity of uniform long-sustained lateral pressure in relatively deep regions of the earth's crust. On the other hand the nonuniform rocks transformed by crystallization of "weathering minerals" [sericite, chlorite, epidote, calcite] mostly belong to the higher levels of the younger mountain chains. Here tangential movements extend themselves in more irregular eddies.

Here the emphasis is upon depth as the principal factor controlling conditions of metamorphism and accompanying deformation. Sederholm (1891, p. 139) also recognized the important indirect role of stress in accelerating metamorphic reactions by increasing "almost ad infinitum" the area of the reacting surfaces of the crushed mineral grains.

The present century has witnessed a series of attempts to interpret metamorphic mineral assemblages more specifically, with increasing emphasis on the principles of thermodynamics and the data of laboratory

---

[1] Compare also Williams, 1890, p. 209.

experiments. By Becke (1903) and Grubenmann (1904) the conditions of metamorphism were seen as a function mainly of depth. Goldschmidt (1911) envisaged each metamorphic assemblage as a system in divariant equilibrium governed by a limited range of pressure and temperature, and he applied the requirements of the phase rule as a test of equilibrium. Johnston and Niggli (1913) wrote an influential essay on the general application of thermodynamic principles to metamorphism. Eskola (1915, 1920) marshalled the more familiar paragenetically associated mineral assemblages into groups that he termed metamorphic facies. Following Goldschmidt's use of the phase rule, he correlated individual facies with broad fields of temperature and pressure. Much research in metamorphism since 1925 has centered on elaboration of metamorphic facies, investigation of their field occurrence and associations, and evaluation of their individual limits of temperature and pressure in the light of experiment. To each of these topics we shall now turn.

METAMORPHISM AS A FUNCTION OF DEPTH

Depth Zones of Becke

In 1903 Becke presented to the Vienna Academy of Sciences a paper (Becke, 1913) in which he treated metamorphic assemblages as systems in thermodynamic equilibrium. He recognized that temperature and pressure, both of which increase with depth, have opposite effects upon most metamorphic reactions. In modern terms, the slope of the curve of univariant equilibrium drawn for such a reaction on a pressure-temperature field is positive (Fig. 2-1). In other words, the reaction proceeds with simultaneous increase (or decrease) both in entropy and in volume.

On the above basis, Becke proposed two depth zones of regional metamorphism:

1. In the upper zone reactions were said to proceed with decreasing volume and to conform to a *volume law* (for example, $Q \rightarrow P$ in Fig. 2-1). Among the typical reaction products are dense minerals such as garnet, and many hydrous silicates (chlorites, micas, epidotes, amphiboles) that are dense compared with chemically equivalent minerals plus water as a separate phase. The conversion of gabbro (plagioclase-pyroxene) plus water to garnet amphibolite or to chlorite-epidote-albite schist would exemplify a reaction of Becke's upper zone. But other reactions in the upper zone, such as those concerned in the low-grade metamorphism of pelitic sediments, involve progressive expulsion of water. On a diagram such as Fig. 2-1 they would proceed, contrary to Becke's generalization, from left to right in opposition to the volume law.

2. In the lower zone reactions proceed, according to Becke, in the sense opposite to that required by the volume law ($P \rightarrow Q$ in Fig. 2-1).

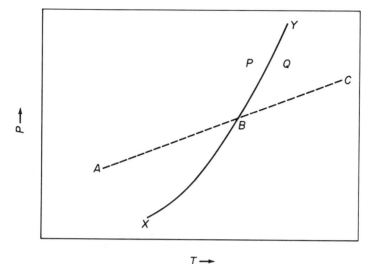

Fig. 2-1. Hypothetical curve of univariant equilibrium (*XY*) for a metamorphic reaction $P \rightleftharpoons Q$. *ABC* is a hypothetical metamorphic gradient depending on depth.

The influence of increasing temperature was said to overshadow that of increasing pressure. Today we visualize the reaction products simply as the result of progressive dehydration or decarbonation under increasing temperature. They include feldspars, pyroxenes, garnets, sillimanite, olivine, etc.

Depth Zones of Grubenmann

Grubenmann's (1904) great work on "*The Crystalline Schists*," later rewritten and modified by Niggli (Grubenmann and Niggli, 1924), has strongly influenced European conceptions of metamorphism, especially during the first four decades of this century. Like Sederholm and Becke, Grubenmann stressed mineralogical and textural differences that were supposed to exist between Archaean metamorphic rocks and the schists of younger fold-mountain chains. Again the principal factor controlling the observed differences was thought to be depth. Accordingly, Gruben-mann assigned metamorphic rocks to three depth zones. But apart from the original supposed distinction between Archaean and younger meta-morphic rocks, the criteria of depth are purely textural and mineralogical:

1. *Upper or epi zone*. Typical minerals are muscovite, chlorite, chloritoid, stilpnomelane, talc, actinolite, epidotes, glaucophane, car-bonates, and others. Cataclastic textures with structural relics of an earlier state are characteristic; folded, finely schistose and lineated structures are common. The inferred physical conditions are relatively low temperatures

and pressures combined with high nonhydrostatic pressure (stress). The epi zone is exemplified by the chlorite zones of regions such as the Highlands of Scotland and southern New Zealand.[1]

2. *Middle or meso zone.* Typical minerals include biotite, muscovite, staurolite, kyanite, hornblende and other amphiboles, plagioclase, epidote, garnet and calcite. Characteristic, too, are mineral assemblages including minerals of the epi and of the meso zone. Widely prevalent is a regular planar foliation (*crystallization schistosity*) marked by parallel dimensional orientation of micas and other tabular minerals, which were thought to have crystallized with their long dimensions normal to the axis of maximum principal stress. Laminated and linear fabrics are common. Metamorphism in the meso zone was envisaged as chemical reconstitution governed by moderate temperatures and pressures, with highly variable nonhydrostatic pressures. The meso zone of Grubenmann would embrace all of Barrow's zones in the Dalradian except the zone of sillimanite.

3. *Lower or kata zone.* Characteristic minerals are biotite, potash feldspar, calcic plagioclase, sillimanite, hornblende, pyroxenes, garnets, and others. The typical texture is granulitic, with thin elongate lenses of quartz and feldspar aligned to give a planar foliation. Migmatitic structures are common. Metamorphism in the kata zone was conceived to be a protracted process of chemical reconstitution under high pressure and temperature, with nonhydrostatic pressure relatively weak or lacking. The kata zone was said to be exemplified chiefly by Archaean rocks. This is true of high-grade Archaean granulites; but the mineral assemblages of most Archaean rocks turn out to belong mainly to the meso zone (Eskola, 1939, p. 340).

Grubenmann framed a general classification of regionally metamorphosed rocks on a dual basis: the threefold division in terms of depth, and a twelvefold subdivision based on bulk chemical composition (Al-silicate rocks, Mg-silicate rocks, marbles, and so on). Thus he clearly demonstrated the twofold dependence of every common metamorphic assemblage upon its present chemical composition and the physical conditions of metamorphism. Of course there were anomalies in the classification. Some low-temperature high-pressure minerals such as jadeite and some high-temperature low-pressure minerals such as periclase and cordierite were assigned to the kata zone. Other low-temperature high-pressure minerals, notably lawsonite and glaucophane, are placed in the epi zone.[2] The complete gamut of physical conditions encompassed by metamorphism is too wide and varied to be expressed by any single parameter such as age or depth.

---

[1] Today generally assigned to considerable crustal depth.

[2] The anomaly is even greater in Niggli's revision (Grubenmann and Niggli, 1924) which forces the products of low-pressure contact metamorphism into the kata zone.

In Grubenmann's scheme the individual mineral is the index of metamorphism. Today the emphasis has shifted to the mineral assemblage as an entity. Potash feldspar is a constituent of metamorphic rocks formed over a wide range of conditions. The same may be said of sillimanite, and of almandine. But the assemblage orthoclase-sillimanite-almadine is found only in the highest grades of metamorphism; and on this fact rests the subdivision of the sillimanite zone in New England (cf. p. 29). It remained for Goldschmidt and Eskola to demonstrate the significance of the metamorphic mineral assemblage; and so arose the concept of metamorphic facies.

METAMORPHIC FACIES

The Facies Concept

In the Oslo region of Norway (Goldschmidt, 1911), a mixed series of pelitic, sandy, and calcareous sediments of Paleozoic age has been invaded by igneous plutons ranging in composition from alkali gabbro to granite. Close to the igneous contacts in the resulting aureoles the hornfelses show a remarkably uniform paragenesis. In spite of their wide diversity in chemical composition the common mineral assemblages are relatively simple. Each consists essentially of four or five out of ten widely prevalent minerals: quartz, potash feldspar, plagioclase, andalusite, cordierite, hypersthene, diopside, wollastonite, grossularite, and biotite. Certain pairs of these appear consistently to the exclusion of chemically equivalent pairs; thus anorthite-hypersthene is common, but the equivalent pair andalusite-diopside is unknown.

$$CaMgSi_2O_6 + Al_2SiO_5 \rightarrow CaAl_2Si_2O_8 + MgSiO_3$$

Moreover, for a given range of chemical composition, the mineral assemblage in the Oslo hornfelses is always the same; e.g., quartz-orthoclase-andalusite-cordierite in pelitic rocks, diopside-wollastonite-grossularite-calcite in calcareous hornfelses.

Shortly after the publication of Goldschmidt's work on the Oslo hornfelses, Eskola (1914, 1915) described the effects of contact metamorphism and mineralization associated with Precambrian granites of the Orijärvi mining region of Finland. Again the mineral assemblages were found to be simple and consistently related to rock composition. Some assemblages such as diopside-grossularite and andalusite-cordierite-plagioclase are common to the two regions. But there are consistent mineralogical differences between chemically equivalent assemblages as shown in Table 2-1. These differences Eskola attributed to different physical conditions of metamorphism. He considered it likely that temperatures

Table 2-1. Chemically equivalent mineralogical assemblages in hornfelses of Oslo and of Orijärvi

Oslo	Orijärvi
Potash feldspar + Andalusite	Muscovite + Quartz
Potash feldspar + Cordierite	Biotite + Muscovite
Potash feldspar + Hypersthene + Anorthite	Biotite + Hornblende
Hypersthene	Anthophyllite

were higher and pressures lower in the Oslo aureoles than at Orijärvi—a conclusion that has been upheld by subsequent experimental work.

On the basis of the above comparison, Eskola (1915, pp. 114, 115) proposed the term *metamorphic facies* to include any association of metamorphic rocks within which there is constant correlation between mineral and chemical composition. The rocks of Orijärvi constitute one facies, those of the Oslo aureoles another. Each facies has since been recognized in other parts of the world. In Eskola's original definitions, in his subsequent writings on facies, and in later discussion of the same topic by many writers, there is a good deal of confusion as to the relative significance of observed petrological data and inferred physical conditions of metamorphism as criteria for defining facies (cf. Fyfe, Turner, and Verhoogen, 1958, pp. 8–10, 18). Facies refer to mineral assemblages of associated rocks—not to inferred metamorphic conditions. Accordingly, any definition of facies in general, or of individual facies such as that of Oslo, must be framed in terms of criteria that may be observed in metamorphic rocks. A recent definition of facies (Fyfe and Turner, 1966) is here adopted:

> A metamorphic facies is a set of metamorphic mineral assemblages, repeatedly associated in space and time, such that there is a constant and therefore predictable relation between mineral composition and chemical composition.

This definition requires amplification in several respects:

1. Any facies is recognized on the basis of a set of mutually associated rocks collectively covering a wide range of composition. It cannot be defined in terms of a single rock type, even though each facies is customarily named after some characteristic rock: greenschist, amphibolite, and so on. Contrary to a view repeatedly expressed in the literature (e.g., Becke, 1921; Tilley, 1924), the facies concept is unsuited for use in developing a comprehensive classification of individual rock types.

2. The relation between the mineral and the chemical composition of rocks belonging to any facies is such that, given the chemical analysis, it is possible to predict the corresponding mineral assemblage. Thus in the

greenschist facies rocks having the composition of basalt will always be represented by one of the assemblages

Albite-chlorite-actinolite-epidote-sphene

Albite-chlorite-epidote-sphene

Albite-chlorite-epidote-calcite-sphene

Which of these three assemblages is developed, and whether quartz is present as a minor additional phase, depends upon the particular chemical composition within the general basaltic range. Typical pelitic assemblages in the same facies are

Quartz-muscovite-chlorite (-albite-epidote)

Quartz-muscovite-chlorite (-biotite-garnet)

Quartz-muscovite-biotite (-garnet)

All three may have virtually identical chemical compositions. Which of the three develops in any particular locality depends upon some factor other than composition—almost certainly the values of temperature and pressure within some restricted range.

3. What determines the mineral assemblage in a given rock within any facies is the present composition as shown by a chemical analysis. The facies concept throws no light upon the initial state of the rock nor upon any change in bulk composition that may have accompanied metamorphism. Rocks of one composition in the greenschist facies are composed of actinolite and calcite. The parent rock may have been a pure dolomite, a siliceous dolomite, or a peridotite. The initial state can be reconstructed only on the basis of chemical, textural, and field data.

During his lifetime, Eskola increased the number of facies recognized by him from five to eight. More have been added by other writers. Some of these have later been abandoned or redefined. Many have been divided into subfacies. For example the greenschist facies was originally defined to include rocks of the chlorite and biotite zones of regional metamorphism. The diagnostic assemblage in greenschists (derivatives of basic igneous rocks) is albite-epidote-chlorite-sphene-quartz, with or without actinolite or calcite. It was later redefined and divided into subfacies on the basis of pelitic assemblages (Turner and Verhoogen, 1960, p. 533). More recently Lambert (1965) has criticized the use of subfacies as having become both confused and cumbersome. Accordingly it is now proposed to discontinue attempts to divide facies into minor units of more than local significance (Fyfe and Turner, 1966), and to revert to Eskola's original usage regarding the greenschist facies. It seems that ten or a dozen facies will prove sufficient to encompass the complete gamut of metamorphic rocks; this number is small enough to permit the general petrologist to remain familiar with their essential characteristics.

The confusion that still exists regarding nomenclature arises mainly from differences in opinion as to where arbitrarily to draw boundaries between facies which necessarily show transitional relations to one another. Such transitions, of course, reflect the gradational relations that are now recognized between mineral assemblages on either side of any of the generally recognized isograds. If we no longer attempt to set up clear-cut subfacies of worldwide significance, nomenclature becomes simplified to the point where metamorphic phenomena can be discussed with a minimum of ambiguity by any geologist. In any given region it will still be possible to define locally significant subfacies corresponding to the various meta-morphic zones that can be mapped between the isograds that limit the facies in question in the field. But to attempt any rigid application of such a series of subfacies to the same facies, as it is developed elsewhere, is to ignore the differences which are just as important as the resemblances between the respective metamorphic parageneses of the two regions.

Most serious divergences of opinion are apparent with regard to what metamorphic conditions may be inferred from the combined mineral assemblages of any given facies. Even in this area, however, opinion is much more nearly unanimous on some questions than was the case a dozen years ago. This growing consensus reflects the influence of laboratory experiment and thermodynamic reasoning in clarifying the conditions of critical metamorphic reactions.

The Metamorphic Assemblage as a System in Equilibrium

Petrographic and chemical evidence. Ever since Williams (e.g., 1890, p. 39) wrote of the "equipoise" or "delicate balance" between metamorphic mineral assemblages and the physical conditions of metamorphism, the classic writers on metamorphic petrology have seen each common mineral assemblage as a system approximating internal equilibrium controlled by a limited range of temperature and pressure conditions (e.g., Becke, 1913, p. 4; Goldschmidt, 1911, p. 118; Eskola, 1915, pp. 114–115; Harker, 1932, pp. 10–11). There is abundant cumulative petrographic evidence to support this contention *as a first approximation.* Minerals belonging to most isomorphous series tend to be remarkably uniform in composition within domains ranging from a thin section to a metamorphic zone. Optical measurements made on hundreds of grains of plagioclase in schists of the chlorite and biotite zones of Otago, New Zealand (an area 30,000 km^2 in extent) indicate compositional variations no greater than An_0 to An_7. Even this limited range probably reflects error in measurement rather than variation in anorthite content. Perhaps the true range is no greater than An_0 to An_1 (cf. Evans, 1964, p. 175, 177). The chlorite series is one in which there is a wide range of possible substitution between Mg^{2+}, Fe^{2+}, Al^{3+} and between Al^{3+} and Si^{4+}. Yet such chlorites of New Zealand and Japanese greenschists as have been analyzed are highly restricted in compositional range: they are prochlorites in which the ratio FeO/MgO is about 0.8 to 1.1. Optically recognizable zoning in plagioclase and amphibole crystals, although by no means unknown, is relatively rare in metamorphic rocks. Garnet of pelitic schists, however, is commonly zoned.

The rapidly growing analytical data on metamorphic minerals have already demonstrated many consistent and widely prevalent correlations between composition of mineral series and paragenesis (i.e., facies). For example, in coexisting ferromagnesian silicates of any facies, the partitioning of Fe and Mg follows consistent patterns. Thus the respective distribution coefficients for Mg and Fe in the pairs diopside-hypersthene and hypersthene-garnet in granulites have been shown to be constant (Kretz, 1961). Francis (1964, pp. 177–178) finds that in a group of associated, high-grade pelitic schists from Scotland, the biotite of biotite-muscovite-kyanite-almandine schists has a Mg/Fe ratio of about 0.6; in biotite of biotite-almandine-kyanite schists, Mg/Fe < 0.6; in that of schists lacking almandine the ratio Mg/Fe > 0.6. The almandine, as is usually the case in high-grade pelitic schists, has a consistently low Mg/Fe ratio (not greater than 0.3). Again the white micas of low-grade muscovite-chlorite and glaucophane schists usually contain significant amounts of MgO, FeO, and Fe_2O_3 and have been called phengites (Tilley, 1926; Ernst, 1963). In biotite-muscovite schists of higher grade, on the other hand, the white mica more closely approximates the ideal composition of muscovite. Generalizations such as these collectively constitute strong evidence for approximate internal equilibrium in metamorphic rocks.

In no way invalidating this general conclusion is the fact that many metamorphic rocks show textural and mineralogical evidence of more than one episode of metamorphism. A new mineral assemblage may be seen in process of development from an older one. Biotite and garnet are commonly partially chloritized; kyanite or andalusite may be partly converted to white mica; crystals of plagioclase or of amphibole may show optically recognizable simple zoning. Here indeed is evidence of disequilibrium resulting from partial conversion of an older to a newer equilibrium assemblage. Moreover on a very small scale compositional variation within optically homogeneous grains is being increasingly revealed by means of the electron microprobe analyzer (cf. Evans, 1964). Some of this variation probably represents the expectable small-scale adjustments to postmetamorphic conditions in microsystems sufficiently small for ionic diffusion to be effective during postmetamorphic time.

Application of the phase rule. The number of phases that can coexist in a system in equilibrium at constant temperature and pressure is limited by the phase rule. V. M. Goldschmidt (1911, p. 123) applied this restriction as a test of equilibrium in metamorphic mineral assemblages. Arguing that any common assemblage (e.g., diopside-grossularite-wollastonite-quartz) must be able to crystallize over a range of both temperature and pressure, he treated such assemblages as systems in divariant equilibrium. For such the phase rule[1]

$$w = c + 2 - \varphi$$

becomes $\varphi = c$

This simple relation, which Goldschmidt termed the *mineralogical phase rule*, states that for equilibrium the number of minerals (phases) in a metamorphic rock equals the number of components of the system. There is nothing peculiar to mineralogy about this statement, which indeed applies to any heterogeneous system in divariant equilibrium; so the term "mineralogical phase rule" will not be used further.

There is some degree of ambiguity attached to rigorous application of the phase rule to mineral assemblages, which arises from the possibility of choice as to the number of components in the system. In Goldschmidt's equation c is the smallest number of independent components necessary to define the compositions of all phases in the system. This is the usage followed here. But should all ten principal oxides that appear in a typical rock analysis be treated as separate components? Is it permissible, on the other hand, to combine oxides that have the capacity for isomorphous substitution into components such as $(Mg, Fe, Mn)O$, $(Al, Fe)_2O_3$, and so on? Ambiguity of this kind can be avoided if the precise composition of each of the associated minerals is known. Without identifying the individual components it is necessary only to list the associated phases (φ in number) and note the number r of possible independent equations relating any of the listed phases. Then by definition (cf. Turner and Verhoogen, 1960, p. 29)

$$c = \varphi - r$$

and the phase rule becomes

$$w = 2 - r$$

In most cases it must be assumed that the associated phases include an interstitial gas, e.g., water in a system containing hydrated silicates such as micas and amphiboles, CO_2 in a system containing carbonates and their breakdown products (diopside, forsterite, etc.).

The possibilities that arise in evaluating common mineral assemblages are few. They are listed in Table 2-2. Contrary to Goldschmidt's generaliza-

---

[1]The phase rule as stated here applies only when the number of intensive variables is *two*, for example, P,T. To take into account any third variable, such as position in a gravitational field, 3 is substituted for 2 on the right.

Table 2-2. Application of the phase rule as a test of equilibrium in metamorphic mineral assemblages

Number of reactions r	Variance w	Likely significance	
0	2	Divariant equilibrium	
1	1	Univariant equilibrium	Disequilibrium
2	0		Disequilibrium
3	-1		Disequilibrium

tion, we think univariant equilibrium is likely to be represented among assemblages including hydrous silicates and carbonates. In rocks of low permeability such that diffusion of gas into or out of the system is necessarily slow, a hydration or carbonation reaction is likely to become "frozen" on a curve of univariant equilibrium (p. 58).

As a first example, consider a metamorphosed dolomitic limestone consisting of calcite-diopside-quartz (with CO_2 as a gas phase). Counting the components in the routine manner as CaO, MgO, SiO_2, CO_2 ($c = 4$), since $\varphi = 4$,

$$w = 2$$

Alternatively $r = 0$, and $w = 2$. The assemblage is a common one, consistent with Goldschmidt's interpretation as a system in divariant equilibrium.

Now consider the assemblage dolomite-diopside-quartz (plus CO_2 gas). This is not nearly so common as the calcite-bearing assemblage; but it does occur in nature. If the components are counted as CaOMgO, SiO_2, CO_2 ($c = 3$), then since $\varphi = 4$,

$$w = 1$$

Alternatively $r = 1$ and $w = 1$; for it is possible to write an equation

$$\underset{\text{Dolomite}}{CaMg(CO_3)_2} + \underset{\text{Quartz}}{2SiO_2} \rightleftharpoons \underset{\text{Diopside}}{CaMgSi_2O_6} + 2CO_2$$

The dolomitic assemblage may be interpreted alternatively (cf. Table 2-1) as a system in univariant equilibrium or as one in disequilibrium.

In the pyrophyllite deposits of North Carolina (Zen, 1961) there are many two- and three-mineral assemblages in the general system Al_2O_3–SiO_2–H_2O. Allowing for the presence of an additional gaseous phase (essentially water) at the time of metamorphism, these become three- and four-phase assemblages in systems of three components. The four-phase assemblages such as pyrophyllite-kaolinite-quartz (-water) and pyrophyllite-diaspore-kaolinite (-water) are consistent with univariant equilibrium.[1] This is a situation that is not only possible but likely in a system sufficiently impermeable to permit only slow diffusion of water into or out of the rock. The three-phase assemblages such as pyrophyllite-kaolinite (-water) are consistent with divariant equilibrium.

Now consider the common high-grade pelitic assemblage quartz-orthoclase-biotite-almandine-kyanite (with H_2O as an additional gas phase): $\varphi = 6$. At one time the components would have been listed as SiO_2, K_2O, $(Mg, Fe)O$, Al_2O_3, and H_2O: $c = 5$. On this assessment of components the highest variance consistent with equilibrium would be

$$w = 5 + 2 - 6 = 1$$

The inference would be that the assemblage could not be widely prevalent in a state of equilibrium (divariant) in metamorphic rocks. But this conclusion is invalidated by more detailed knowledge of the composition of associated biotite and garnet. It is indeed possible to write a generalized equation relating all six associated phases:

$$K(Mg,Fe)_3(AlSi_3O_{10})(OH)_2 + Al_2SiO_5 + 2SiO_2$$
$$\text{Biotite} \qquad\qquad\qquad \text{Kyanite} \qquad \text{Quartz}$$

$$\rightleftharpoons (Mg,Fe)_3Al_2(SiO_4)_3 + KAlSi_3O_8 + H_2O$$
$$\text{Garnet} \qquad\qquad \text{Orthoclase}$$

But this cannot apply to the normal natural assemblage where the biotite is magnesian, perhaps $KMg_2Fe(AlSi_3O_{10})(OH)_2$, and the garnet a typical almandine $Mg_{\frac{1}{2}}Fe_{2\frac{1}{2}}Al_2(SiO_4)_3$. For natural assemblages, regardless of how the components are identified, $r = 0$, and w consequently is 2. Therefore divariant equilibrium is possible and likely.

The same assemblage, with muscovite as an additional phase, represents only univariant equilibrium (or disequilibrium with higher variance). Since one can write an equation.

$$KAl_2(AlSi_3O_{10})(OH)_2 + SiO_2 \rightleftharpoons KAlSi_3O_8 + Al_2SiO_5 + H_2O$$
$$\text{Muscovite} \qquad\qquad \text{Quartz} \qquad \text{Orthoclase} \qquad \text{Kyanite}$$

$r = 1$ and $w = (2 - 1) = 1$. For the two-mica assemblage, the temperatures and pressures at which equilibrium is possible are, of course, those on the reaction curve corresponding to the above equation for the breakdown of muscovite in the presence of quartz (cf. Evans, 1965).

The accumulated data of petrography support the original contention of Goldschmidt and Eskola that metamorphic mineral assemblages tend to consist of but a few principal phases; and that in the light of the phase rule,

---

[1] This is considered by Zen (1961, pp. 62, 63) to be most unlikely in a geological situation.

φ phases.   C components.   .3/km
                                        = 15 kb = 50km

GENERAL SIGNIFICANCE OF METAMORPHIC MINERAL ASSEMBLAGES   59

this strongly suggests but does not prove the general prevalence of equilibrium. Strict application of the phase rule to systems in which the compositions of the minerals are accurately known is consistent with the same conclusion. The inferred equilibrium is commonly divariant; but some assemblages, such as diopside-hypersthene-hornblende-plagioclase in hornblende granulites, could well represent univariant equilibrium between phases participating in a dehydration or hydration reaction.

In the above discussion, no assumption is made as to whether the metamorphic system was open to one or more components. The phase rule tells us all we need to know as to the possibilities of equilibrium and variance in the mineral assemblage as it now exists. All we need assume is that, where metamorphic reactions involve hydration, carbonation or the reverse process, the final phase assemblage included a gas of appropriate composition. To reconstruct the possible effects of metasomatism on the final mineral assemblage, we must turn to field and textural evidence. The phase rule supplies no additional information here, nor is it profitable to consider the system as open to some (mobile) and closed to other (inert) components. This approach, which has been attempted by some geologists, has added little or nothing to our understanding of the metamorphic process beyond the information already afforded by field and textural criteria (cf. Weill and Fyfe, 1964).

The pressure variables of metamorphic equilibrium. A large rock mass undergoing metamorphism is in a state of stress induced by external forces. These include the vertical load of the overlying rock pile, and lateral forces of tectonic origin which are structurally expressed by contemporary folds and foliations. From a thermodynamic standpoint, a mineral assemblage is usually considered on a small scale, that of a hand specimen or a thin section. On this scale, the state of stress is likely to vary from one such small domain to another. But, as a first approximation, we may conceive the local stress system as controlled principally by load, and influenced to some degree by lateral constraints imposed by the surrounding rock which is itself in a state of stress.

One component of any stress system is hydrostatic. This is the pressure P postulated in thermodynamic argument. It has usually been equated with a hydrostatic pressure which would develop in a viscous body under the weight of an overlying column of rock (about 300 bars per kilometer of depth). The other component is a shearing stress whose magnitude is limited by the rheologic state of the body. The prevalence of isostatic compensation, and the widespread occurrence of flow structures (foliations and lineations), in regionally metamorphosed rocks indicate that a rock mass, during protracted recrystallization in the deeper levels of the crust, behaves essentially as a viscous body. Within it, shearing stresses of high magnitude could not be sustained for the long periods (perhaps a few million years) required for a cycle of regional metamorphism. We therefore write the thermodynamic pressure variable P as a hydrostatic load pressure P_l, in some cases augmented by an increment of "tectonic overpressure." Since the equivalent viscosity of a rock decreases exponentially with temperature (cf. Heard, pp. 182, 192–194), the increment of "tectonic overpressure" may possibly be considerable at temperatures of two or three hundred degrees (even at very low rates of strain).

In a thermodynamic system, the pressure P acts uniformly on all the associated phases. In a porous rock saturated with a fluid phase, the hydrostatic pressure within the fluid is not necessarily the same as the hydrostatic component of the stress system within the continuous aggregate of mineral grains. The difference is likely to be substantial at shallow depths, where the rock is strong and where the fluid in the pores extends continuously through joints and fissures to the earth's surface. At depths of a few km, however, experience in deep drilling for petroleum and gas shows a strong tendency for the fluid pressure P_f to approach the load pressure P_l. In our simplified model of metamorphism, we therefore assume that at depths of 10 km or more, $P_f = P_l$. This is consistent with our earlier assumption that the rock undergoing metamorphism is essentially viscous. There is one possibly significant exception: where metamorphism involves progressive upward expulsion of fluid (such as CO_2 from limestone or water from mudstone), P_f may rise to a value significantly above P_l, with the expulsion of fluid accelerated by the pressure difference.

A further simplification of the model is proposed to permit evaluation of metamorphic mineral assemblages in the light of experimental data. Progressive metamorphism commonly proceeds by a sequence of reactions involving dehydration; retrogressive metamorphism proceeds by a corresponding series of reactions of hydration. If we assume that the gas phase in such cases is pure water, we may write the partial pressure of water $P_{H_2O} = P_f = P_l$. This, we believe, closely approximates the actual conditions of metamorphism in such common instances as conversion of slate through mica schist to granulite, or in metamorphism of basalt to amphibolite or greenschist. Similarly, in considering decarbonation reactions in metamorphism of impure limestones, we may write $P_{CO_2} = P_f = P_l$. Here, however, the composition of the gas phase is likely to vary progressively during metamorphism, especially when the limestones are interbedded with shales. At the outset P_{H_2O} is likely to be high and P_{CO_2} correspondingly low. At the height of reaction, the condition postulated above ($P_{CO_2} = P_f$) may or may not be closely approximated. In the waning stages, when decarbonation ceases, water from the environment diffuses inward so that P_{H_2O} rises once more toward the limiting value when $P_{H_2O} = P_f$. This explains certain common features of metamorphic assemblages in calcareous rocks: the relatively large number of associated phases in some assemblages, the

widespread petrographic evidence of late hydration reactions (Forsterite →
Serpentine, and Periclase → Brucite), and the irregular field distribution of
particular assemblages.

Finally we turn briefly to the role of shearing stress as an independent
pressure variable. First the free energy of a stressed solid phase at constants P_l and T is increased by an amount proportional to its molar volume
(Turner and Verhoogen, 1960, p. 475). The stability fields of individual
metamorphic minerals may be changed significantly by shearing stress.
Sixty years ago Grubenmann (1904, p. 43) wrote:

> The modification of a mineral incompatible with the influence of stress
> dissolves and goes over to the corresponding heteromorphous com-
> plementary form. Augite is transformed into finely fibrous uralite or
> hornblende, andalusite into pinacoidal kyanite . . . .

Harker (1919, pp. lxxvii, lxxviii; 1932, pp. 147–151) noted that certain minerals, such as kyanite, almandine, epidotes, and staurolite occur
mainly in schists whose foliated structure bears witness to metamorphic
deformation. These he termed *stress minerals* in the belief that their
fields of stability on a *P-T* diagram are extended under the influence of
shearing stress. This extension might even be a necessary condition for the
stability of some species. By contrast, other minerals, such as andalusite,
cordierite, and forsterite, which occur mainly in undeformed rocks such as
hornfelses, were classed as *antistress minerals*. It was thought that shearing
stress reduces their stability fields, perhaps in some instances even to zero.
This hard-and-fast distinction has not been substantiated by the growing
mass of petrographic data on associations and distribution of metamorphic
minerals. Today the concept of stress and antistress minerals has fallen
into general disrepute. Instead the shearing stress is assessed simply as
an increment, perhaps not a substantial one, to the pressure factor P_l.

Shearing stress has a much more significant role in accelerating metamorphic reactions, especially at relatively low temperatures. The stress
causes the accumulation of lattice defects (dislocations), so that a strained
crystal has significantly more free energy than an unstrained crystal of the
same phase.[1] Moreover, by causing flow in a mineral aggregate, the shearing stress increases the total area of grain surface (by granulation and
fracture), renews the surface contacts between grains, and may inter-
mittently augment the permeability to fluids. Thus, shearing stress indirectly supplies the activation energy for reactions which otherwise
would be too sluggish to be effective.

---

[1] M. S. Paterson (personal communication) finds that ΔG for strained as compared
with unstrained limestone at room temperature and pressure is of the same order as ΔG
for the Calcite → Aragonite transition.

This function of stress has long been recognized as significant. Grubenmann (1904, p. 41) spoke of "the work of stress . . . in stimulation and encouragement of the chemical and mineralogical rock transformations." Field and petrographic evidence suggest that at low temperatures metamorphism is generally effective only because of the accelerating influence of the deformation caused by shearing stress. Thus in the Southern Alps of New Zealand (Lillie and Gunn, 1964), indurated graywacke has become transformed into quartz-albite-muscovite-chlorite schist in sharply limited zones of intense deformation a few thousand feet in width. Although the stability fields of the resulting low-grade mineral assemblages are defined by the variables T and P_{H_2O} ($= P_l$), the trigger that sets metamorphism in motion commonly is shearing stress.

Conclusion: An Ideal Model for Interpretation of Facies

In this book the individual metamorphic facies is interpreted in terms of an ideal simplified model, from which there may be considerable departures in specific cases. The basic assumptions are as follows:

1. The ideal mineral assemblage is a system which, at the time of its crystallization, was in equilibrium. Typically the variance is 2; but there are some assemblages which represent univariant equilibrium.

2. The assemblages belonging to any particular facies represent a rather broad range of conditions permitting some degree of mineralogical variation in some rocks of identical composition.

3. The metamorphic pressure P is determined essentially by load pressure due to the superincumbent rock column. It may thus be designated P_l. For common reactions of progressive dehydration and decarbonation, the fluid pressure P_f is assumed to equal P_l. This is the situation in progressive metamorphism of pelitic, semipelitic and calcareous rocks. For assemblages containing hydrous minerals the further assumption is made that $P_{H_2O} = P_f = P_l$; for carbonate-bearing assemblages, $P_{CO_2} = P_f = P_l$.*

4. The zonal sequences of facies corresponding to the classic zones of progressive metamorphism in the Scottish Highlands and elsewhere represent gradients in T and P ($P_l = P_f$). These are conceived as gradients in space, the dimension in time being usually of less significance.

Metamorphism usually seems to approximate the ideal model just described. Otherwise it would be hard to explain the general simplicity and regularity of metamorphic paragenesis which is the basis of the facies concept. But there are also obvious departures, some of which are enumerated below:

1. An increment of "tectonic overpressure" (stress) above the load

---

*These are the actual conditions in many experiments on metamorphic reactions involving hydrous minerals and carbonates, respectively.

pressure is always possible. It is unlikely to be large except in strong rocks at low temperatures.

2. Judging from the wide incidence of hydrous silicates and carbonates in metamorphic rocks (and in the parent sediments from which most are derived), the principal components of the pore fluid at the time of metamorphism are water and CO_2. The assumption that P_{H_2O} or $P_{CO_2} = P_f$ must in many instances be incorrect. For example where metamorphism has affected thin beds of limestone interstratified with mudstone layers, P_{H_2O} and P_{CO_2} in any given bed are likely to fluctuate inversely between a maximum (approaching P_f) and a minimum value (approaching zero).

3. On a small scale (within a thin section, a hand specimen or an outcrop), it is common to find a facies transition in time as well as in place. For example, a mass of high-grade amphibolite (hornblende-andesine) may be transformed marginally into a low-grade greenschist (chlorite-actinolite-epidote-albite-calcite) (e.g., Wiseman, 1934, p. 399). Mineral assemblages of both facies may be intimately associated in a single specimen from the zone of transition. But texture and field relations clarify the history of the rock, and demonstrate the existence of two metamorphic episodes, the second of which has partially or locally obliterated the mineralogical effects of the first. There is an element of time as well as of place in the physical gradient—falling temperature, rising water pressure, or both. Replacement of a higher by a low-grade assemblage is termed retrogressive or retrograde metamorphism (cf. Becke, 1909; Knopf, 1931; Turner, 1948, pp. 299–304). The reactions usually involve hydration, carbonation, or both.

THERMODYNAMICS OF METAMORPHIC REACTIONS

The Problem

The chemical equivalence of two mineral assemblages, each typical of a different metamorphic facies, may be brought out by writing an ideal metamorphic reaction in which the two assemblages are equated. For example,

$$SiO_2 + KAl_2(AlSi_3O_{10})(OH)_2 \rightleftharpoons KAlSi_3O_8 + Al_2SiO_5 + H_2O$$

Quartz   Muscovite   K-Feldspar   Sillimanite

and

$$4SiO_2 + 3Mg_3Fe_2Al(AlSi_3O_{10})(OH)_8 \rightleftharpoons 3Fe_2MgAl_2(Si_3O_{12})$$

Quartz   Prochlorite   Almandine

$$+ Mg_6(Si_4O_{10})(OH)_8 + 8H_2O$$

Antigorite

Such reactions are usually simplified versions of the more complex changes occurring in metamorphic rocks, for in nature all the phases represented in a metamorphic assemblage usually participate in the reaction leading to a new assemblage that is more stable under the new conditions. Nevertheless it is profitable to study as a first approximation the simplified ideal reaction, especially where this can be investigated experimentally.

Metamorphic reactions are of course subject to the laws of thermodynamics. This aspect of metamorphism was the subject of the classical essay of Johnston and Niggli (1913). It has been elaborated in some detail by J. Verhoogen and W. S. Fyfe (Fyfe, Turner, and Verhoogen, 1958, pp. 21–148; Turner and Verhoogen, 1960, pp. 458–487). Our present discussion, based mainly on these latter works, will be limited to a few fundamental problems treated as simply as possible. We would like to evaluate the pressure-temperature limits of stability of common metamorphic assemblages. We ask ourselves at what temperatures and pressures are critical metamorphic reactions (1) possible and (2) likely to occur. What is the effect of the presence of an additional mineral phase E upon a reaction

$$A + B \rightleftharpoons C + D$$

Why do metamorphic assemblages formed at high pressure and temperature so often survive as metastable assemblages at surface pressure and temperature?

Thermodynamics can supply at least partial answers to such questions, given adequate experimental data. Present uncertainties, as we shall see later, stem from current inadequacy of thermodynamic data relating to metamorphic minerals at the temperatures and pressures of metamorphism. Thermodynamics, moreover, can supply us with the only rigorous definitions and criteria of stability and equilibrium—concepts that loom large in the modern literature of metamorphic petrology.

Reversibility of Reactions

At some constant temperature T and pressure P, a reaction

$$A + B \rightleftharpoons C + D$$

is reversible if it tends to proceed from left to right for an infinitesimal change in either condition, while for an infinitesimal change of opposite sign it tends to proceed from right to left. At temperature T and pressure P the assemblage of phases $(A + B + C + D)$ is in equilibrium; assemblages $(A + B)$ and $(C + D)$ are equally stable. Thus at 0°C and 1 bar the system water-ice is in univariant equilibrium. The two phases are equally stable. Conversely, an irreversible reaction

$$A + B \rightarrow C + D$$

is one that may occur spontaneously at some other constant temperature T_1 and pressure P_1. The phase assemblage $(A + B + C + D)$ is in disequilibrium, and the assemblage (C + D) is more stable than (A + B). Such is the case with the polymorphic transition

Aragonite → Calcite

at 400°C and 1 bar.

Between 0 and 25°C and 1 bar, neither calcite nor aragonite shows any tendency to change to the other polymorph. Yet according to the phase rule the variance of the system calcite-aragonite is 1, so that at a given pressure (1 bar) the two-phase assemblage cannot be in equilibrium over a range of temperature (0 to 25°C). One phase must be more stable than the other. To evaluate their relative stabilities we must turn from direct experimental observation to another thermodynamic property: the entropy of each polymorph.

Entropy of Reaction ΔS

The reader is reminded that the entropy S of a system (a quantity reflecting the degree of internal disorder in the system) is defined by the statement that in any *reversible* reaction

$$\Delta S = \frac{\Delta q}{T}$$

where q is the quantity of heat absorbed and T is the temperature, Kelvin ($T°K$). The third law of thermodynamics assumes that, with certain qualifications (cf. Fyfe, Turner, and Verhoogen, 1958, pp. 27–28), the entropy of a perfect crystal at $0°K$ is zero. From measurements of molar heat capacity c at $P = 1$ bar over the interval 0 to 298°K, the molar entropy S of a phase at room temperature (298°K) and pressure (1 bar) may be calculated thus:[1]

$$S = \int_0^{298} \frac{dq}{T} = \int_0^{298} \frac{c\ dT}{T} = \int_0^{298} c\ d(\ln T)$$

To calculate S for mineral phases at metamorphic pressures and temperatures it would be necessary to have additional data over the appropriate range of conditions—specific heats, molar volumes, compressibilities, and coefficients of thermal expansion. These are lacking for most minerals. However, in the realm of inorganic chemistry, values of entropy from room temperature to several hundred degrees centigrade at atmospheric pressure are known for a host of compounds (Kelley and King, 1961; Kelley, 1960).

---

[1] Experimental procedure is outlined, and entropy data for many inorganic compounds including some minerals are given, in Kelley and King (1961).

General experience has shown that, without known exception, in any *irreversible* reaction,

$$\Delta S > \frac{\Delta q}{T}$$

This important conclusion, known as the *second law of thermodynamics*, is the basis of an unequivocal definition of irreversibility of reactions. It is also a means of rigorously defining the relative stability of chemically equivalent phase assemblages.

For example, take the reaction, at 298°K and 1 bar (Kracek, Neuvonen, and Burley, 1951):

$$\underset{\text{Jadeite}}{NaAlSi_2O_6} + \underset{\text{Quartz}}{SiO_2} \rightarrow \underset{\text{Albite}}{NaAlSi_3O_8}$$

$$T \Delta S = 2.5 \text{ kcal/mole}$$

$$\Delta q = 0.6 \text{ kcal/mole}$$

So albite at room temperature and pressure is more stable than jadeite-quartz. The reaction is irreversible even though no one has yet succeeded in converting (jadeite + quartz) to albite under the specified conditions.[1]

Free Energy of Reaction ΔG: A Criterion of Stability

The Gibbs free energy G of a system at constant temperature T and pressure P is written

$$G = E + PV - TS$$

where E is the internal energy, V the volume, and S the entropy of the system. For any reaction within the system

$$\Delta G = \Delta E + P \Delta V - T \Delta S$$
$$= (\Delta q - P \Delta V) + P \Delta V - T \Delta S$$
$$= \Delta q - T \Delta S$$

For a reaction at constant pressure this may be written

$$\Delta G = \Delta H - T \Delta S$$

where ΔH is the enthalpy of reaction at constant pressure.

The expression ΔG is a convenient index of the relative stability of phase assemblages and of the reversibility of reactions connecting them. For a reaction

$$A + B \rightarrow C + D$$

---

[1] For this reason, ΔH was determined indirectly from the respective heats of solution of the three phases in hydrofluoric acid.

if ΔG is negative, the reaction is irreversible and may occur spontaneously; if ΔG is zero, the reaction is reversible.

In the latter case, (A + B) and (C + D) are equally stable, and the system (A + B + C + D) is in equilibrium. But there may be a third chemically equivalent assemblage (E + F) such that for both the reactions

$$A + B \rightarrow E + F \quad \text{and} \quad C + D \rightarrow E + F$$

ΔG is negative. Then (E + F) is the most stable assemblage. (A + B + C + D) is a metastable equilibrium; an example is aragonite in contact with its saturated solution in water at room temperature and pressure. Assemblages (A + B) or (C + D) may show no tendency to change to the stable assemblage (E + F). They are termed metastable assemblages. Many metamorphic mineral assemblages, though presumed to be stable at metamorphic temperatures and pressures, are metastable under ordinary room conditions.

With respect to petrologic problems the terms stable, metastable, and equilibrium should be used only in the strict thermodynamic sense as defined in terms of free energy.

Coupled Reactions

Statement of the principle. Most experimental data bearing on metamorphic reactions refer to simple changes, such as polymorphous inversions, or the breakdown and synthesis of pure mineral phases such as muscovite, tremolite, phlogopite, wollastonite, and so on. On the other hand natural metamorphic reactions (with rare exceptions) are complex. They generally involve transformation of one multi-phase assemblage into another, with active participation of all phases present (cf. Tilley, 1926). Moreover, since many metamorphic minerals are members of isomorphous series, survival of a phase such as biotite or ilmenite (present in both assemblages) more often than not is accompanied by marked change in its chemical composition.[1]

The application of experimental data to problems of metamorphic paragenesis is limited by two axiomatic principles:

1. The stability field of any phase assemblage (A + B) must encompass the stability fields of all other assemblages (A + B + C) etc. of which A and B are both members. Thus the temperature-pressure range over which jadeite has been found by experiment to be stable cannot be extended in nature by the presence of additional associated minerals such as lawsonite or glaucophane.

---

[1] The nature and widespread incidence of such compositional changes in isomorphous series is only now beginning to be appreciated as a result of detailed studies of mineral compositions made possible by modern methods of separation and analysis and especially by use of the electron microprobe analyzer.

2. Under appropriate conditions the stability field of a phase assemblage $(A + B)$[1] may be reduced in the presence of an additional phase C. For example, at any given temperature, jadeite alone is stable over a range of pressures below those at which (jadeite + quartz) is stable.

To explore further the conditions that make possible a reduction of the stability fields of individual metamorphic minerals we turn to the concept of the coupled reaction (Turner and Verhoogen, 1960, p. 469; Fyfe, Turner, and Verhoogen, 1961). Consider the primary reaction at some specified temperature and pressure:

(1) $A + B \rightarrow C + D$

with free energy change ΔG_1. The boundaries of the respective fields of stability of $(A + B)$ and $(C + D)$ on a pressure-temperature diagram may become significantly changed by the presence of an additional phase E, if a coupling reaction of the form

(2) $C + E \rightarrow F + H$

with free energy change ΔG_2, is possible. The two may then combine as a coupled reaction

(3) $A + B + E \rightarrow D + F + H$

with free energy change

$$\Delta G_3 = \Delta G_1 + \Delta G_2$$

As possible products of this series of reactions there are three chemically equivalent three-phase assemblages: $(A + B + E)$, $(C + D + E)$, and $(D + F + H)$.

$(A + B + E)$ is stable when ΔG_1 and ΔG_2 are both positive; or when ΔG_1 is positive and ΔG_2 negative, with ΔG_1 arithmetically greater than ΔG_2.

$(C + D + E)$ is stable when ΔG_1 is negative and ΔG_2 positive.

$(D + F + H)$ is stable when ΔG_1 and ΔG_2 are both negative; or when ΔG_1 is positive and ΔG_2 negative, with ΔG_1 arithmetically less than ΔG_2.

Which of these conditions may be possible at any given temperature and pressure depends upon three factors:

1. The respective signs of the entropies of reaction ΔS_1 and ΔS_2 for reactions (1) and (2), respectively.

2. The relative values of the respective equilibrium temperatures t_1 and t_2 for reactions (1) and (2) at the given pressure.

---

[1] This wording most clearly expresses to a geologist what he may infer as to *P-T* conditions of metamorphism from some index mineral assemblage. The criticism of this usage by Fawcett and Yoder (*Am. Mineral.*, vol. 51, p. 373, 1966) seems to be a quibble in semantics.

3. The relative slopes of the curves for ΔG_1 and ΔG_2 plotted against temperature at the same pressure. Since for any reaction (cf. Fyfe, Turner, and Verhoogen, 1958, p. 25)

$$\left(\frac{\partial \Delta G}{\partial T}\right)_P = -\Delta S$$

the curve $\Delta G/T$—with T plotted horizontally—will be steep for a reaction with large ΔS.

All possible combinations of the above conditions can be expressed in terms of four general cases which will be presented below. In every case the stability field of $(C + D + E)$ is restricted to the area of overlap of the respective fields of $(C + D)$ and $(C + E)$. The fields of $(A + B)$ and of $(F + H)$ may or may not be reduced in the presence of E and of D, respectively. In some cases one of the three-phase assemblages may have no field of stability. In discussing the significance of the four cases in metamorphism, it must be remembered that most metamorphic reactions involve either dehydration, decarbonation, reapportionment of cations in isomorphous mineral series, participation of quartz as a reacting phase, or some combination of these processes.

Case 1. Let ΔS_1 and ΔS_2 both be positive, with $t_1 < t_2$ (Fig. 2-2a).[1] There is no field for which ΔG_1 is positive and ΔG_2 at the same time negative, so the stability fields of $(A + B)$ and $(F + H)$ are unaffected by coupling. At any pressure p there is a temperature t_3, between t_1 and t_2, at which ΔG_3 is zero. Here there is *metastable* equilibrium between $(A + B + E)$ and $(D + F + H)$; but both assemblages are less stable than $(C + D + E)$. This situation will occur in progressive metamorphism where a particular phase (cf. C above) appears as the product of an early reaction and disappears at some higher grade of metamorphism.

According to Thompson (1957, p. 856) a possible sequence of reactions in progressive metamorphism of pelitic rocks is

(1) Staurolite + Quartz → Almandine + Sillimanite + Water

(2) Sillimanite + Biotite → Almandine + Cordierite + Potash feldspar
$$+ \text{ Water}$$

The breakdown of staurolite [reaction (1)] is unaffected by the presence of biotite.

---

[1] Each case can be stated in an alternative form by interchanging, renumbering, and reversing reactions (1) and (2):

(1) $\qquad\qquad\qquad\qquad F + H \rightarrow C + E$
(2) $\qquad\qquad\qquad\qquad C + D \rightarrow A + B$
(3) $\qquad\qquad\qquad\qquad D + F + H \rightarrow A + B + E$

Case (1) can then be restated:

$\qquad\qquad\qquad \Delta S_1$ and ΔS_2 both negative $\quad t_1 > t_2$

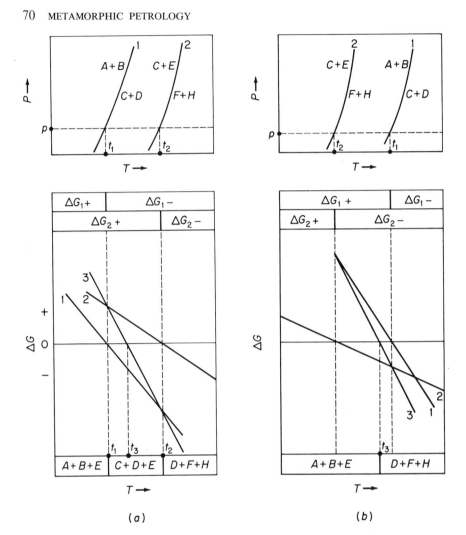

Fig. 2-2. Hypothetical curves illustrating coupled reactions. The upper part of each figure shows the equilibrium curves for the reactions (1) $A + B \rightleftharpoons C + D$ and (2) $C + E \rightleftharpoons F + H$. The lower figure, drawn for constant pressure P, shows the fields of stability of chemically equivalent three-phase assemblages. Numbers refer to reactions similarly numbered in the text.

Similarly, the reaction

(1)   Analcite + Quartz → Albite + Water

marking the transition from what we shall later term the zeolitic to the greenschist facies in low-grade progressive metamorphism, is unaffected by

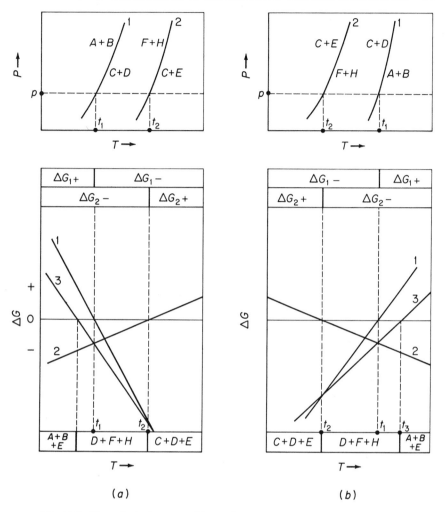

Fig. 2-3. Hypothetical curves illustrating coupled reactions. The upper part of each figure shows the equilibrium curves for the reactions (1) $A + B \rightleftharpoons C + D$ and (2) $C + E \rightleftharpoons F + H$. The lower figure, drawn for constant pressure P, shows the fields of stability of chemically equivalent three-phase assemblages. Numbers refer to reactions similarly numbered in the text.

the presence of clinozoisite, even though at higher temperatures there is a reaction

(2) Albite + Clinozoisite + Al_2O_3* → Plagioclase + Water

*Derived from a coexisting aluminous mineral such as chlorite.

At some intermediate temperature equilibrium in the coupled reaction

(3) Analcite + Quartz + Clinozoisite + $Al_2O_3 \rightleftharpoons$ Plagioclase + Water

is metastable. The stable assemblage is albite + clinozoisite + water.

   Case 2. Let ΔS_1 and ΔS_2 both be positive, with $t_1 > t_2$ (Fig. 2-2b). There is no field in which ΔG_1 is negative and ΔG_2 is positive, so (C + D + E) is nowhere stable. Coupling reduces the stability field of (A + B) in the presence of E and of (F + H) in the presence of D. A necessary condition is that some phase C which becomes unstable in the presence of E at a low temperature should appear at some higher temperature associated with phase D. There are only two situations where such conditions are likely to arise in metamorphism: (1) where C and E are members of a solid-solution series (albite-anorthite; spessartite-almandine); (2) where silica is a product of reaction (1).

   Spessartite commonly appears in somewhat manganiferous sediments in the chlorite zone of regional metamorphism. With increasing metamorphic grade, its presence might permit the wholesale development of almandine-rich garnet [reaction (3), below] at temperatures somewhat lower than would be the case in the absence of spessartite.

(1) Micas$_1$* + Chlorites → Almandine + Micas$_2$ + Water

(2) Almandine + Spessartite → Spessartite-almandine

(3) Micas$_1$ + Chlorites + Spessartite → Spessartite-almandine
$$+ \text{Micas}_2 + \text{Water}$$

Again the breakdown of grossularite to anorthite + wollastonite at high temperatures and low pressures should be accelerated by the presence of albite:

(1)   Grossularite → Anorthite + Wollastonite

(2)   Anorthite + Albite → Oligoclase-andesine

(3)   Grossularite + Albite → Wollastonite + Oligoclase-andesine

Exemplifying this reaction is the association of the assemblages calcite-diopside-wollastonite-oligoclase and calcite-diopside-grossularite in contact aureoles of the western Sierra Nevada of California (Durrell, 1940, pp. 58–60).

   Case 3. Let ΔS_1 be positive, ΔS_2 be negative, and $t_1 < t_2$.† From

---

*The micas change composition and relative abundance during reaction.

†This case can be rewritten [by reversing and interchanging reactions (1) and (2)] as ΔS_1 positive, ΔS_2 negative, $t_1 > t_2$.

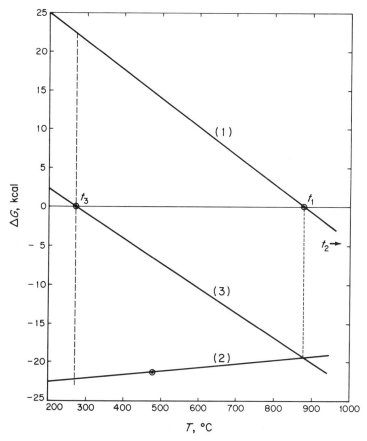

Fig. 2-4. Variation in ΔG with temperature for reactions at $P_{CO_2} = 1$ bar: (1) $CaCO_3 \rightarrow CaO + CO_2$; (2) $CaO + SiO_2 \rightarrow CaSiO_3$. Curves drawn from standard thermochemical data at $700°K$, $P_{CO_2} = 1$ bar. (*Turner*, 1967, p. 4.) Curve for coupled reaction (2), (3) $CaCO_3 + SiO_2 \rightarrow CaSiO_3 + CO_2$, is constructed from curves 1 and 2. Equilibrium temperatures are t_1, t_2, t_3.

Fig. 2-3*a*, it will be seen that coupling reduces the stability fields of (A + B + E) compared with (A + B), and of (D + F + H) compared with (F + H). If the ΔG curve for reaction (1) in the lower half of the figure is flatter than that for reaction (2), then there is no field of stability for (A + B + E). There are many metamorphically significant reactions of this type, especially where reaction (2) represents the synthesis of a silicate from its component oxides. Consider, for example, the breakdown of muscovite at high grades of metamorphism:

(1)   Muscovite → Potash feldspar + Corundum + Water

(2)   Corundum + Quartz → Sillimanite

(3)   Muscovite + Quartz → Potash feldspar + Sillimanite + Water

Since reaction (1) involves liberation of a fluid phase, ΔS_1 must be considerably greater than ΔS_2; so the curve $\Delta G_1/T$ must be steeper than $\Delta G_2/T$ (cf. Fig. 2-3a).[1] Thus there is a limited range of temperature below t_1 for which muscovite will break down in the presence of quartz. Experimental data (Evans, 1965) show that at $P_{H_2O} = 2000$ bars, reaction (1) takes place at 670 to 680°C, and reaction (2) at some 80° lower.

A familiar example is the reaction between calcite and quartz to produce wollastonite in metamorphism of limestone (illustrated quantitatively in Fig. 2-4):

(1) $CaCO_3 \rightarrow CaO + CO_2$

(2) $CaO + SiO_2 \rightarrow CaSiO_3$

(3) $CaCO_3 + SiO_2 \rightarrow CaSiO_3$

At $P_{CO_2} = 1$ bar the equilibrium temperature of reaction (1) is estimated as about 870°C (Turner, 1967, p. 9). The coupling effect of reaction (2) is to lower the temperature of stability of calcite (in the presence of quartz) by about 600° [equilibrium temperature of reaction (3) is about 270°C].

Case 4. Let ΔS_1 be negative, ΔS_2 positive, and $t_1 > t_2$† (Fig. 2-3b). As in case 3, (A + B + E) has no stability field if the ΔG curve for reaction (1) is flatter than that for reaction (2). In metamorphism this combination of reactions is likely to be significant where reaction (2) expresses the mixing of end members in an isomorphous mineral series. For example:

(1)   Albite → Jadeite + Quartz

(2)   Jadeite + Aegirine → Aegirine-jadeite

(3)   Albite + Aegirine → Aegirine-jadeite + Quartz

The curve of univariant equilibrium for reaction (1.) has been determined experimentally (e.g., Robertson, Birch, and MacDonald, 1957; Fyfe and Valpy, 1959). At 8 to 10 kb the equilibrium temperature is perhaps only 100°C, or even less. However, from Fig. 2-3b it follows that for any such pressure range the (D + F + H) assemblage (aegirine-jadeite solid solution + quartz) will be stable up to temperatures that may be much beyond

---

[1] If the reverse were the case there would be no field in which (A + B + E) were stable.
† This can be rewritten [by reversing and interchanging reactions (1) and (2)] as ΔS_1 negative, ΔS_2 positive, $t_1 < t_2$.

the stability range of the (A + B + E) assemblage (pure jadeite + quartz). This explains the wide prevalence of aegirine-bearing jadeites associated with quartz in many glaucophane-schist terranes. The much rarer assemblage (aegirine + albite) represents higher temperatures (or lower pressures).

KINETICS OF METAMORPHIC REACTIONS

On the basis of free-energy data, thermodynamics can predict whether a reaction is possible. To predict further whether a possible reaction is likely to occur spontaneously under given conditions, we turn to experimental experience on reaction rates interpreted in terms of theory in which the system is viewed on the molecular scale.

Any reaction between minerals involves relative motion and re-grouping of ions and atoms. Before this can occur, bonds must be broken and ions must be able to diffuse through intergranular fluids, along grain boundaries, or even through crystal structures, to reach favorable sites where nucleation of new phases is in progress. Obviously, there are energy barriers which must be surmounted before a thermodynamically possible reaction becomes a reality. Moreover, nucleation of new phases plays an important role in reaction. The new nuclei must be able to grow to sufficient size to be truly stable if the reaction is to be effective. Ions must be able to diffuse (through fluid or solid) sufficiently fast for nuclei to develop to stable proportions before they spontaneously break down because of instability inherent in very small size.

In order to treat rigorously the problem of whether the velocity of a possible reaction will be appreciable under given conditions, we need to take account of molecular fluctuations within macroscopically homogeneous phases. Essential to reaction is the transient development of particles of high free energy (the *activated complex*) which spontaneously regroup or break down to yield stable nuclei of the newly growing phases of minimal free energy. A full treatment of the problem is beyond the scope of this book. But it is helpful to note some general conclusions drawn from more rigorous discussion elsewhere and verified by experiment (Fyfe, Turner, and Verhoogen, 1958, pp. 53–103; Turner and Verhoogen, 1960, pp. 48–49, 478–484):

1. A metamorphic reaction involves three interdependent processes: liberation of particles from the structural networks that make up crystals of the initial phases, diffusion of particles to sites where regrouping is possible, and nucleation of the new stable phases at such sites. The rate of a given reaction is the rate of the slowest of these processes.

2. Reaction rates have been found by experiment to increase exponentially with temperature. A general equation relating the experi-

mentally measured rate K to temperature, and to energy or heat of activation E, is

$$K = Ae^{-E/RT}$$

E is a measure of the energy barrier that separates the initial form from the final state. A is a "frequency factor" representing the number of activated particles that enter into reaction in unit time. E may be determined experimentally by measuring K at different temperatures (over a range for which A varies slightly) and plotting $\ln K$ against $1/T$. It is found that K is not greatly affected by change in pressure.

3. Reaction rates increase exponentially with the activation entropy $\Delta S^{\ddagger}$. This usually has the same sign as the entropy of reaction ΔS.

4. Rates of diffusion through ionic crystals are extremely slow. They may be significantly accelerated by lattice defects due to strain or impurities, and by increase in the total proportion of disorganized surface matter due to small grain size in an aggregate.

5. Nucleation tends to be slow since a small nucleus, by the very nature of its large ratio surface/volume, is unstable compared with a larger grain. The nucleus, presumably as a result of fluctuations, must reach a critical size before it becomes stable and can survive under given conditions.

6. Because of high activation energies necessary to disrupt crystal lattices and slow rates of solid diffusion and nucleation, reaction between solids is very slow in the range of metamorphic temperatures and pressures.

7. Most reactions are accelerated by the presence of water; it must be remembered that in metamorphism an aqueous intergranular film is widely prevalent. The equilibrium temperature T_e must be overstepped to a temperature T at which solution, diffusion and nucleation are rapid enough for the reaction to proceed spontaneously. The degree of overstepping, $\Delta T = (T - T_e)$ increases with temperature, but varies inversely with the reaction entropy ΔS.

Metastable Metamorphic Minerals

From time to time the question has been raised as to whether common metamorphic minerals, especially the index minerals of metamorphic zones and subfacies, crystallize as metastable phases or persist metastably from an earlier stage and so survive as constituents of the later and principal stage of metamorphism. If this were indeed so our treatment of standard metamorphic assemblages as equilibria would be seriously at fault.

We have seen that solid $\rightleftharpoons$ solid reactions among anhydrous silicates are usually accompanied by only slight changes in entropy and free energy. This fact has been referred to (Fyfe, Turner, and Verhoogen, 1958, p. 22) as "the plague of small ΔG's" in metamorphic reactions. Simple instances are certain first-order polymorphous transitions such as andalusite $\rightleftharpoons$ sillimanite $\rightleftharpoons$ kyanite, anthophyllite $\rightleftharpoons$ cummingtonite and calcite $\rightleftharpoons$ aragonite. So the possibility arises that, in some spontaneous reactions, other factors than minimization of free energy may determine which of two polymorphs crystallizes. Chemists have long recognized a principle known as Ostwald's step rule, which states that there is a tendency for preference of that reaction which involves minimum ΔS rather than minimum ΔG. Such is the crystallization of cristobalite from silica glass within the temperature range over which α-quartz is the truly stable phase. Again adularia, crystallizing in low-temperature veins, usually has the structure of sanidine, the high-temperature polymorph of $KAlSi_3O_8$. The coexistence of andalusite, sillimanite and kyanite in some pelitic schists, and perhaps the association of cummingtonite and anthophyllite in magnesian hornfelses, possibly reflect the metastable condition of one or more of the phases concerned. It is likely, then, that kyanite, sillimanite, or andalusite may be a metastable member of the metamorphic assemblage even when occurring alone. The well-known tendency for sillimanite to replace mica suggests that crystallization of this particular phase, rather than andalusite or kyanite, may be due in some instances to a smaller value of ΔS in the breakdown of mica to sillimanite as contrasted with andalusite or kyanite. Sillimanite could then be metastable from the moment of its formation.

Crystallization of metastable phases is also likely in the earliest stages of metamorphism, represented by the zeolite facies and by rocks of the chlorite zone. Here, low temperatures slow down metamorphic reaction rates. At temperatures of perhaps 200 to 300°C, a parent aggregate of clay minerals, feldspar, and quartz in a mudstone is highly unstable. The respective values of ΔG for a number of possible metamorphic reactions are all correspondingly high. When the temperature rises to a point where reaction velocities become appreciable, the nature of the product is likely to depend upon such factors as minimal change in entropy or favorable conditions of nucleation, rather than attainment of minimal possible free energy. Moreover, even within an isochemical rock series, the temperature and products of reaction will depend partly upon the mineralogical nature of the parent material, especially the nature of the clay minerals (cf. Yoder, 1955, p. 513). On these grounds one might expect considerable mineralogical variation among the zeolites, chlorites, micas, etc. that appear in the earlier stages of metamorphism. Some such variety is indeed encountered. But, perhaps surprisingly, there is a remarkable degree of uniformity among the reaction products: the common zeolites are heulandite and laumontite, the mica is phengitic muscovite, and the chlorite is at first celadonite, later a prochlorite.

Other questions relating to metastability may be raised. One concerns the possible survival of metastable phases from early episodes of metamorphism. For example, in eastern Otago, New Zealand, the common metamorphic assemblage in derivatives of graywacke is quartz-albite-chlorite-muscovite-epidote. But there are local areas in which the same minerals are accompanied by biotite and almandine garnet (Brown, 1963, p. 858). Is one or both of these a metastable survival from an earlier episode of crystallization at relatively high temperature? Or are they co-members, along with quartz, albite, chlorite and muscovite, of an equilibrium assemblage? Progressive chloritization of garnet and biotite in ploymetamorphic rocks elsewhere may supply an answer, testifying to the metastable status of the partly destroyed phases. In the Otago rocks there is no such textural evidence of metastability; an answer—in this case favoring true equilibrium—can be provided only by generalizations regarding rates of hydration reactions (see below). On these grounds, too, we cannot accept the proposition put forward by Yoder (1952, pp. 620-622) that some or all of the currently recognized isograds are determined by kinetics of reaction rather than by equilibrium temperatures and pressures.

With these possibilities and doubts in mind, this writer nevertheless upholds the earlier postulate (pp. 54-55) that the common metamorphic mineral assemblages approximate equilibria, each governed by a rather narrow range of temperature and pressure. Metastability of phases with respect to conditions of metamorphism is considered to be the exception, not the rule. Isograds, contrary to the view of Yoder, are thought to be but little influenced by kinetic factors. Behind these statements lie two important generalizations, each based on a multitude of observations. First is the simplicity of commonly occurring mineral assemblages, and the comparative uniformity of their development and mutual field relations in many parts of the world. Second is a significant generalization drawn from experiment and theory of reaction rates. Most metamorphic reactions involve hydration or dehydration, or (in calcareous rocks) the participation of a fluid rich in CO_2. Entropies of such reactions are high; and the overstepping beyond equilibrium temperature to a point where reaction is rapid must be correspondingly low. Failure to react is to be expected only in completely dehydrated systems impermeable to water from an external source, or in those rare reactions such as sillimanite $\rightleftharpoons$ kyanite whose entropies are small and in which a gas phase does not participate.

> Barring the case of utterly dry rocks or of reactions with very small entropies, the physical factors which affect the reaction kinetics are not very different from those that govern equilibrium: the physical conditions that determine equilibrium are likely to determine kinetic conditions as well. It is unlikely, under geologic conditions, that assemblages characteristic of different facies could develop under identical conditions of temperature and pressure merely because of differences in reaction kinetics . . . . Progressive metamorphism in nature represents gradients in temperature and pressure variables. (Fyfe, Turner, and Verhoogen, 1958, p. 103)

Survival of High-grade Facies

During unloading by erosion, any high-grade mineral assemblage that has crystallized in the depths becomes subjected to progressively decreasing temperatures and pressures over a time interval measured in millions of years. Elsewhere the same conditions have resulted in low-grade metamorphism. How, then, can high-grade assemblages survive, with little or no change, prolonged exposure to the temperature-pressure range of low-grade metamorphism? The same problem is posed by survival of igneous mineral assemblages during cooling of a pluton. Why does the assemblage plagioclase-pyroxene-olivine of gabbros survive postconsolidational cooling from 800°C, when it is converted to the low-grade assemblage albite-epidote-chlorite-actinolite by regional metamorphism at perhaps 300 to 400°C?

A partial answer was proposed by Becke (1903, p. 34). He assumed that metamorphic reactions proceed much more rapidly with rising than with falling temperatures. This view found general acceptance (e.g., Harker, 1932, p. 11; Eskola, 1939, p. 318; Turner, 1948, p. 301); the common mineral assemblages of metamorphic rocks have been widely interpreted as equilibria expressing the maximum temperatures attained during the cycle of burial, deformation and unloading. There is indeed experimental evidence of, and theoretical justification for, difference between the respective rates of forward and backward reaction (cf. Fyfe, Turner, and Verhoogen, 1958, pp. 97–98). The difference could be great for reactions in which the overstepping ΔT is high; for instance, where the reaction entropy ΔS is small. This is the case for most reactions between dry solids, such as polymorphic transitions. Here the high-temperature polymorph or mineral assemblage is likely to persist unchanged during a period of slowly falling temperature. Most metamorphic reactions, however, involve participation of a fluid phase such as water or CO_2. Here ΔS is large, ΔT is correspondingly small, and the high-temperature assemblage is unlikely to survive prolonged exposure to lower temperatures.[1] The fact that such assemblages do survive must be due to some other factor, most probably to the special role of water (or CO_2).

Progressive metamorphism of sediments involves steady expulsion of a fluid phase. Reactions will be, geologically speaking, rapid, and overstepping of the equilibrium temperature is likely to be small. Thus it is probable that the pelitic assemblage of the sillimanite zone has in turn passed through the successive states represented by all the zones of lower grade. Associated anhydrous rocks may also become hydrated at the lower

---

[1] High pressure reduces the value of ΔS for hydration reactions and so increases the chance of survival of the high-grade assemblage.

grades provided they are sufficiently permeable. Contemporary deformation seems to facilitate this process. Such is the conversion of basalt or diabase to greenschist (albite-chlorite-epidote-actinolite) in the chlorite zone.[1] Here the rate of reaction is determined by the rate of inward diffusion of water. This is generally negligible in the central portions of thick sills, for in many such bodies a relatively unaltered central zone is margined by a border of greenschist or amphibolite.

The climax of metamorphism in the high-grade zones is expressed by relatively anhydrous coarse-grained rocks. Recrystallization and crystal growth outlasting deformation have sealed the intergranular pores and reduced the permeability to very low values. In the absence of water, the mineral assemblages of such rocks tend to survive subsequent cooling unchanged. There may be microscopic evidence of incipient changes along grain boundaries, e.g., growth of amphibole by incipient hydration of pyroxene. Probably more general is a microscopically invisible marginal redistribution of cations resulting from diffusion across grain boundaries, e.g., zonal variation in ratios $Fe/Mg/Mn$ revealed in crystals of garnet and iron ores by the electron microprobe analyzer. Coronas of hypersthene around olivine grains and of garnet, pyroxene, and spinel around iron ores in metamorphosed gabbro and anorthosite are similarly interpreted as products of incomplete reaction between dry mineral grains. Here, however, the high-temperature parent assemblages are igneous.

Retrogressive Metamorphism

There are circumstances in which high-grade mineral assemblages fail to survive exposure to lower metamorphic temperatures. They then become converted to low-grade assemblages, the process being termed retrogressive metamorphism or diaphthoresis (Becke, 1909; Knopf, 1931; Harker, 1932, pp. 342–356). It can be recognized with certainty only when its effects are incomplete, as when a low-grade quartz-muscovite-chlorite-carbonate schist contains undestroyed remnants of garnet and staurolite crystals surviving from the parent high-grade assemblage. So there is always a possibility that some low-grade schists lacking such relics may in reality be products of retrogressive metamorphism carried to completion.

The problem of retrogressive metamorphism has been generally visualized as one of reaction kinetics. Retrogressive effects are characteristically displayed by strongly foliated or lineated rocks (schists and phyllonites) showing textural evidence of intense deformation preceding or accompanying crystallization of the low-grade mineral assemblage. Elsewhere (pp. 59–62) we have discussed the role of shearing stress and resultant

---

[1] Even though this reac 'on occurs in response to an episode of rising temperatures it is in fact a "backward" reaction; for the parent assemblage was stable at a higher temperature than the metamorphic product.

strain effects in accelerating metamorphic reactions. This role was emphasized by Becke and Knopf and was considered by them to be essential in stepping up the rates of reactions at low temperature to the point where retrogressive metamorphism becomes effective.

> If adjustment to the new pressure-temperature field is to take place, the instigating force or trigger of the reaction must be furnished by a strong differential movement of the constituent parts before or together with diaphthoresis. (Knopf, 1931, p. 7)

More fundamental still is free accessibility of an aqueous or CO_2-rich fluid, capable of penetrating the reacting system on a microscopic scale (Schwarz and Todd, 1941). Such a fluid not only greatly accelerates reaction rates by increasing rates of diffusion, but also is an essential phase participating in retrogressive reactions; for, except for polymorphic transformations, these involve either hydration or carbonation or both. It is not unlikely that the principal role of deformation in retrogressive metamorphism is to increase, at least temporarily, the permeability of rocks, and on a larger scale to localize and accelerate diffusion of fluids in zones of dislocation. The widespread tendency for segregation of individual minerals in laminae and veins in foliated low-grade metamorphic rocks testifies to the effectiveness of diffusion—probably through the medium of pore fluids—in rocks affected by deformation at low temperatures and high pressures.

Reaction Kinetics and the Significance of Isograds

Isograds in an area of progressive regional metamorphism are generally interpreted as corresponding to points on a temperature-pressure gradient. It follows, from our assumption that the critical mineral assemblages of each of the intervening zones approximate equilibria, that the appearance of each index mineral at an isograd marks attainment of the equilibrium temperature and pressure of a corresponding metamorphic reaction. Thus the garnet isograd in pelitic rocks is thought to express a point on the curve of univariant equilibrium of a garnet-producing reaction.

The validity of this viewpoint has been challenged by Yoder (1952, pp. 620–623) who regards "the appearance of garnet in progressive metamorphism . . . as being dependent on the rate of growth and not on the attainment of a particular pressure and temperature." He states in support of this conclusion

> Since reaction rates vary with grain size, composition (including volatiles), and temperature, it should not be uncommon to find reversals of the normal sequence of mineral isograds (for example see Goldschmidt, 1920, p. 48). Statistically, however, the normal sequence will obtain. This may be interpreted to mean that, in general, the rate of growth of chlorite > biotite > garnet.

This writer can find no evidence to justify Yoder's contention, except with respect to the "chlorite isograd" marking the initiation of metamorphism (cf. Yoder, 1955, p. 513). Here we are concerned with transition from a metastable clay-mineral assemblage to a stable metamorphic mica-chlorite assemblage. The temperature and pressure of reaction will depend on the nature of the starting materials and to some degree upon kinetics of reaction. But the "chlorite isograd," if indeed it is ever shown on a map, must always be arbitrarily drawn. The only question regarding the possible role of kinetics in determining the other isograds is this: what degree of overstepping of the equilibrium temperature is necessary to initiate the various reactions responsible for first appearance of the index minerals biotite, almandine, staurolite, and so on? These reactions, almost without exception, involve dehydration; so the reaction entropy ΔS is relatively high, and water is present as a participating phase. For such reactions overstepping is minimal. The mineral assemblages "should remain adjusted, with a lag of not more than a few degrees, to the prevailing temperature" (Fyfe, Turner, and Verhoogen, 1958, p. 103).

The conclusion just stated justifies the attempt to assign possible temperature-pressure ranges to the critical mineral assemblages of recognized facies and subfacies. Ideally this could be done by constructing what Bowen (1940, pp. 272–274) termed a *petrogenic grid* of equilibrium curves for metamorphically significant reactions, plotted against temperature-pressure coordinates. Much of the effort of experimental petrologists and geochemists during the past two decades has been directed to this end. This aspect of the theory of metamorphism will be reviewed in the chapter which follows.

REFERENCES

Becke, F.: Über Mineralbestand und Struktur der kristallinischen Schiefer, *Akad. Wiss. Vienna Denkschr., Math.-Natv. Kl.*, vol. 75, pp. 1–53, 1913 (first published, 1903).

———: Ueber Diaphthorite, *Mineral. Petrog. Mitt.*, vol. 28, pp. 369–375, 1909.

———: Zur Faciesklassifikation der metamorphen Gesteine, *Mineral. Petrog. Mitt.*, vol. 35, pp. 215–230, 1921.

Bowen, N. L.: Progressive metamorphism of siliceous limestone and dolomite, *J. Geol.*, vol. 48, pp. 225–274, 1940.

Brown, E. H.: The geology of the Mt. Stoker area, eastern Otago, Part 1, *New Zealand J. Geol. and Geophys.*, vol. 6, pp. 847–871, 1963.

Durrell, C.: Metamorphism in the southern Sierra Nevada northeast of Visalia, California, *Univ. Calif. Publ. Geol. Sci.*, vol. 25, no. 1, pp. 1–118, 1940.

Ernst, W. G.: Significance of phengitic micas from low-grade schists, *Am. Mineralogist*, vol. 48, pp. 1357–1373, 1963.

Eskola, P.: On the relations between the chemical and mineralogical composition in the metamorphic rocks of the Orijärvi region, *Bull. Comm. Geol. Finlande*, no. 44 (English summary pp. 109–145), 1915.

———: The mineral facies of rocks, *Norsk Geol. Tidsskr.*, vol. 6, pp. 143–194, 1920.

———: Die metamorphen Gesteine, "Die Entstehung der Gesteine" (T. F. W. Barth, C. W. Correns, P. Eskola), pp. 263–407, Springer, Berlin, 1939.

Evans, B. W.: Coexisting albite and oligoclase in some schists from New Zealand, *Am. Mineralogist*, vol. 49, pp. 173–179, 1964.

———: Application of a reaction-rate method to the breakdown equilibria of muscovite and muscovite plus quartz, *Am. J. Sci.*, vol. 263, pp. 647–667, 1965.

Francis, G. H.: Further petrological studies in Glen Urquhart, Inverness-shire, *Bull. Brit. Museum Nat. Hist.*, vol. 1, pp. 165–199, 1964.

Fyfe, W. S., and F. J. Turner: Reappraisal of the concept of metamorphic facies, *Beit. Mineral. Petrog.*, vol. 12, pp. 354–364, 1966.

———, ———, and J. Verhoogen: Metamorphic reactions and metamorphic facies, *Geol. Soc. Am. Mem.*, 73, 1958.

———, ———, and ———: Coupled reactions in metamorphism; a correction, *Bull. Geol. Soc. Am.*, vol. 72, pp. 169–170, 1961.

———, and G. W. Valpy: The analcime-jadeite phase boundary: some indirect deductions, *Am. J. Sci.*, vol. 257, pp. 316–320, 1959.

Goldschmidt, V. M.: Die Kontaktmetamorphose im Kristianiagebiet, *Oslo Vidensk. Skr., I, Math.-Nat. Kl.*, no. 11, 1911.

Grubenmann, U.: "Die Kristallinen Schiefer," Borntraeger, Berlin, 1904.

———, and P. Niggli: "Die Gesteinsmetamorphose," Borntraeger, Berlin, 1924.

Harker, A.: Anniversary address of the president, *Geol. Soc. London Proc.*, 1917–1918, vol. 74, 51–80, 1919.

———: "Metamorphism," Methuen, London, 1932.

Heard, H.: Effects of large changes in strain rate in the experimental deformation of Yule marble, *J. Geol.*, vol. 71, pp. 162–195, 1963.

Johnston, J., and P. Niggli: The general principles underlying metamorphic processes, *J. Geol.*, vol. 21, pp. 481–516, 588–624, 1913.

Kelley, K. K.: High-temperature heat-content, heat-capacity and entropy data for elements and inorganic compounds, *U.S. Bur. Mines Bull.*, 584, 1960.

———, and E. G. King: Entropies of the elements and inorganic compounds, *U.S. Bur. Mines Bull.*, 592, 1961.

Knopf, E. B.: Retrogressive metamorphism and phyllonitization, *Am. J. Sci.*, vol. 21, pp. 1–27, 1931.

Kracek, F. C., J. J. Neuvonen, and G. Burley: A thermodynamic study of the stability of jadeite, *Washington Acad. Sci. J.*, vol. 41, pp. 373–383, 1951.

Kretz, R.: Some applications of thermodynamics to coexisting minerals, *J. Geol.*, vol. 69, pp. 361–387, 1961.

Lambert, R. St. J.: The metamorphic facies concept, *Mineral. Mag.*, vol. 34, pp. 283–291, 1965.

Lillie, A. R., and B. M. Gunn: Steeply plunging folds in the Sealy Range, Southern Alps, *New Zealand J. Geol. Geophys.*, vol. 7, pp. 403–423, 1964.

Lyell, C.: "Principles of Geology," 7th edition, J. Murray, London, pp. 170–175, 1847.

Robertson, E. C., F. Birch, and G. J. F. MacDonald: Experimental determination of jadeite stability relations to 25,000 bars, *Am. J. Sci.*, vol. 255, pp. 115–137, 1957.

Schwartz, G. M., and J. H. Todd: Comments on retrograde metamorphism, *J. Geol.*, vol. 49, pp. 177–189, 1941.

Sederholm, J. J.: Studien über archäische Eruptivgesteine aus dem südwestlichen Finnland, *Tschernaks Mineral. Petrog. Mitt.*, vol. 12, pp. 97–142, 1891.

Thompson, J. B.: The graphical analysis of mineral assemblages in pelitic schists, *Am. Mineralogist*, vol. 42, pp. 842–858, 1957.

Tilley, C. E.: The facies classification of metamorphic rocks, *Geol. Mag.*, vol. 61, pp. 167–171, 1924.

———: On some mineralogical transformations in crystalline schists, *Mineral. Mag.*, vol. 21, pp. 34–36, 1926.

Turner, F. J.: Thermodynamic appraisal of steps in progressive metamorphism of siliceous dolomitic limestones, *Neues Jahrb. Mineral. Monatsh.*, 1967, pp. 1–2, 1967.

———, and J. Verhoogen: "Igneous and Metamorphic Petrology," 2d ed., McGraw-Hill, New York, 1960.

Weill, D. F., and W. S. Fyfe: A discussion of the Korzhinski and Thompson treatment of thermodynamic equilibrium in open systems, *Geochim. Cosmochim. Acta*, vol. 28, pp. 565–576, 1964.

Williams, G. H.: The greenstone schist areas of the Menominee and Marquette regions of Michigan, *U.S. Geol. Surv. Bull.*, no. 62, 1890.

Yoder, H. S.: The MgO-Al_2O_3-SiO_2-H_2O system and the related metamorphic facies, *Am. J. Sci.*, Bowen vol., pp. 569–627, 1952.

———: Role of water in metamorphism, *Geol. Soc. Am. Spec. Paper 62*, pp. 505–524, 1955.

Zen, E-an: Mineralogy and petrology of the system Al_2O_3-SiO_2-H_2O in some pyrophyllite deposits of North Carolina, *Am. Mineralogist*, vol. 46, pp. 52–66, 1961.

Experimental Approach
to Metamorphic Problems

PHYSICAL CONDITIONS OF METAMORPHISM

Regional metamorphism is a phenomenon of the deeper levels of the earth's crust. Metamorphism in contact aureoles may occur relatively close to the surface—at depths of 1 or 2 km—while rock fragments enclosed in dikes and lava flows may show striking metamorphic effects brought about at magmatic temperatures and near-surface pressures. The total range of metamorphic pressure, calculated as load pressure P_l, thus lies between a few bars and 10 kb.

The upper limit of metamorphic temperatures is set by partial or complete fusion of more fusible rocks such as graywacke and shale. This is generally assumed to be 650 to 700°C at pressures of a few thousand bars, for these are the minimal temperatures of melting in granite systems in the presence of excess water. However, rocks such as granulites, from which all water has been expelled during progressive metamorphism, will remain unfused up to considerably higher temperatures. So also will xenoliths

85

enclosed in magma at near-surface pressures. Thus metamorphic temperatures in the depths probably extend to 800°C or more, and near the suface perhaps occasionally reach or exceed 1000°C. The lower limit is the temperature at which reaction rates in common rocks first become high enough for effective metamorphism within periods of the order of a million years. There is some experimental evidence on this point (Fyfe, Turner, and Verhoogen, 1958, pp. 93–95, 100). Studies of rates of dehydration of clay minerals suggest that metamorphism is unlikely to be effective at temperatures below 200°C. This figure agrees with observations that sediments may remain almost unaltered after burial for millions of years at depths consistent with temperatures of 100 to 150°C.

Our task, then, is to explore the behavior and stability relations of common metamorphic minerals and mineral assemblages at $T = 200$ to 1000°C, and $P = 100$ bars to 10 kb. Most significant will be experiments on hydrous minerals in which $P_{H_2O} = P_l$ and on carbonate systems in which $P_{CO_2} = P_l$. It is also desirable, especially in systems in which FeO and/or MnO are components, to explore the effects of variation in the partial pressure of oxygen P_{O_2} as fixed (for any given T and P) by buffers (combinations of graphite, magnetite, haematite, and ilmenite), all of which occur widely in metamorphic rocks.

SCOPE OF EXPERIMENTS

The aim of most experiments in the chemistry of metamorphic reactions is to determine the respective stability fields of individual minerals and simple assemblages upon a temperature-pressure diagram. The boundary of any field is a curve of univariant equilibrium between chemically equivalent phase assemblages expressible by a reversible reaction

$$A + B \rightleftharpoons C + D$$

e.g., $\underset{\text{Muscovite}}{KAl_2(AlSi_3O_{10})(OH)_2} + \underset{\text{Quartz}}{SiO_2} \rightleftharpoons \underset{\text{Microcline}}{KAlSi_3O_8} + \underset{\text{Sillimanite}}{Al_2SiO_5} + \underset{\text{Water}}{H_2O}$

There are two broad approaches to the problem. Each is simple in principle but difficult in execution. The first approach is to observe directly the conversion of $A + B \rightarrow C + D$, and also the reversed reaction, at a number of temperatures and pressures. The equilibrium curve lies between the respective fields of the reactions $A + B \rightarrow C + D$ and $C + D \rightarrow A + B$. The second approach is to use standard entropy and heat data for the participating phases, from which the free energy of the reaction ΔG may be calculated for a range of conditions in the vicinity of the equilibrium curve. The curve itself connects all points for which ΔG is zero.

Any equilibrium, whether established by experiment or calculated from thermochemical data, may prove to be metastable. Thermochemical calculation gives the equilibrium temperature of the reaction

$$\text{Dolmite} + 2 \text{ Quartz} \rightleftharpoons \text{Diopside} + 2CO_2$$

at $P_{CO_2} = 1$ bar as $200°C$. The equilibrium temperature at the same pressure similarly calculated for the alternative reaction

$$2 \text{ Dolomite} + \text{Quartz} \rightleftharpoons \text{Forsterite} + 2 \text{ Calcite} + 2CO_2$$

is $290°C$. At this temperature and pressure all five phases (dolomite, quartz, forsterite, calcite, and carbon dioxide) can coexist in equilibrium. But the equilibrium is metastable; for at $T = 290°C$ and $P_{CO_2} = 1$ bar, the most stable known chemically equivalent assemblages are diopside-dolomite-CO_2 and diopside-quartz-CO_2 (cf. Turner, 1967, p. 9). Contrary to the statement of Fawcett and Yoder (1966, p. 373, footnote) "that any heterogeneous reaction can take place only within the stability limits of the reactants and their products" many experimentally investigated reactions involving mineral phases represent metastable equilibria and can be reversed at temperatures and pressures over which one or more of the participating phases is not stable. For example, the metastable equilibrium

$$\text{Muscovite} + \text{Quartz} \rightleftharpoons \text{Sanidine} + \text{Kyanite} + H_2O$$

as determined by Evans (1965) at $P_{H_2O} = 2$ kb and $T = $ about $670°C$ is well outside the stability field of kyanite (cf. Fig. 4-3).

Also accruing from experimental work are data concerning reaction rates. From these something may be predicted regarding the possibility that some minerals or assemblages may appreciably overstep the limits of their stability fields. It has been found, for example, that over much of the range of metamorphic temperatures and pressures mutual inversions of the three polymorphs of Al_2SiO_5 are impossible or difficult to induce. Geologists should watch for instances in which andalusite, sillimanite, or kyanite occur as metastable minerals. On the other hand, the inversion of aragonite to calcite, especially in the presence of water, has been found to be so rapid that aragonite, crystallized at high pressure, cannot be expected to survive reduction of pressure to near-surface values except when cooled from initial temperatures below two or three hundred degrees centigrade (Brown, Fyfe, and Turner, 1962).

DIRECT DETERMINATION OF EQUILIBRIUM CURVES

The difficulties that beset experimental determination of equilibrium curves by the direct method are many. For some reactions, especially in the lower temperature range where rates are low, they have not yet been surmounted. For this reason many so-called "curves of univariant equilibrium" are valueless or dubious. Those that appear acceptable are constantly being revised in the light of new experiments. The geologist must therefore scrutinize with care the experimental procedure and the nature of the data presented in order to evaluate the published curves referring to any particular reaction. He must ask himself questions such as these: Was the reaction really reversed; that is, were the initial phases used for the backward reaction identical with the phases formed as the products of the forward reaction? How were the reaction products identified? If X-rays alone were used for identification is it possible that a critical phase present in small amount passed unnoticed? Was the quenching procedure such that products of reaction at high temperature and pressure have survived unchanged to laboratory temperature and pressure at which they were identified? Is it possible—especially in complex high-pressure equipment such as squeezers—that strong pressure-temperature gradients develop within the charge, and that the instrumentally recorded values of P and T differ from those at which reaction actually occurred?

Some of the grounds upon which published "equilibrium" diagrams are subject to criticism or even outright rejection have been summarized for the benefit of the geologist by Fyfe (1960). To his remarks may be added a warning that the latest set of data are not necessarily the best—especially if there is reason to suspect defective instrumental recording of P and T values, or where the author of new data fails to give a critical appraisal of earlier records. Against this background we can now review briefly some of the methods currently used in determining curves of univariant equilibrium by direct observation of the reactions concerned.

Experimentally Reversed Reactions

Figure 3-1 shows the curve of univariant equilibrium established by Harker and Tuttle (1955, p. 218) for the reaction

$$\underset{\text{Magnesite}}{MgCO_3} \rightleftharpoons \underset{\text{Periclase}}{MgO} + CO_2$$

The plotted points represent runs in which the starting materials were the participating phases magnesite or periclase in an atmosphere of CO_2. Two dubious points, at $T > 800°C$ and $P = 20,000$ psi, were rejected because the final products included magnesite formed during slow quenching. The reaction was reversed over narrow temperature intervals at pressures ranging up to 3 kb. So the curve can be regarded as satisfactorily established within a few degrees, and it is not likely to be modified by later experiments.

Somewhat less satisfactory is the curve (Fig. 3-2) of inversion for the reaction

$$Kyanite \rightleftharpoons Sillimanite$$

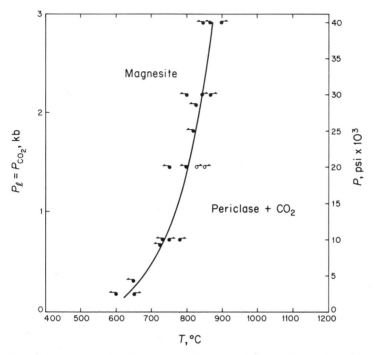

Fig. 3-1. Curve of univariant equilibrium for reaction Magnesite ⇌ Periclase + CO_2 experimentally established by *R. I. Harker and O. F. Tuttle* (1955). Solid circles show experimentally determined points, with arrows indicating directions of reaction. Open circles are dubious points rejected because of imperfect quenching procedure.

as determined by Clark, Robertson, and Birch (1957) and later modified somewhat by Clark (1964). The value of ΔG for this reaction is so small that the reaction velocity becomes appreciable only at temperatures and pressures beyond the metamorphic range. Reversal was successfully accomplished at temperatures of 1200 to 1500°C and pressures in excess of 18 kb. The points so determined are scattered sufficiently to permit drawing curves with slopes varying between about 10 and 20 bars/deg. A slope of about 20 bars/deg around 800°C is consistent with the best available data for ΔS and ΔV of inversion (Skinner, Clark, and Appleman, 1961). Moreover such an equilibrium curve would show kyanite as the stable phase at pressures about 4 to 6 kb in the temperature range 500 to 600°C; this is consistent with conditions to be expected at sites of regional metamorphism deep within the crust. A gradient of 13.2 bars/deg (broken line in Fig. 3-2) was nevertheless preferred by Clark on the basis of synthesis data which, on grounds to be discussed later, are here considered to be no criterion of equilibrium.

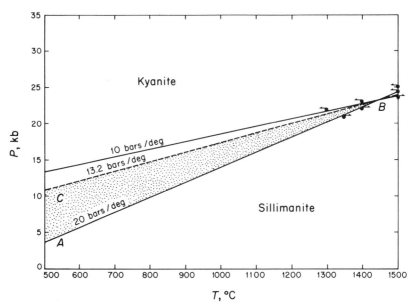

Fig. 3-2. Reversal of the reaction Kyanite ⇌ Sillimanite by *S. P. Clark* (1964): solid circles with arrows showing direction of reaction. Possible inversion curves consistent with the data are shown with gradients of 10 and 20 bars/deg. Broken line is Clark's inversion curve.

The sluggish nature of many reactions stems from failure of stable nuclei of new phases to form spontaneously, close to the reaction temperature. To overcome this difficulty it is now customary to start with mixes of all participating phases, and to hold these at constant temperature and pressure for long periods until the reaction, in one or other direction, has proceeded to completion. Nuclei of all phases are thus already provided in the initial charge, and one of the principal kinetic barriers to reaction is thus removed. In their classic investigation of the system $MgO-SiO_2-H_2O$, Bowen and Tuttle (1949, p. 450) were unable to synthesize anthophyllite. They concluded, and on the basis of his own experiments Yoder (1952, p. 587) agreed, that pure magnesian anthophyllite has no stability field in the presence of water. The chemically equivalent stable assemblages at $P_{H_2O} = 1$ kb and $T = 700$ to 800°C were thought to be enstatite-talc and enstatite-quartz. Fyfe (1962) found that at $P_{H_2O} = 1$ to 2 kb, talc-anthophyllite-quartz and enstatite-anthophyllite-quartz mixes can be converted largely to anthophyllite by prolonged heating over this range of temperature. He concluded that anthophyllite is stable with respect to talc-quartz and enstatite-quartz over a temperature range of 100°C, with 760° ± 10°C as the upper limits, at $P_{H_2O} = 2$ kb. An independent and

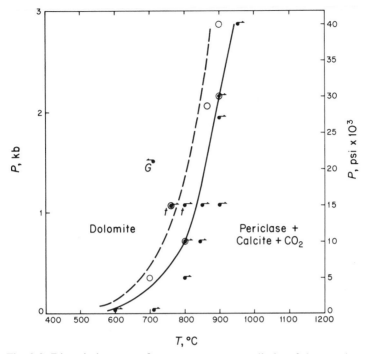

Fig. 3-3. Dissociation curve for upper temperature limits of the reaction Dolomite → Calcite + Periclase + CO_2 experimentally established by *R. I. Harker and O. F. Tuttle* (1955). Open circles indicate recrystallization of dolomite unchanged. Broken curve is the Magnesite ⇌ Periclase + CO_2 curve of Fig. 3-1. Point *G* corresponds to a reversal of the reaction by *D. L. Graf and J. R. Goldsmith* (1955, *p.* 123).

more detailed study by Greenwood (1963, p. 325) using the same technique, gives the stability range at the same pressure as 675 to 760°C.

One-way Reactions

Many reactions proceed too slowly in the direction of decreasing entropy for reversal to be achieved except possibly in experimental runs of very long duration. For this reason there are a number of published curves based solely or largely on points representing only the "forward" reaction with increasing entropy. These are useful as they set upper limits to reaction temperatures; but they are not curves of univariant equilibrium. The accepted "equilibrium" curve for the reaction

$$CaMg(CO_3)_2 \rightleftharpoons CaCO_3 + MgO + CO_2$$
$$\text{Dolomite} \qquad \text{Calcite} \qquad \text{Periclase}$$

is that of Harker and Tuttle (1955, pp. 216–219) shown in Fig. 3-3. Their data include no records of reversal, that is, of synthesis of dolomite from a calcite-periclase mix. Runs in which dolomite recrystallized unchanged were interpreted as indicating stability of dolomite; but this conclusion has no thermodynamic justification. Of no significance are runs in which a calcite-magnesite mix was employed as starting material. Where this was converted to dolomite the latter was assumed to be truly stable; but where the end product was periclase and calcite, periclase was pronounced metastable if the plotted point fell to the left of the reaction curve based on the other data. An unexplained anomaly is raised by two points (*t* in Fig. 3-3) in which small amounts of calcite and periclase were detected in prolonged runs starting with natural dolomite.

Reactions of Synthesis

At the relatively low temperatures comprising a large part of the metamorphic range, reactions between silicates, even those in which water participates, are notoriously slow. The experimenter often finds that it is impossible to induce metamorphically significant reactions even in runs of weeks or months duration. Faced with this dilemma, some have investigated alternative reactions in which the desired mineral phases are synthesized under controlled conditions from reactive materials such as glass or oxide mixes. Unfortunately such reactions can yield no direct information as to the primary metamorphic reaction (cf. Fyfe, 1960, pp. 553–562).

Suppose that the primary reaction to be investigated is

$$A \rightleftharpoons B$$

and that the synthesis reactions that are actually studied, starting with a glass or an oxide mix C are

$$C \rightarrow A \quad \text{and} \quad C \rightarrow B$$

Near the $A \rightleftharpoons B$ equilibrium conditions, ΔG for the primary reaction is small compared with ΔG for either reaction starting from C. Thus there is a strong potential favoring crystallization of both A and B. Which of the two actually crystallizes depends less on the sign of ΔG for the $A \rightarrow B$ reaction than on kinetic factors favoring preferential nucleation and growth of A or B. Clearly an important influence is exerted by the very nature of the starting material. For example, at 375°C and $P_{H_2O} = 2$ kb, kaolinite-quartz crystallizes from a mixture of amorphous Al_2O_3 and quartz, while pyrophyllite-cristobalite crystallizes from a mixture of kaolinite and amorphous silica of the same bulk composition (Carr and Fyfe, 1960). In the absence of direct data relating to the reaction $A \rightleftharpoons B$, it has been tentatively concluded by some workers that A is likely to be stable in a temperature-pressure field where it can be synthesized from different starting materials. Such a conclusion must, however, be viewed with caution when it conflicts with geological evidence, and it must be rejected outright when results of synthesis conflict with one-way data directly relating to A → B or to B → A.

As an example consider data on the reaction

$$\text{Muscovite} \rightleftharpoons \text{K-feldspar} + \text{Corundum}$$

as published by Yoder and Eugster (1955, pp. 235–242). Figure 3-4 shows the curve of "univariant equilibrium" drawn by these authors and the experimentally established points directly relating to the reaction. Only one of these, at 350°C, represents a successful attempt to reverse the reaction from right to left. In the absence of reversal over narrow temperature intervals, the curve was located as shown on the basis of alternative synthesis of muscovite or of sanidine-corundum from reactive starting materials such as glass, kaolinite-$KAlSiO_4$, and leucite-sillimanite, in the presence of water. If such points are discarded, as has been done in Fig. 3-4, it is clear that the true curve of univariant equilibrium lies somewhere to the left (at least 30°) of that shown in Fig. 3-4. Subsequent work by Evans (1965), based on reaction rates, shows that the equilibrium curve should indeed be displaced some 40° to the left; this conclusion has been verified independently by Velde (1965).

We have already seen that reversal of the kyanite ⇌ sillimanite inversion at temperatures above 1300°C has set limits on the curve of univariant equilibrium in this range. Extrapolation to lower temperatures of possible metamorphic significance has been attempted (Clark, Robertson, and Birch, 1957; Clark, 1964) on the basis of alternative synthesis of the two polymorphs from initial charges of metakaolinite, some of which were first seeded with sillimanite and andalusite. The starting material is highly unstable. Such extrapolation (curve *BC*, Fig. 3-2) is therefore of dubious value, especially since it conflicts with available thermodynamic data and has geological implications incompatible with current general opinion. These difficulties can be avoided by tentatively accepting the curve *AB*. This alternative[1] (preferable in the opinion of this writer) merely implies that there is a strong tendency, within the stippled field of Fig. 3-2, for the high-entropy polymorph sillimanite to nucleate from unstable metakaolinite, and grow as a metastable phase in preference to the more stable kyanite. There is nothing unlikely in this supposition. Indeed some of the earlier experiments in which the reactant was kaolinite + pyrophyllite consistently produced the undoubtedly metastable association corundum-quartz. It has been pointed out, in justification of the procedure of extrapolation of curve *BC*, that low-temperature syntheses give

[1] Now experimentally established by R. C. Newton.

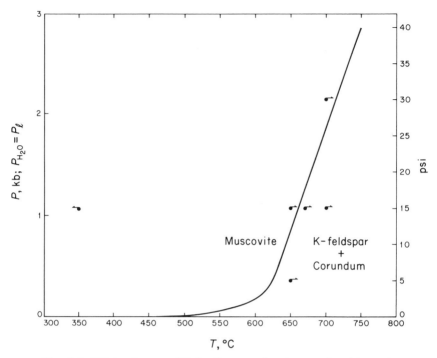

Fig. 3-4. "Univariant equilibrium" curve for the reaction Muscovite ⇌ Sanidine + Corundum + H_2O. (*After H. S. Yoder and H. P. Eugster,* 1955.) Solid circles show experimentally determined points with arrows indicating directions of reaction.

a curve continuous with the high-temperature segment based upon valid reversed reactions (Clark, 1964, p. 162). But this condition must hold whether the low-temperature synthesis curve is an equilibrium curve or not; for in the region where the two segments meet (at 20 kb, Fig. 3-2), the rate of the reaction kyanite ⇌ sillimanite becomes high enough to outweigh the possible effects of preferential nucleation of one phase or the other.[1]

USE OF THERMODYNAMIC DATA

If accurate data were available for entropy S and enthalpy ΔH of common metamorphic minerals over a wide range of temperature and pressure, it would be a simple matter to draw a curve of univariant equilibrium for any metamorphic reaction. Unfortunately, such information

---

[1] This generalization, although almost a truism, has escaped the notice of many experimenters. It was pointed out to this writer by W. S. Fyfe.

applies mainly to simple minerals under standard conditions $[T = 25°C$ and $P = 1$ bar (e.g., Robie, 1966)] supplemented by additional data determined at higher temperatures but still at a pressure of 1 bar (Kelley, 1960). Such information may be extrapolated to cover the range of metamorphic pressures and temperatures, given yet other data relating to heat capacity, compressibility, and thermal expansion; but at the present time such data are not available. For some minerals, such as garnet, aegirine, and hornblende, thermodynamic data are completely lacking; for others, such as the polymorphs of Al_2SiO_5, the best available figures (in this case enthalpy values) are far from precise. And there is the added complication that many metamorphic minerals have compositions markedly different from those of the pure phases whose thermodynamic properties are known.

In spite of the paucity of thermodynamic data geologically useful inferences may be drawn from those that are available (see Myiashiro, 1960; Ramberg, 1964*; Turner, 1967). On the same basis we can also test the probable validity of equilibrium diagrams based on direct experiment. In the discussion which follows, emphasis is placed on some simple relations and approximations that can readily be grasped and applied by geologists who are unfamiliar with the more complicated and sophisticated aspects of thermodynamic calculation and reasoning.

Stability of Phase Assemblages at Room Temperature and Pressure

For many oxides and simple minerals such as quartz, calcite, forsterite and so on, there are experimentally determined values of molar volume $V°$, entropy $S°$ and enthalpy (heat of formation, $\Delta H_f°$)[1] at $T = 25°C$ and $P = 1$ bar (e.g., Kelley, 1962; Robie, 1966).

Values of $S°$ are available for most oxides. In reactions involving only solid phases the entropy change ΔS is generally small, so as a first approximation, $S°$ of any anhydrous silicate may be estimated roughly as the sum of the respective entropies of the component oxides (Kelley's rule). The value so obtained may be further refined by applying various corrections discussed in some detail in Fyfe, Turner, and Verhoogen (1958, pp. 25–34).

First is a correction relating to density; for in general there is a direct correlation between S and V among compounds made up of various combinations of the same oxides. For silicates of Ca, K, Na, and Al, the entropy estimated from S of the component oxides should be increased by 0.5 cal for every cubic centimeter by which $V°$ of the silicate exceeds the sum of the respective values of $V°$ for the component oxides. This is

---

*Reference. p. 170.

[1] $\Delta H_f°$ is conventionally tabulated as heat of formation of a compound from its elements, except for silicates, when it is the heat of formation from the component oxides.

illustrated by known $V°$ and $S°$ data tabulated in Table 3-1. The sum of $S°$ of the component oxides of anorthite is 41.44 ± 0.27 cal. $V°$ of anorthite is 13 cm^3 greater than the sum of $V°$ values of the component oxides; and the corresponding entropy correction is 6.5 cal. So the corrected estimated value of $S°$ of anorthite is 47.94 ± 0.27 cal compared with the experimentally determined value 48.45 ± 0.3 cal. $S°$ of jadeite, estimated as a first approximation from known values of $S°$ for albite and quartz, is $(50.2 - 9.88) \pm 0.42 = 40.32 \pm 0.42$ cal. Since jadeite is much denser than other aluminosilicates of sodium (albite, nepheline) there is a corresponding

Table 3-1. Values of molar volume $V°$ and molar entropy $S°$ of some oxides and mineral phases (Robie, 1966)

Phase	$V°$, cm^3/mole	$S°$, cal/mole°
Al$_2$O$_3$:Corundum	25.57 ± 0.01	12.18 ± 0.03
CaO	16.76 ± 0.01	9.5 ± 0.2
SiO$_2$:α-quartz	22.69 ± 0.005	9.88 ± 0.02
KAlSiO$_4$:Kaliophillite	59.90 ± 0.08	31.85 ± 0.3
KAlSi$_2$O$_6$:Leucite	88.39 ± 0.05	44.05 ± 0.4
CaAl$_2$Si$_2$O$_8$:Anorthite	100.73 ± 0.15	48.45 ± 0.3
NaAlSiO$_4$:Nepheline	54.17 ± 0.15	29.72 ± 0.3
NaAlSi$_2$O$_6$:Jadeite	60.98 ± 0.4	31.90 ± 0.3
NaAlSi$_3$O$_8$:Albite	100.21 ± 0.19	50.20 ± 0.4

correction of $(-8.2$ cal$)$. Thus corrected estimated value of $S°$ for jadeite is 32.12 ± 0.42; which is within the limits of error of the experimentally determined value, 31.90 ± 0.3 cal. Listed values of $S°$ for magnesium silicates indicate that it is unsafe to apply any density correction to the value estimated from $S°$ of component oxides. However, if the entropy of a magnesium-bearing silicate such as diopside or forsterite is calculated from standard data for the silicate clinoenstatite ($S° = 16.22 \pm 0.1$ cal; $V° = 31.47 \pm 0.07$ cm^3) combined with those for the other component oxides, the correction of 0.5 cal/cm^3 can still be used. An alternative method, long known to chemists, by which entropies of silicates of Ca, Mg, Na, K, and Fe may be estimated to within about ± 2 cal,* is based on the observation that at high temperatures, entropies of such silicates are nearly proportional to their molecular weights. Newton and Kennedy (1963, p. 2975 and fig. 4) apply this approximation to entropies calculated

---

*A discrepancy of the order of 2 cal/mole° would lead to large errors in ΔG at metamorphic temperatures (1.5 kcal at 500°C).

at $P = 1$ bar and $T = 410°C$. If W is the molecular weight, then

$$S^{410°C} = 0.356W$$

The second entropy correction concerns the contribution of combined water to $S°$ of hydrated silicates. This correction is not so simple as the first. It depends on the structural role of water in the minerals in question. For many simple compounds such as brucite and kaolin, the contribution of water to $S°$ is close to the entropy of ice, 9.4 cal. For analcite, where the water is loosely held, the $S°$ contribution of H_2O has been determined experimentally as 14.1 cal (compared with 16.7 cal for liquid water at 25°C). For muscovite, the contribution of water is much less—about 4.3 cal (Weller and King, 1963).

Given $S°$ and $\Delta H_f°$ for all phases in two chemically equivalent mineral assemblages, it is possible to say which is the more stable at $T = 298°K$ (25°C) and $P = 1$ bar. Consider, for example,

$$\underset{\text{Calcite}}{CaCO_3} + \underset{\text{Quartz}}{SiO_2} \rightarrow \underset{\text{Wollastonite}}{CaSiO_3} + \underset{\text{Gas}}{CO_2}$$

Pertinent data (Robie, 1966) are given in Table 3-2.

Table 3-2. Thermochemical data for wollastonite reaction ($T = 25°C$; $P = 1$ bar)

Phase	$\Delta H_f°$ (from oxides), cal/mole	$S°$, cal/mole°
$CaCO_3$	$-42,290 \pm 250$	22.2 ± 0.2
SiO_2	0	9.88 ± 0.02
$CaSiO_3$	$-21,250 \pm 700$	19.6 ± 0.2
CO_2 (ideal gas)	0	51.07 ± 0.02

From these values

$$\Delta H° = 42.29 - 21.25 = 21.04 \pm 0.95 \text{ kcal/mole}$$

$$\Delta S° = 70.67 - 32.08 = 38.59 \pm 0.44 \text{ cal/mole°}$$

$$\Delta G° = \Delta H° - 298\Delta S° = 9.54 \pm 1.1 \text{ kcal/mole}$$

Clearly the stable assemblage is (calcite + quartz). Since this is the low-entropy assemblage the equilibrium temperature must be greater than 25°C, and the large value of ΔG indicates that it must be at least a few hundred degrees centigrade.

Evaluation of equilibrium on the basis of thermodynamic data is subject to error inherent in the standard values of ΔH and ΔS for the reaction in question. For most simple minerals the recorded values of $S°$ are accurate to $\pm$ 0.5 to 1 percent; for oxides the error is much less than this. Values of $\Delta H_f°$ for most oxides and carbonates are accurate to $\pm$ 0.5 to 1 percent, but the error for silicates may be as high as 3 or 4 percent. Against this background it is possible to generalize as follows:

1. For reactions involving a change of state, notably those of dehydration and decarbonation, both ΔH and ΔS are commonly large compared with possible errors. Equilibrium conditions calculated from such data can be accepted with some confidence. Fortunately, many metamorphic reactions fall in this category. Accuracy of the calculated equilibrium temperatures is likely to be $\pm$ 30 to 50°.

2. For reactions between solids when one or more is an oxide phase, although ΔS is small, ΔH may be large enough to permit meaningful inferences to be drawn from thermodynamic data. For example, for the reaction

$$CaSiO_3 \rightarrow CaO + SiO_2$$

at $T = 298°K$ and $P = 1$ bar, $\Delta H = 21.3 \pm 0.7$ kcal/mole, $\Delta S = 0$ (within limits of error), and ΔG is thus 21.3 ± 1 kcal/mole (data from Robie, 1966).

3. For reactions between solids exclusive of oxides, ΔS is again insignificant, and ΔH may be so small that the value of ΔG and even its sign are in doubt. Such is the case for polymorphic inversions such as sillimanite $\rightleftharpoons$ andalusite and calcite $\rightleftharpoons$ aragonite. At $T = 298°K$ and $P = 1$ bar (several kilobars below the equilibrium pressure), ΔG for the Aragonite $\rightarrow$ Calcite transition is only 250 cal/mole and the possible error is around $\pm$ 400 cal/mole (Robie, 1966, p. 448).

Stability of Phase Assemblages at Elevated Temperatures

Kelley (1960) has tabulated experimentally determined increments in S and in ΔH_f for a number of simple minerals over temperatures covering the metamorphic range, but at uniform pressure $P = 1$ bar. For any given reaction, $T \Delta S$ and ΔH are linear functions of T. In Fig. 3-5, curves for ΔH (AB) and for $T \Delta S$ (CD) have been plotted from Kelley's data for the reaction

$$\underset{\text{Calcite}}{CaCO_3} + \underset{\text{Quartz}}{SiO_2} \rightarrow \underset{\text{Wollastonite}}{CaSiO_3} + \underset{\text{Gas}}{CO_2}$$

These cross at the equilibrium temperature $T_e = 550°K$ (277°C) at which point

$$\Delta G = \Delta H - T \Delta S = 0$$

The limits of possible error in enthalpy and entropy data are such that the

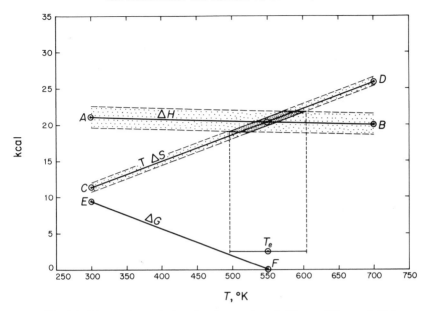

Fig. 3-5. Thermodynamic data for the reaction $CaCO_3 + SiO_2 \rightarrow CaSiO_3$ $+ CO_2$ at $P = 1$ bar. Broken lines and stippled bands indicate possible limits of error. Possible error in T_e is indicated by the shaded area around $550°K$.

calculated value of T_e is accurate only to ± 30 to $50°$. For this reason, all calculated equilibrium temperatures henceforth cited in this book are rounded to the nearest multiple of $10°$—in this case $280°C$.

Where high-temperature values of ΔH_f and S are not available, T_e at $P = 1$ bar can still be calculated from the relation (cf. Fyfe, Turner, and Verhoogen, 1958, p. 25)

$$\left(\frac{\partial \Delta G}{\partial T}\right)_P = -\Delta S$$

At the equilibrium temperature for any given pressure

$$T_e = \frac{\Delta H}{\Delta S}$$

Now $\Delta H/\Delta S$ varies only slightly over a temperature interval of a few hundred degrees, so within the limits of accuracy of the thermochemical data (Table 3-2),

$$T_e = \frac{\Delta H}{\Delta S^\circ} = \frac{21,040}{38.59} = 545°K = 270 \pm 45°C$$

Danielson (1950) adopting a more rigorous thermodynamic approach, but using the same basic data for the participating phases at 298°C and 1 bar, calculated T_e for the wollastonite reaction at $P = 1$ bar as 280°C.

There has been some discussion among petrologists (e.g., Bowen, 1940; Harker and Tuttle, 1956, pp. 250–255) as to the relative order of appearance of wollastonite and periclase in progressive contact metamorphism of calcareous rocks. Harker and Tuttle (1955, 1956) have given experimentally determined curves for the pertinent reactions

(1) $\qquad$ Calcite + Quartz $\rightleftharpoons$ Wollastonite + CO_2

and

(2) $\qquad$ Dolomite $\rightleftharpoons$ Calcite + Periclase + CO_2

Their curves are subparallel, and at pressures below $P_{CO_2} = 1000$ bars the curve for reaction (1) is drawn at temperatures 130 to 150°C lower than that for reaction (2). Thermodynamic data for reaction (2) (Robie, 1966) are as follows ($T = 298$°C; $P = 1$ bar):

$$\Delta S° = 42.62 \text{ cal/mole}°$$

$$\Delta H° = 31,700 \text{ cal}$$

$$\Delta G° = 18,500 \text{ cal}$$

From the equation

$$T_e = \frac{\Delta H}{\Delta S}$$

the equilibrium temperature $T_e = 470$°C. Again there is a possible error of perhaps ± 40°. In the above calculation we assumed that at $P = 1$ bar $\Delta H/\Delta S$ is unaffected by temperature in the range 25 to 470°C. No data are available for variation in entropy of dolomite with temperature. However, over the same temperature interval, ΔS for the dissociation of *magnesite* decreases by 2.11 cal/mole° and ΔH by 1100 cal. This same correction would change the calculated value of T_e for the dissociation of dolomite from 470 to 480°C. The difference of 200° between the respective values of T_e thus calculated for dissociation of dolomite and appearance of wollastonite in siliceous limestones cannot be reduced to less than 140°, even by allowing maximum possible error in the basic enthalpy and entropy data. There is no conflict between the conclusions reached from thermodynamic reasoning and those of Harker and Tuttle drawn from direct experiment.

Stability of Phase Assemblages at Elevated Pressure

For some reactions between solids, ΔV is relatively high and the equilibrium pressure P_e at 298°K is a few kilobars. Given $\Delta G°$ and ΔV, and assuming that ΔV remains constant over the pressure interval 1 bar to P_e, it follows from the relation

$$\left(\frac{\partial \Delta G}{\partial P}\right)_T = \Delta V$$

that

$$P_e = \frac{-\Delta G^\circ}{\Delta V} \times 41.3*$$

For reactions between anhydrous silicates, ΔH° is usually small and subject to relatively high possible error; and ΔS°, though more accurately known, is also relatively small. So ΔG° is too small, and the possible error too high, to permit evaluation of equilibrium pressure, except between wide limits. For example, consider the reaction

$$\text{Jadeite} + \text{Quartz} \rightarrow \text{Albite}$$

From standard data (Robie, 1966), at $T = 25°C$ and $P = 1$ bar,

$$\Delta V^\circ = 16.54 \pm 0.60 \text{ cm}^3$$

$$\Delta S^\circ = 8.42 \pm 0.72 \text{ cal/mole}^\circ$$

$$\Delta H^\circ = 600 \pm 2500 \text{ cal}$$

$$\Delta G^\circ = -1900 \pm 2700 \text{ cal}$$

P_e calculated from these data is 5 ± 7 kb. This result (though certainly far from precise!) is by no means valueless. It shows that albite is almost certainly the stable phase at room temperature and pressure. Since ΔS is positive and relatively large, ΔG must decrease rapidly with increase in temperature, so that at 200 to 300°C it will have a relatively high negative value even within the wide limits of possible error. At 600°K (327°C), ΔG (from Kelley, 1962, pp. 25, 26) is -4300 cal (again $\pm$ 3000 cal). Assuming that ΔV is constant from 298 to 600°K,

$$P_e \text{ at } 600°K = \frac{4300 \times 41.3}{16.54} = 9 \pm 6\text{kb}$$

It is safe to conclude that jadeite-quartz can be stable only at high pressures and low temperatures of metamorphism. Moreover, thermodynamic reasoning limits the range of temperature and pressure within which it

---

*The conversion factor 1 cal $= 41.3$ bar/cm^3 is derived directly from the equation

$$PV = RT$$

in which R has the dimensions of energy, equivalent to 1.985 cal. The work done when 1 mole of a perfect gas (22,412 cm^3) is generated at $P = 1$ bar and $T = 0°C = 273°K$ is

$$1 \times 22,412 \text{ bar/cm}^3 = 273 \times 1.985 \text{ cal}$$

whence $41.3 \text{ bar/cm}^3 = 1 \text{ cal}$

might be profitable to explore the reaction by direct experimental reversal. When one of the phases participating in a reaction is a gas, both ΔV and ΔS (and hence ΔG) vary markedly with temperature and pressure, especially in the low-pressure field. Fortunately, V and S of both water (Kennedy, 1950; Sharp, 1962) and CO_2 (Kennedy, 1954; Price, 1955) have been determined accurately for the full span of metamorphic temperatures and a considerable range of pressure. To determine the equilibrium temperature T_e of a reaction in which water or CO_2 participates at some given pressure P_e, it may further be assumed that at some convenient temperature T_1, close to T_e the contribution of the solid phases to ΔG of the reaction is unaffected by pressure. To this fixed contribution is added that of the gas phase at T_1 and pressure P_e. From ΔG, so calculated for T_1 and P_e, the equilibrium temperature (in $^\circ$K) is calculated as

$$T_e = \frac{\Delta G}{\Delta S}$$

Example 1. Consider the reaction

Calcite + Quartz $\rightarrow$ Wollastonite + CO_2 at $P_{CO_2} = 1000$ bars

Pertinent data (Kelley, 1960) for solid phases at 700°K and 1 bar are: ΔH_f, with reference to oxides at 298°K and 1 bar:

	Calcite	$-32,400$ cal
	Quartz	$+5630$ cal
	Wollastonite	$-11,100$ cal
S:	Calcite	42.77 cal/mole°
	Quartz	21.5 cal/mole°
	Wollastonite	40.72 cal/mole°

For reaction at 700°K and any pressure up to 1000 bars,

ΔH, solids only $= +15,670$ cal

ΔS, solids only $= -23.55$ cal/mole°

At 700°K and $P = 1000$ bars (Price, 1955[1]) for CO_2,

ΔH_f (based on ideal gas, 298°K, 1 bar) $= 3660$ cal

$S = 44.90$ cal/mole°

---

[1] Price tabulates increments in ΔH_f and in S with reference to the zero point (base), 273°K (0°C) and 1 bar. To apply these data to the base 298°K and 1 bar employed in the tables of Kelley and of Robie, a correction of -220 cal must be made to Price's ΔH_f increments, and -0.76 cal to Price's S increments.

For the complete reaction (solid plus fluid phases) at 700°K and P_{CO_2} = 1000 bars,

$$\Delta H = (15{,}670 + 3{,}660) = 19{,}330 \text{ cal}$$

$$\Delta S = (44.90 - 23.55) = 21.35 \text{ cal}$$

$$T_e = \frac{19{,}330}{21.35} = 905°\text{K} = 630°\text{C (rounded value)}$$

Since the possible error is at least as great as that for T_e at $P = 1$ bar (perhaps $\pm 50°$) the above figure is consistent with that (612°C) calculated from the same data, but with a more rigorous approach, by Danielsson (1950) and revised by Ellis and Fyfe (1956). Nor is there any conflict with the experimentally determined value, 670°C, of Harker and Tuttle (1956).

Example 2. Consider the reaction

Brucite → Periclase + H_2O at $P_{H_2O} = 500$ bars

Data (Kelley, 1960) for the solid phases at 700°K and 1 bar are:

ΔH_f:	Periclase	$4{,}100 \pm 100$ cal
	Brucite	$-11{,}300 \pm 500$ cal
S:	Periclase	$15.04 \pm .04$ cal
	Brucite	$32.99 \pm .05$ cal

For reaction at 700°K and any pressure up to 500 bars

$$\Delta H, \text{ solids only } = \quad 15{,}400 \pm 600 \text{ cal}$$

$$\Delta S, \text{ solids only } = - \ 17.95 \pm .09 \text{ cal}$$

At 700°C and $P_{H_2O} = 500$ bars (Sharp, 1962) for H_2O,

$$\Delta H_f \text{ (based on ideal gas, 298°K, } P = 1 \text{ bar)} = -2010 \text{ cal}$$

$$S = 33.59 \text{ cal}$$

For the complete reaction (solid plus fluid phases) at 700°K and $P_{H_2O} = 500$ bars,

$$\Delta H = (15{,}400 - 2{,}010) = 13{,}390 \pm 600 \text{ cal}$$

$$\Delta S = (33.59 - 17.95) = 15.64 \pm 0.1 \text{ cal}$$

$$T_e = \frac{13{,}390}{15.64} = 856°\text{K} = 583°\text{C}$$

This figure is recorded as $580 \pm 30°$C. It is consistent with Fyfe's (1958) value $555 \pm 5°C$ determined by experimental reversal of the reaction at the same pressure.

The above examples show that equilibrium temperatures calculated for pressures of a few kilobars from thermochemical data, using simple approximate methods, are likely to fall within a few tens of degrees of temperatures determined by experimental reversal of reactions. The calculated values are not subject to the uncertainty attached to "equilibrium" temperatures inferred from synthesis. Accuracy of this order is probably sufficient for interpreting geological systems; these must always be complicated by uncertainty as to relative values of P_f, P_{H_2O}, and P_{CO_2}, variation in compositions of natural phases, and the uncertain role of time in metamorphic crystallization.

Slopes of Univariant Equilibrium Curves

One of the most broadly applicable and generally reliable inferences to be drawn from thermodynamic data concerns the slope of an equilibrium curve on a pressure-temperature diagram. The fundamental equation is a version of the Clausius-Clapeyron relation

$$\frac{dP}{dT} = \frac{\Delta S}{\Delta V} \times 41.3 \text{ bars/deg}$$

Reasonably accurate values of both $\Delta S°$ and $\Delta V°$ are available for many metamorphic reactions at $T = 298°K$ and $P = 1$ bar. These data, supplemented by values for ΔS at higher temperatures and atmospheric pressure, can be extrapolated without great error to metamorphic temperatures and pressures.

The Aragonite $\rightleftharpoons$ Calcite transition was reversed by Clark (1957) at temperatures between 400 and 600°C and pressures of 10 to 14 kb. Clark's equilibrium curve is compatible with that obtained by Jamieson (1953), using a different technique, for temperatures below 100°C. The slope is about 16.5 bars/deg and the corresponding transition pressure at 298°K is 4.7 kb. Values of $\Delta H°$ and $\Delta G°$ are too inaccurate to be of use in testing the validity of this equilibrium pressure. But the slope of the curve can be checked independently from the following data for inversion of aragonite to calcite at $T = 298°K$ and $P = 1$ bar.

$$\Delta S° = +1.0 \pm 0.5 \text{ cal/mole}° \qquad \Delta V° = +2.78 \pm 0.04 \text{ cm}^3/\text{mole}$$

thus
$$\frac{dP}{dT} = \frac{1}{2.78} \times 41.3 = 15 \pm 8 \text{ bars/deg}$$

The slope of the Clark-Jamieson curve is well within these limits, in spite of the small value of ΔS inherent in a polymorphous transition.

In reactions involving a gas phase, both ΔS and ΔV are sensitive to change in temperature and pressure. Consequently it may not be assumed that $\Delta S/\Delta V$ is constant, except over very limited ranges of T and P. However, no great error is involved in the assumption, though only an approximation, that ΔV of the solid phases is independent of both temperature and pressure and that ΔS of the solids is independent of pressure. From this assumption several generalizations emerge regarding the slopes of equilibrium curves for many metamorphically significant reactions:

1. At any given temperature and pressure the slopes of all dehydration curves of hydroxyl-bearing compounds will be almost identical. The same may be said of reactions involving liberation of carbon dioxide from calcite and dolomite. For a dehydration reaction at temperature T and pressure P,

$$\frac{dP}{dT} = \frac{\Delta S}{\Delta V} = \frac{\Delta S_{\text{solids}}^T + S_{\text{water}}^{TP}}{\Delta V_{\text{solids}}^\circ + V_{\text{water}}^{TP}} \times 41.3$$

2. At pressures not greater than a few hundred bars, the behavior of the gas phase with increasing temperature approximates more and more closely that of a perfect gas. Consequently, with increasing temperature the slope dP/dT of the equilibrium curve decreases. Figure 3-6 shows a family of typical dehydration curves based on calculation from thermodynamic data (Fyfe, Turner, and Verhoogen, 1958, p. 119). Figure 3-7 shows some experimentally determined equilibrium curves for reactions involving calcite and magnesite.

3. The density correction applied to values of S° estimated according to Kelley's rule implies that for reactions (including inversions) involving solid phases only, $\Delta S^\circ/\Delta V^\circ$ will be rather constant: 0.5 ± 0.1 cal/cm^3. So the univariant equilibrium curves for such reactions on a $P - T$ diagram, at temperatures ranging up to a few hundred degrees, generally have a positive slope not far from 20 bars/deg. There are exceptions, such as the andalusite $\rightleftharpoons$ sillimanite curve, where both ΔS and ΔV are very small.

We can now examine some published "equilibrium" curves (Fig. 3-8) for the reaction

$$\underset{\text{Muscovite}}{\text{KAl}_2(\text{AlSi}_3\text{O}_{10})(\text{OH})_2} \rightleftharpoons \underset{\text{Sanidine}}{\text{KAlSi}_3\text{O}_8} + \underset{\text{Corundum}}{\text{Al}_2\text{O}_3} + \underset{\text{Gas}}{\text{H}_2\text{O}}$$

Curve A (Yoder and Eugster, 1955, p. 267) is straight between the points $(T = 660°C, P = 1 \text{ kb})$ and $(T = 715°, P = 2 \text{ kb})$. At $T = 700°C$ and $P = 2$ kb (X in Fig. 3-8),

$$V_{\text{water}} = 35.3 \text{ cm}^3 \qquad \text{and} \qquad S_{\text{water}} = 37.3 \text{ cal/mole}°$$

$$\Delta V_{\text{solids}}^\circ = (109.0 + 25.6) - 140.6 = -6.0 \text{ cm}^3$$

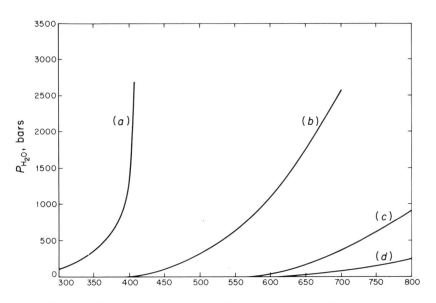

Fig. 3-6. Curves of univariant equilibrium (calculated) for dehydration of hydrates. ΔG at $T = 25\,°C$ and $P = 1$ bar is (*a*) 5, (*b*) 8.5, (*c*) 12, and (*d*) 15 kcal/mole. (*After W. S. Fyfe, F. J. Turner, and J. Verhoogen.*)

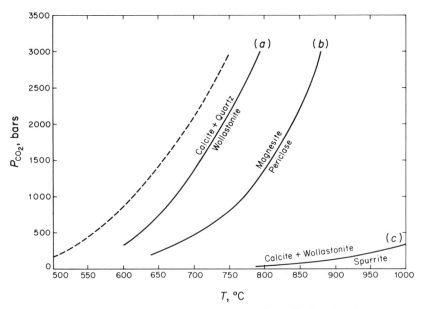

T, °C

Fig. 3-7. Experimentally determined curves of equilibrium for decomposition of carbonates. Same scale as Fig. 3-5. Dashed line is Danielsson's computed curve for the wollastonite reaction. Curve (*a*) *after R. I. Harker and O. F. Tuttle* (1955); curve (*b*) *after R. I. Harker and O. F. Tuttle* (1956); curve (*c*) *after O. F. Tuttle and R. I. Harker* (1957).

106

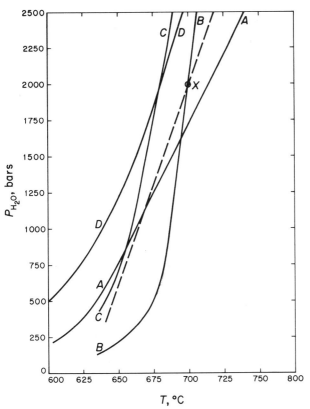

Fig. 3-8. Four experimentally determined "equilibrium" curves for the reaction   Muscovite $\rightleftharpoons$ Sanidine + Corundum + Water.   The   dashed line is the slope estimated approximately from thermodynamic data for a curve passing through X.

ΔS_{solids} at $700°C = (129.3 + 42.3) - 189.1 = -17.5$ cal/mole°

$$\frac{dP}{dT} = \frac{-17.5 + 37.3}{-6.0 + 35.3} \times 41.3 = 28 \text{ bars/deg}$$

The slopes of the experimentally determined curves passing through or close to X are as follows: A (Yoder and Eugster), 20 bars/deg; B (Crowley and Roy, 1964, p. 354), 100 bars/deg; C (Velde, 1966), 50 bars/deg; D (Evans, 1965), 25 bars/deg. Clearly curves B and C are in error as to slope. They imply that the entropy of water vapor at $T = 700°C$ and $P = 2$ kb is about 53 or 88 cal, respectively, whereas the actual value is 37.3 cal/mole°. Even less acceptable are dehydration "equilibrium" curves whose slopes on a $P - T$ diagram are vertical, e.g., Halferdahl's (1961, p. 99) preliminary curve for destruction of chloritoid.

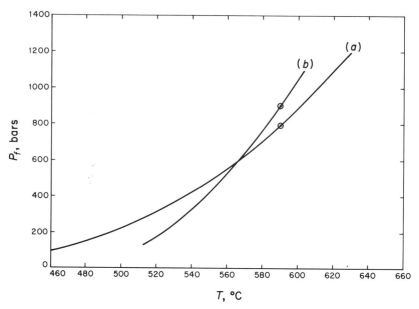

Fig. 3-9. Curves of univariant equilibrium (*a*) Calcite + Quartz ⇌ Wollastonite + CO₂. (*After A. Danielsson.*) (*b*) Brucite ⇌ Periclase + Water. (*After W. S. Fyfe.*)

The relative slopes of dehydration and decarbonization curves at similar temperatures and pressures of a few hundred bars are illustrated by comparing the reactions

$$\underset{\text{Calcite}}{CaCO_3} + \underset{\text{Quartz}}{SiO_2} \rightleftharpoons \underset{\text{Wollastonite}}{CaSiO_3} + \underset{\text{Gas}}{CO_2}$$

and

$$\underset{\text{Brucite}}{Mg(OH)_2} \rightleftharpoons \underset{\text{Periclase}}{MgO} + \underset{\text{Gas}}{H_2O}$$

Danielsson's (1950) curve (*a* in Fig. 3-9) for the wollastonite reaction is based on rigorous thermodynamic calculation. It passes through the point ($T = 590°C$, $P = 790$ bars), at which the slope is 8.5 bars/deg. (The slope estimated by the approximate method outlined above is 8 bars/deg.) Fyfe's (1958) experimentally determined equilibrium curve (*b* in Fig. 3-9) for the brucite decomposition passes through the nearby point ($T = 590°C$, $P = 900$ bars). The slope is 15 bars/deg, compared with an approximately estimated slope of 16 bars/deg. The difference in the two curves is due mainly to a marked difference in ΔV, reflecting the large molar volume of CO_2 (122 cm³) as compared with that of water vapor (52 cm³).

Conclusion

Sufficient thermodynamic data are now available to permit construction of approximate curves of univariant equilibrium for some simple metamorphic reactions. The temperatures on such curves are subject to possible error of at least $\pm$ 40 to 50°C. Thermodynamic tests may also be applied in evaluating equilibrium curves based on the data of direct experiment. To apply any such curves to problems of metamorphism, account must be taken of widely prevalent differences in composition between pure materials used in experiments and natural metamorphic minerals, and also of the range of possible error in standard thermodynamic data.

REFERENCES

Bowen, N. L.: Progressive metamorphism of siliceous limestone and dolomite, *J. Geol.*, vol. 48, pp. 225–274, 1940.

———, and O. T. Tuttle: The system $MgO - SiO_2 - H_2O$, *Bull. Geol. Soc. Am.*, vol. 60, pp. 439–460, 1949.

Brown, W. H., H. S. Fyfe, and F. J. Turner: Aragonite in California glaucophane schists, and the kinetics of the aragonite-calcite transition, *J. Petrol.*, vol. 3, pp. 566–582, 1962.

Carr, R. M., and W. S. Fyfe: Synthesis fields of some aluminium silicates, *Geochim. Cosmochim. Acta*, vol. 29, pp. 99–109, 1960.

Clark, S. P.: A note on the calcite-aragonite equilibrium, *Am. Mineralogist*, vol. 42, pp. 564–566, 1957.

———: A redetermination of equilibrium relations between kyanite and sillimanite, *Am. J. Sci.*, vol. 259, pp. 641–650, 1964.

———, E. C. Robertson, and F. Birch: Experimental determination of kyanite-sillimanite equilibrium relations at high temperatures and pressures, *Am. J. Sci.*, vol. 255, pp. 628–640, 1957.

Crowley, M. S., and R. Roy: Crystalline solubility in the muscovite and phlogopite groups, *Am. Mineralogist*, v. 49, pp. 348–362, 1964.

Danielsson, A.: Calcite-wollastonite equilibrium, *Geochim. Cosmochim. Acta*, vol. 1, pp. 55–69, 1950.

Ellis, A. J., and W. S. Fyfe: A note on the calcite-wollastonite equilibrium, *Am. Mineralogist*, vol. 41, pp. 805–807, 1956.

Evans, B. W.: Application of a reaction-rate method to the breakdown equilibria of muscovite and muscovite plus quartz, *Am. J. Sci.*, vol. 263, pp. 647–667, 1965.

Fawcett, J. J., and H. S. Yoder, Phase relations of chlorites in the system $MgO-Al_2O_3-SiO_2-H_2O$, *Am. Mineralogist*, vol. 51, pp. 353–380, 1966.

Fyfe, W. S.: A further attempt to determine the vapor pressure of brucite, *Am. J. Sci.*, vol. 256, pp. 729–732, 1958.

———: Hydrothermal synthesis and determination of equilibrium between minerals in the subsolidus region, *J. Geol.*, vol. 68, pp. 553–566, 1960.

————: On the relative stability of talc, anthophyllite, and enstatite, *Am. J. Sci.*, vol. 260, pp. 460–466, 1962.

————, F. J. Turner, and J. Verhoogen: Metamorphic reactions and metamorphic facies, *Geol. Soc. Am. Mem. no. 73*, 1958.

Graf, D. L., and J. R. Goldsmith: Dolomite-magnesian calcite relations at elevated temperatures and CO_2 pressures, *Geochim. Cosmochim. Acta*, vol. 7, pp. 109–128, 1955.

Greenwood, H. J.: The synthesis and stability of anthophyllite, *J. Petrol.*, vol. 4, pp. 317–351, 1963.

Halferdahl, L. B.: Chloritoid: its composition, X-ray and optical properties, stability, and occurrence, *J. Petrol.*, vol. 2, pp. 49–135, 1961.

Harker, R. I. and O. F. Tuttle: Studies in the system $CaO–MgO–CO_2$, Part 1, *Am. J. Sci.*, vol. 253, pp. 209–224, 1955.

———— and ————: Experimental data on the $P_{CO2} - T$ curve for the reaction: calcite + quartz $\rightleftharpoons$ wollastonite + carbon dioxide, *Am. J. Sci.*, vol. 254, pp. 239–256, 1956.

Jamieson, J. C.: Phase equilibrium in the system calcite-aragonite, *J. Chem. Phys.*, vol. 21, pp. 1385–1390, 1953.

Kelley, K. K.: High-temperature heat-content, heat-capacity and entropy data for the elements and inorganic compounds, *U.S. Bur. Mines Bull.*, 584, 1960.

————: Heats and free energies of formation of anhydrous silicates, *U.S. Bur. Mines Rep. Invest.*, 5901, 1962.

Kennedy, G. C.: Pressure-volume-temperature relations in water at elevated temperatures and pressures, *Am. J. Sci.*, vol. 248, pp. 540–564, 1950.

————: Pressure-volume-temperature relations in CO_2 at elevated temperatures and pressures, *Am. J. Sci.*, vol. 252, pp. 225–241, 1954.

Kracek, K., K. J. Neuvonen and G. Burley, Thermochemistry of mineral substances, *Washington Acad. Sci. J.*, vol. 41, pp. 373–383, 1951.

MacDonald, G. J.: Experimental determination of calcite-aragonite equilibrium relations at elevated temperatures and pressures, *Am. Mineralogist*, vol. 41, pp. 744–756, 1956.

Miyashiro, A.: Thermodynamics of reactions of rock-forming minerals with silica, *Jap. J. Geol. Geog.*, vol. 31, no. 1, pp. 71–84; no. 2, pp. 107–111, 1960.

Newton, R. C., and G. C. Kennedy: Some equilibrium reactions in the join $CaAl_2Si_2O_8–H_2O$, *J. Geophys. Res.*, vol. 68, pp. 2967–2983, 1963.

Price, D., 1955: Thermodynamic functions of carbon dioxide, *Ind. Eng. Chem.*, vol. 47, pp. 1649–1652, 1955.

Robie, R. A.: Thermodynamic properties of minerals, in S. P. Clark (ed.), "Handbook of Physical Constants", *Geol. Soc. Am. Mem. 97*, pp. 459–482, 1966.

Sharp, W. E.: The thermodynamic functions for water, *Univ. Cal. Lawrence Radiation Lab. Rept.*, 1962.

Skinner, B. J., S. P. Clark, and D. E. Appleman: Molar volumes and thermal expansions of andalusite, kyanite, and sillimanite, *Am. J. Sci.*, vol. 259, pp. 651–668, 1961.

Turner, F. J.: Thermodynamic appraisal of steps in progressive metamorphism of siliceous dolomitic limestones, *Neues Jahrb. Mineral. Monatsh.*, 1967, pp. 1–22, 1956.

Tuttle, O. F., and R. I. Harker: Synthesis of spurrite, *Am. J. Sci.*, vol. 255, pp. 226–234, 1957.

Velde, B.: Upper stability of muscovite, *Am. Mineralogist*, vol. 51, pp. 924–929, 1966.

Weller, W. W., and E. G. King: Low-temperature heat capacity and entropy at 298.15°K of muscovite, *U.S. Bur. Mines Rept.*, 6281, 1963.

Yoder, H. S.: The $MgO–Al_2O_3–SiO_2–H_2O$ system and the related metamorphic facies, *Am. J. Sci.*, Bowen vol., pp. 569–627, 1952.

———, and H. P. Eugster: Synthetic and natural muscovites, *Geochim. Cosmochim. Acta*, vol. 8, pp. 225–280, 1955.

Experimental Appraisal
of Critical
Metamorphic Reactions

LIMITING FACTORS IN APPRAISAL OF EXPERIMENTAL DATA

During the past two decades many metamorphic reactions have been investigated through the medium of laboratory experiment. Most experiments have been conducted upon phases whose compositions are simpler than those of corresponding minerals. Where hydrous phases or carbonates are involved, it has been customary—with certain exceptions—to investigate the system at a fluid pressure (P_{H_2O} or P_{CO_2} as the case may be) equal to the load pressure P_l. The resulting data are directly applicable to our simplified model of metamorphic conditions as set out on p. 62.

In some systems, data are complete enough to permit construction of a curve of univariant equilibrium for the reaction in question. More usually experiments have defined only an upper-temperature limit to a reaction of dehydration or decarbonation. Of comparatively little value are numerous experiments in which metamorphic phases have merely been synthesized from reactive initial materials of high free energy (glasses, oxide mixes, oxalates, and so on). Experiments on polymorphic transitions, some of great potential interest to the geologist, have been somewhat disappointing. An inversion that takes place rapidly in the laboratory will occur equally readily under natural conditions; so a metamorphic high-temperature polymorph is likely to be represented in the outcrop specimen by its low-temperature counterpart. Such is the α-quartz $\rightleftharpoons$ β-quartz inversion. On the other hand, an inversion that is difficult to induce experimentally could possibly lead to crystallization of metastable polymorphs during metamorphism.

Different experimenters using different techniques all too commonly disagree regarding the same reaction. And it is by no means safe to assume that the latest data obtained by some complex new technique are necessarily superior to older data resulting from simpler experiments. The standard entropy and heat capacity data referred to in the previous chapter provide a useful means of checking the validity of experimentally determined reaction curves, and of testing the mutual compatibility of curves for reactions involving participation of some of the same phases.

This chapter is devoted to reviewing some of the experimental data that throw light upon the temperature and pressure of reactions considered to be significant in metamorphism. Such a review is necessarily critical and tentative, and reflects the prejudices of the writer. The reader is urged to turn to the original literature and make his own judgments.

REACTIONS IN PELITIC PHASE ASSEMBLAGES

The Al_2SiO_5 Polymorphs

The three polymorphs of Al_2SiO_5 are widely distributed in pelitic schists and hornfelses and consequently have been the subject of a good deal of experimental investigation with a view to their use as indices of temperature and pressure (P_l). This work unfortunately has been hampered by an almost insurmountable obstacle—the small values of ΔG for the three inversion reactions. At room temperature and pressure these are at most a few hundred calories per mole, and available data are subject to error of perhaps 50 percent. Moreover, for the Andalusite $\rightleftharpoons$ Sillimanite inversion in particular, ΔS and ΔH are both small and published data are subject to similar error. It is not surprising, therefore, that until recently inversions have been reversed experimentally only at very high temperatures, or (at metamorphic temperatures) by means of equipment which induces intense strain in the starting material, and so raises significantly its free energy before inversion is effected. There are many records of synthesis of the three polymorphs from glasses, oxide mixes and other unstable starting materials over a wide range of temperature. But here ΔG of the actual reaction is many times greater than that of the polymorphic inversion, and so the data thus obtained are more than usually suspect (cf. pp. 92–93).

Figure 4-1 is a tentative equilibrium diagram, showing also the limits of probable error, deduced by Fyfe (Fyfe and Turner, 1966, fig. 2) from five independent sets of data, with all of which the diagram is compatible.

1. Reversal of the Kyanite $\rightleftharpoons$ Sillimanite transition by Clark at $T = 1300$ to $1500°C$ and $P = 20$ to 25 kb (cf. Fig. 3-2).

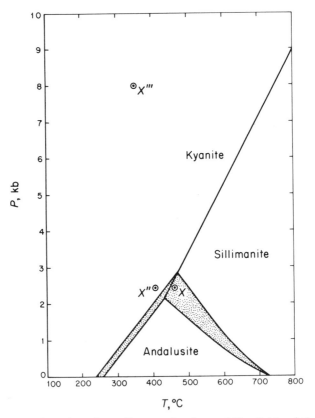

Fig. 4-1. Tentative phase diagram showing stability fields of the polymorphs of Al_2SiO_5. (*After W. S. Fyfe.*) Stippled area shows limits of probable error with respect to boundaries of the andalusite field. Triple points recorded by various workers are X (*W. S. Fyfe*), X'' (D. Weill), X''' (*P. M. Bell*). The first two are mutually consistent within limits of error of experimental data.

2. Reversal of the metastable kyanite-andalusite transition between 700 and 800°C at P_{H_2O} = 6 to 7 kb by Newton (1966).

3. Evans' (1965) data on the experimentally reversed equilibria

$$\text{Muscovite} + \text{Quartz} \rightleftharpoons \text{Sillimanite} + \text{Sanidine} + \text{H}_2\text{O}$$

and $$\text{Muscovite} + \text{Quartz} \rightleftharpoons \text{Andalusite} + \text{Sanidine} + \text{H}_2\text{O}$$

at P_{H_2O} = 2 kb and T = 600 ± 20°C.

4. Solubilities of andalusite and sillimanite in fused cryolite at 600 to 1000°C and atmospheric pressure (Weill and Fyfe, 1961; Weill, 1966).

5. Standard entropy, enthalpy, and volume data.

Fyfe's diagram (Fig. 4-1) and the almost identical diagram of Newton (1966) conflict markedly with previously published phase diagrams of Bell (1963) and Khitarov (1963), which unfortunately have been accepted uncritically by a number of geologists as the quantitative basis of theories and propositions, now invalidated, on pressure-temperature regimes in terranes of regional metamorphism. The reader is referred to Newton (1966), Fyfe (1966), and Turner (1967b) for critical discussion of the whole problem. Newton's later data[1] place the triple point near 500°C, 4 kb, but, allowing for possible error, are still compatible with Fig. 4-1. Althaus[2] has since advocated a triple point at 595°C, 6.5 kb. His clearly established inversions agree with Fig. 4-1. But extension of the andalusite field to 6.5 kb rests on less convincing reported incipient reactions. The starting materials, moreover, were intensely strained (and hence activated) powders.

At high temperatures and low pressures the stable equivalent of Al_2SiO_5 is mullite, $\text{Al}_6\text{Si}_2\text{O}_{13}$, plus quartz. There are still no reliable experimental data, consistent with Fig. 4-1, on the stability of mullite-quartz with respect to andalusite or sillimanite. Another chemically equivalent pair, corundum-quartz, seems to have no metamorphic stability field.

Pyrophyllite

At low temperatures and high values of P_{H_2O}, hydrated aluminum silicates such as kaolin $\text{Al}_2(\text{Si}_2\text{O}_5)(\text{OH})_4$ or pyrophyllite $\text{Al}_2(\text{Si}_4\text{O}_{10})(\text{OH})_2$ are stable phases rather than the anhydrous Al_2SiO_5 polymorphs. Thus there has been a good deal of experimental work and much speculation on the equilibrium

$$\underset{\text{Pyrophyllite}}{\text{Al}_2(\text{Si}_4\text{O}_{10})(\text{OH})_2} \rightleftharpoons \underset{\text{Andalusite}}{\text{Al}_2\text{SiO}_5} + \underset{\text{Quartz}}{3\text{SiO}_2} + \text{H}_2\text{O}$$

Some geologists have placed the equilibrium temperature close to 600°C at water pressures of a few kilobars (e.g., Kennedy, 1955; Aramaki and Roy,

[1] *Science*, vol. 153, pp. 170–172, 1966.
[2] *Contrib. Mineral. Petrol.*, vol. 16, pp. 29–44, 1967.

1963). This temperature is much too high to reconcile readily with the widespread occurrence of Al_2SiO_5 polymorphs and relatively few records of pyrophyllite in pelitic schists and hornfelses, even in rocks of low metamorphic grade. Other experiments suggest much lower equilibrium temperatures at P_{H_2O} = about 2 kb: 480 to 490°C (Althaus, 1966, p. 33); 420°C (Carr and Fyfe, 1960); 420°C (Kerrick, 1966). To this writer, admittedly prejudiced in favor of geologically acceptable data determined in the Berkeley laboratory, it seems likely that the rarity of pyrophyllite in pelitic rocks reflects a narrow stability range of quartz-chlorite-pyrophyllite assemblages between about 400°C (at P_{H_2O} = 2 kb) and the only slightly lower equilibrium temperature of reactions such as

$$Al_2(Si_2O_5)(OH)_4 + 2SiO_2 \rightleftharpoons Al_2(Si_4O_{10})(OH)_2 + H_2O$$

Kaolin   Quartz   Pyrophyllite

In typical chlorite-bearing pelites the stability field of pyrophyllite is likely to be even further reduced by reactions leading to aluminous chlorites.

Generation of Micas and Chlorites

The low-grade muscovite-chlorite-quartz assemblage. As diagenesis of shale merges into low-grade metamorphism, sedimentary assemblages of clay minerals, quartz, and feldspar detritus give rise to metamorphic assemblages in which the principal phases are quartz, white micas, chlorites, and albite. Micas at this early stage may be phengitic muscovite, paragonite-muscovite solid solutions, or muscovites approaching the ideal composition $KAl_2(AlSi_3O_{10})(OH)_2$. In rather rare, highly aluminous rocks there may be two white micas, one close to muscovite, the other approximating paragonite $NaAl_2(AlSi_3O_{10})(OH)_2$. The typical pelitic chlorites are aluminous varieties (prochlorites). The hydrous aluminum silicate pyrophyllite seems to be confined to highly aluminous rocks low in alkalies.

Nothing accurate can be said about the temperatures and pressures that can be inferred from the first appearance of quartz-mica-chlorite assemblages in low-grade metamorphism. These assemblages can perhaps be regarded as stable over some definite range of temperature and pressure. Such indeed is the assumption made in this discussion. But the initial premetamorphic clay mixture must commonly have been metastable. And the temperature of metamorphism at any given P_{H_2O} (as well as the products of reaction) must be affected to some degree by the composition (especially the acidity) of the initial abundant pore fluid (cf. Hemley, 1959, p. 268).

Early metamorphic temperatures therefore probably cannot be precisely evaluated from experimental data relating to synthesis and destruction of clay mixtures, nor even by experimental determination of clay-mica-chlorite-silica equilibria (cf. Yoder, 1955, p. 513).

Winkler (1964) has crystallized mineral phases such as pyrophyllite, paragonite, and chlorite by heating mixtures of clay minerals and quartz to temperatures of about 400°C at $P_{H_2O} = 2$ kb. This he takes as the lower limit of temperature spanned by what we shall later call the greenschist facies—the field of the stability of the metamorphic quartz-muscovite-chlorite assemblages. Most reactions cited by Winkler (e.g., 1965, pp. 55–56, 154–158) were not reversed experimentally; some of his equilibria seem to be metastable. Velde (1964) has given some preliminary data on experimental conversion of quartz-bearing sedimentary montmorillonoid and illite assemblages to metamorphic mixtures of quartz, white mica and chlorite. At $P_{H_2O} = 2$ kb he places such reactions in the vicinity of 300°C, marking "the appearance of what could be called a greenschist assemblage." Low temperatures and high pressures are found to favor phengitic micas transitional from muscovite toward celadonite, rather than nearly ideal muscovites. Velde's data on the whole substantiate our earlier guess (Fyfe, Turner, and Verhoogen, 1958, p. 173) that the lower limit of stability of metamorphic quartz-muscovite-chlorite assemblages of the greenschist facies is around $T = 300$°C and $P_{H_2O} = 3$ kb, or possibly somewhat lower.

First appearance of biotites. The first appearance of biotite in pelitic rocks is thought to be due to reactions between low-grade muscovites and chlorites (cf. Tilley, 1926; Ernst, 1963; Brown, 1967). The former are commonly phengitic muscovites high in SiO_2, low in Al_2O_3, and containing significant MgO, FeO, and Fe_2O_3. Reaction with chlorite might yield biotite plus a more nearly ideal muscovite and a chlorite of different composition; possibly a variety richer in Al_2O_3. Analytical data relating to low-grade biotites, muscovites and chlorites are still inadequate to demonstrate the true nature of the critical reaction at the biotite isograd (Brown, 1967). A suggestion by McNamara (1966, pp. 405, 412) that biotite forms from chlorite by addition of potash from an external source is here discounted on the ground that the supporting evidence is based on misidentification of weathered chlorite and vermiculite in New Zealand schists as "biotite" (cf. Brown, 1967). But, as Brown and McNamara both point out, it has yet to be shown that muscovites and chlorites undergo significant compositional changes across the biotite isograd. With advancing metamorphic grade muscovite-biotite-chlorite-quartz gives way to such assemblages as musco-vite-biotite-garnet or muscovite-biotite-cordierite. Clearly the biotite-forming reactions are complex and constitute a more or less continuous series of mineral transformations. Again, as with muscovite-chlorite assemblages, there is little direct experimental evidence as to the temperatures and pressures of quartz-biotite-muscovite-chlorite equilibria. Winkler (1957) heated illite-bearing clays with a high Al/K ratio at $P_{H_2O} = 2$ kb. At temperatures below 400°C they had become converted to muscovite-chlorite-quartz. Biotite first appeared at temperatures around 550°C, accompanied by muscovite, cordierite, and quartz. But in the listed reaction products there is obvious evidence of disequilibrium: muscovite and quartz persist abundantly, along with newly formed biotite, up to 670°C—some 70° beyond the stability limit of muscovite-quartz as shown in curve C, Fig. 4-1. All that is suggested by these experiments is that at $P_{H_2O} = 2$ kb reactions leading to the first appearance of biotite in pelitic rocks occur at some temperature (unknown) below 550°C.

Perhaps no more satisfactory are indirect inferences drawn from data on high-temperature dehydration of micas and chlorites. At any given P_{H_2O}, biotite must first appear at temperatures well below those at which the simple pairs muscovite-quartz and chlorite-quartz themselves become unstable. Otherwise quartz-muscovite-biotite and quartz-biotite-chlorite assemblages would not be as widely distributed as they are in medium-grade pelitic schists. At $P_{H_2O} = 2$ kb muscovite-quartz breaks down at 600°C (Fig. 4-2). Throughout the whole span of low to high metamorphic grade the atomic ratio Fe^{2+}/Mg^{2+} in pelitic biotites is close to 1 (Banno, 1964, pp. 261–265). The corresponding temperature span, at a guess, is not likely to be less than 300°C. Moreover, the temperature at which biotites of this kind break down in the presence of quartz may be about 700°C (cf. Fig. 4-4).

All that can safely be concluded on this topic is that available experimental data are consistent with the first development of biotites, under water pressures of a few kilobars, at temperatures between 300 and 400°C. The reactions in question involve partial dehydration so that corresponding equilibrium temperatures will increase slightly with water pressure (cf. Fyfe, Turner, and Verhoogen, 1958, p. 119, fig. 34a).

Breakdown of Micas and Chlorites

Micas and chlorites, like other hydrous silicates, ultimately break down, when progressively heated at constant pressure of a few kilobars, to anhydrous phases and water. The breakdown curve for a given mica or chlorite sets upper temperature limits for its stability in natural assemblages. The presence of other minerals may permit coupled reactions at lower temperatures, thus reducing the stability field of the mica in that particular assemblage. Quartz, which is a member of most common mica- and chlorite-bearing assemblages, is particularly significant in this connection. Dehydration of micas and chlorites in the presence of quartz must always be possible at temperatures considerably lower than those of corresponding reactions in a silica-deficient environment.

Dehydration of micas and chlorites results in notable increase in both volume and entropy. Therefore, the slope of the dehydration curve is positive. The values of ΔV and ΔS decrease with rising pressure as the gas phase becomes denser. But the effect of pressure on ΔV is greater than upon ΔS, so the curve steepens with increase in pressure and assumes a characteristic curved form that is convex toward the high-temperature end of the scale (cf. Fig. 4-2) at low pressures.

Metamorphic biotites and chlorites have a high content of ferrous iron, and among their anhydrous breakdown products are haematite and magnetite. Reactions of this kind are sensitive to differences in partial pressures of oxygen, P_{O_2}. In natural assemblages, P_{O_2} is commonly held between fixed limits ("buffered") in the presence of combinations of haematite, magnetite, ilmenite, or pyrite. So at any given pressure the temperature at which biotite or chlorite will participate in a metamorphic reaction is likely to vary according to the identity of the "opaque ore" in the metamorphic assemblage (cf. Eugster and Wones, 1962, pp. 115–116).

Muscovite. Muscovite breaks down by dehydration according to the equation[1]

(1) $$KAl_2(AlSi_3O_{10})(OH)_2 \rightleftharpoons KAlSi_3O_8 + Al_2O_3 + H_2O$$
       Muscovite   Sanidine   Corundum

Yoder and Eugster (1955, pp. 235–242) decomposed natural muscovite at the following points: 650°C, 350 bars; 650°C, 1000 bars; 700°C, 2100 bars. The reverse reaction was accomplished in a single run at 350°C, 1000 bars. This work for the first time set upper limits (broken curve A' in Fig. 4-2) upon the stability of muscovite at elevated pressures ($P_{H_2O} = P_l$). Most of their other data refer to experimental synthesis of muscovite from unstable starting materials, and so are of doubtful value.

To date, the most satisfactory curve of univariant equilibrium (A in Fig. 4-2) seems to be that of Evans (1965). Using a natural muscovite, he measured the rates of reaction (1) in both directions over wide temperature intervals at 2 kb and at 3 kb, and so arrived at an equilibrium temperature (where the reaction rate is zero) for each pressure. The curve connecting these points was extrapolated, using standard thermochemical data, to lower pressures. A more recent curve published by Velde (1966) agrees with that of Evans in the 1 to 2 kb range; at 1 kb he reversed the reaction in the range 645 to 660 $\pm$ 6°C, and he records the breakdown of muscovite at 2 kb and 685°C. Grossly inconsistent with Evans' data, however, is Velde's record of the synthesis of muscovite at 160 bars, 610°C, and reversal of the reaction at 8 kb between 720 and 735°C. These results imply a slope of the equilibrium curve that seems much too steep (dP/dT too great) to be consistent with well-established values of S and V for water. For

---

[1] See Chap. 3, pp. 93, 105–107, for critical evaluation of some experimental data relating to this reaction.

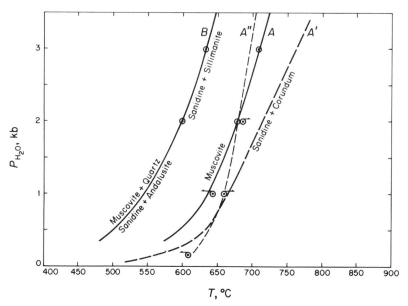

Fig. 4-2. Curves showing limits of stability of muscovite. Curves A (*after B. W. Evans*, 1965), A' (*after H. S. Yoder and H. P. Eugster*, 1955), and A'' (*after B. Velde*, 1966) represent the reaction Muscovite $\rightleftharpoons$ Sanidine + Corundum + H_2O. Circled points with arrows represent points recorded by Velde. Curve B (*after B. W. Evans*, 1965) is the equilibrium curve for Muscovite + Quartz $\rightleftharpoons$ Sanidine + Al_2SiO_5 + H_2O.

this reason Evans' curve is tentatively accepted in preference to that of Velde.

By the same procedure, Evans (1965) has given an equilibrium curve (B in Fig. 4-2) for the reaction

$$(2) \quad \underset{\text{Muscovite}}{KAl_2(AlSi_3O_{10})(OH)_2} + SiO_2 \rightleftharpoons \underset{\text{Sanidine}}{KAlSi_3O_8} + \underset{\text{Andalusite}}{Al_2SiO_3} + H_2O$$

This is the more significant of the two muscovite breakdowns, since among metamorphic rocks, mineral assemblages with quartz and andalusite (or sillimanite) are much more common than silica-deficient assemblages containing corundum. In the presence of quartz the stability field of muscovite is significantly reduced. The 80° interval between curves A and B represents the effect of the negative ΔG of the coupling reaction

$$(3) \qquad \underset{\text{Quartz}}{SiO_2} + \underset{\text{Corundum}}{Al_2O_3} \rightarrow \underset{\text{Andalusite}}{Al_2SiO_5}$$

Within the limits of experimental error there is no significant difference between the equilibrium temperatures (about 600°C) at $P_{H_2O} = 2$ kb, recorded by Evans for the alternative reactions respectively yielding silli-manite-sanidine and andalusite-sanidine as breakdown products of muscovite-quartz. So the two polymorphs are about equally stable at $T = 600°C$ and $P = 2$ kb. It is inferred that at pressures above about 3 kb the denser polymorph, sillimanite, would be the stable aluminum silicate to form by destruction of muscovite. The much denser phase kyanite is unstable at 600°C and 2 kb; so that the temperature of the metastable equilibrium

$$\text{Muscovite} + \text{Quartz} \rightleftharpoons \text{Kyanite} + \text{Sanidine} + H_2O$$

at $P_{H_2O} = 2$ kb is significantly above 600°C. Evans determined it as approximately 675°C.

The melting relations of muscovite in the presence of quartz have obvious possible significance with respect to the intimate association of mica schist and "granitic" rock components in migmatites. Segnit and Kennedy's (1961) curve separating fields of muscovite plus quartz and of sillimanite plus glass is based on experiments starting with mixes of kaolin, $K_2Si_4O_9$, and hydrated silica. It is not consistent with Evans' curve B (Fig. 4-3) for the breakdown of muscovite-quartz. The most reliable information (cf. Evans, 1965, fig. 10) comes from Shaw's (1963) study of the melting of quartz plus sanidine in the presence of water. Shaw's curve intersects Evans' curve B (Fig. 4-3) at $P_{H_2O} = 6$ kb and $T = 715°C$. This must be a point on the melting curve of muscovite-quartz. So at temperatures and pressures (P_{H_2O}) above about 700°C and 6 kb, quartz-muscovite schists should begin to melt without previous breakdown of muscovite to sillimanite (in stippled area of Fig. 4-3).

In Fig. 4-3, Bowen and Tuttle's (1958, p. 58) minimum melting curve of "granite" (quartz-orthoclase-albite) is shown as curve D. Melts on this curve contain twice as much water as does pure muscovite. So such melts could be generated from quartz-feldspar-muscovite schists only by copious introduction of water from an extraneous source. They could coexist in equilibrium with solid quartz-muscovite and quartz-sanidine-muscovite-sillimanite aggregates over temperature-pressure ranges consistent with Fig. 4-3 between curves C and D.

At 700°C the kyanite-sillimanite inversion temperature (Fig. 4-1) is probably close to 7 kb, so there is no significant field of high pressure and temperature within which the assemblage kyanite-sanidine could form as a stable product of the destruction of muscovite. Melting of muscovite would occur before kyanite could form. If the kyanite-sillimanite transition were referred to even higher pressures (cf. Clark, 1964; Bell, 1963), this conclusion would be even stronger. The hypothetical relation between the Kyanite $\rightleftharpoons$ Sillimanite inversion and the breakdown of muscovite pictured by Turner and Verhoogen (1960, p. 551) is clearly invalid. Kyanite of pelitic

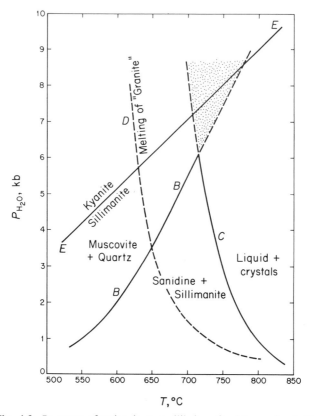

Fig. 4-3. *B*: curve of univariant equilibrium for Muscovite + Quartz $\rightleftharpoons$ Sanidine + Sillimanite + H_2O. (*After B. W. Evans,* 1965.) *C*: melting curve of Sanidine + Quartz + Water. (*After H. R. Shaw,* 1963.) *D*: minimum melting curve of "granite." (*After N. L. Bowen and O. F. Tuttle,* 1958.) *E*: part of inversion curve Kyanite $\rightleftharpoons$ Sillimanite. (*After W. S. Fyfe,* 1966.)

schists, if stable, must have some other origin than by reaction between muscovite and quartz. Indeed the three minerals are frequently associated in pelitic schists.

Paragonite. Dehydration of paragonite, $NaAl_2(AlSi_3O_{10})(OH)_2$, to albite-corundum or albite-andalusite-quartz occurs at temperatures somewhat below those of corresponding dehydrations of muscovite (cf. Eugster and Yoder, 1954). The significance of such reactions in metamorphism of normal pelitic sediments is doubtful. Paragonite, though known in pelitic schists of low and medium grades, is confined to rocks richer than average in alumina; and it is always subordinate to muscovite. Disappearance of paragonite with rising metamorphic temperature has not yet been correlated with incoming of Al_2SiO_5 or corundum. More likely it is eliminated as a separate phase by complex reactions involving crystallization of aluminous minerals such as garnet and staurolite (and perhaps kyanite), and progressive substitution of Na for K in muscovite.

Biotite. Destruction of biotites at high temperatures can be treated in the first instance in terms of the simple reaction

(1) $K(Mg, Fe)_3(AlSi_3O_{10})(OH)_2 + 3SiO_2 \rightleftharpoons KAlSi_3O_8$
            Biotite   Quartz   K-feldspar

$$+ 3(Mg, Fe)SiO_3 + H_2O$$
            Hypersthene

End members of the phlogopite-annite series, corresponding to the biotite in equation (1), have been investigated experimentally by Yoder and Eugster (1954), Eugster and Wones (1962), and Wones and Eugster (1965). Their conclusions are as follows.

They have determined the upper limits of stability of phlogopite as

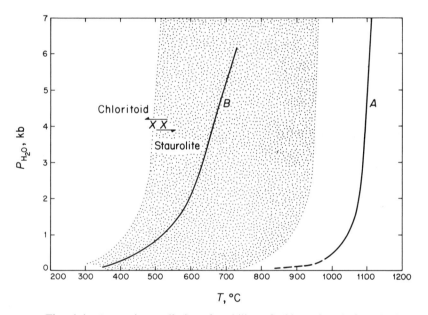

$T,\,°C$

Fig. 4-4. A: maximum limits of stability of phlogopite. (*After H. S. Yoder and H. P. Eugster,* 1954.) B: curve of univariant equilibrium for Muscovite + Quartz $\rightleftharpoons$ Sanidine + Al_2SiO_3 + Water. (*After B. W. Evans,* 1965.) Natural biotites might be expected to react with quartz at points somewhere within the stippled field. Chloritoid assemblages give way to staurolite assemblages at pressures and temperatures such as X.

shown in Fig. 4-4, curve A. To the right of the curve, phlogopite breaks down thus:

(2) $2KMg_3(AlSi_3O_{10})(OH)_2 \rightarrow KAlSi_2O_6 + KAlSiO_4$

      Phlogopite   Leucite   Kalsilite

$$+ 3Mg_2SiO_4 + 2H_2O$$

                           Forsterite

It was synthesized from glass and artificial mixes over a range of conditions to the left of curve A. This diagram, though not an equilibrium curve, is consistent with the known occurrence of phlogopite in quartz-free assemblages, such as marbles, up to the highest grades of metamorphism.

Annite breaks down at temperatures several hundred degrees below those at which phlogopite is destroyed. Here the reactions are more complex and depend on prevailing partial pressures of oxygen; for some of them involve oxidation of ferrous iron to magnetite or haematite. One such reaction is

(3) $KFe_3(AlSi_3O_{10})(OH)_2 + \frac{1}{2}O_2 \rightleftharpoons KAlSi_3O_8 + Fe_3O_4 + H_2O$

      Annite   K-feldspar   Magnetite

For any given water pressure the temperature of reaction increases with increasing P_{O_2}. Thus as P_{O_2} increases from 10^{-22} to 10^{-18} bars, the temperature of reaction (3) at a water pressure of 2 kb rises from about 400 to 800°C. Magnitudes of P_{O_2} under metamorphic conditions between 400 and 700°C might range between 10^{-22} and 10^{-11} bars in the presence of *magnetite-haematite* or between 10^{-30} and 10^{-18} in the presence of *magnetite-fayalite-quartz* (Eugster and Wones, 1962, p. 92).[1]

Clearly the destruction of natural biotites according to reaction (1) at any given water pressure will take place over a wide range of temperatures depending upon the Mg/Fe ratio of the biotite and the value of P_{O_2} maintained by natural buffers. Even pure magnesian phlogopite in quartzose rocks must be eliminated at temperatures considerably lower than those of curve A in Fig. 4-4.[2] Under a given set of conditions an iron-rich biotite

---

[1] The italicized assemblages, known as *buffers*, maintain the P_{O_2} at a constant value at any given pressure and temperature by internal reaction:

$$2Fe_3O_4 + \tfrac{1}{2}O_2 \rightleftharpoons 3Fe_2O_3$$

     Magnetite   Hematite

$$3Fe_2SiO_4 + O_2 \rightleftharpoons 2Fe_3O_4 + 3SiO_2$$

     Fayalite   Magnetite   Quartz

[2] The degree of lowering will depend upon the values (still not accurately known) of ΔG (negative) for reactions

$$KAlSi_2O_6 + SiO_2 \rightarrow KAlSi_3O_8$$

$$KAlSiO_4 + 2SiO_2 \rightarrow KAlSi_3O_8$$

and $\qquad\qquad Mg_2SiO_4 + SiO_2 \rightarrow 2MgSiO_3$

may be expected to react with quartz to give a more magnesian biotite, K-feldspar, hypersthene, magnetite, and water. Other conditions being equal, high partial pressures of oxygen (such as those in assemblages with magnetite-hematite) favor high Mg/Fe in the surviving biotite. Increasing temperature (which in the presence of a given buffer involves increasing P_{O_2}) also favors survival of magnesian biotites. With progressive metamorphism biotite should thus decrease in quantity and become more magnesian. At the same time there should be a progressive increase in the quantity of potash feldspar and orthopyroxene. The range of temperatures and pressures in which such reactions may be expected to occur is shown qualitatively as the stippled field of Fig. 4-4. This covers a wide range of metamorphic conditions; and its boundaries are but vaguely defined.

At present it is unprofitable to attempt any precise estimation of metamorphic temperatures and pressures on the basis of currently available data on stability of biotites. Such an attempt made by Wones and Eugster (1965, pp. 1266–1277) has led to conclusions which few geologists would accept. Taking the conditions $T = 500$ to $600°C$ and $P_l = 2$ to 3 kb (depth 7 to 10 km) deduced by Engel and Engel (1960) for crystallization of quartz-biotite-oligoclase-muscovite and quartz-biotite-oligoclase-garnet gneisses in a sector of the Adirondacks, and making use of the unusually full miner-alogical and chemical data available, Wones and Eugster conclude that water pressures must have been extremely low (0.1 bar at $500°C$; 1 to 10 bars at $600°C$). They further suggest that the occurrence of biotite-magnetite-K-feldspar assemblages in low-grade schists implies common prevalence of exceedingly low P_{H_2O} values in regional metamorphism. Such conclusions are startling to the geologist; for it is hard to visualize how a series of dehydration reactions can proceed in a large mass of pelitic sediments while P_{H_2O} is maintained at a minute fraction of the total fluid pressure. Moreover, even at water pressures of 10 to 100 bars, in quartz-bearing rocks muscovite (an essential constituent of the Adirondack rocks and the characteristic mica of low-grade metamorphism) could not survive temperatures as high as $400°C$ (cf. curve B, Fig. 4-2).

Chlorites. Chlorites of low-grade pelitic schists and greenschists are rich in both ferrous iron and aluminum. From such rocks in southern New Zealand, Hutton (1940, pp. 17–19) records chlorites approximating $Fe_2Mg_{2.8}Al_{1.2}(Si_{2.8}Al_{1.2}O_{10})(OH)_8$. A number of chlorites from Japanese schists are closely similar; a few are higher in iron (Miyashiro, 1957; Banno, 1964, pp. 255–261). Nonaluminous chlorites close to antigorite, $Mg_6(Si_4O_{10})(OH)_8$ occur principally in magnesian schists—metamor-phosed serpentinites.

A good deal of experimental work has been done on synthesis and dehydration breakdown of magnesian and ferrous end members of the aluminous chlorite series (Nelson and Roy, 1958; Fawcett, 1963, 1964; Turnock, 1960; Fawcett and Yoder, 1966). Unfortunately there are very few records of experimental reversal of any reaction. Reaction products are commonly metastable assemblages. Where reactions have been reversed, the temperature interval of reversal may be 150 to 200°C at any given pressure. Moreover, most of the investigated reactions (for example, breakdown of clinochlore and clinochlore-quartz as discussed below) have no obvious application to commonly observed metamorphic transformations in pelitic schists and greenschists.

Facts and inferences of possible petrogenic interest are as follows:

1. Clinochlore alone possibly remains stable up to temperatures of 700 to 800°C over the P_{H_2O} range 2 to 6 kb. The curve drawn by Fawcett and Yoder (1966) to represent the upper stability limits of clinochlore (Fig. 4-5, curve A) is based on two dehydration reactions respectively

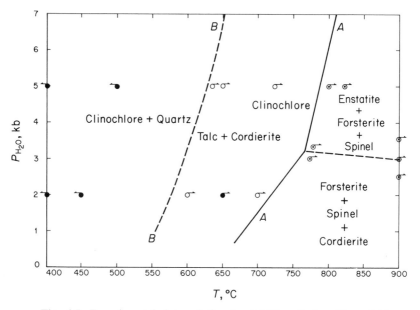

Fig. 4-5. Experimental data relating to stability of clinochlore. (*After J. J. Fawcett and H. S. Yoder.*) A: breakdown of clinochlore to enstatite-forsterite-spinel or to forsterite-spinel-cordierite. Points determined from natural or synthetic chlorite as starting material are shown by circled points (arrows give reaction sense). B: breakdown of clinochlore-quartz to talc-cordierite. Solid circles show points of reversal of reaction (arrows give reaction sense) starting with natural mineral phases. Open circles are points of breakdown of chlorite-quartz mixes synthesized from glasses.

yielding enstatite-forsterite-spinel above 3 kb and forsterite-spinel-cordierite at lower pressures. The first reaction was truly reversed at $P_{H_2O} =$ 10 kb over the interval 825 to 837°C. Dehydration reactions (apparently not reversed) were recorded between 770 to 800°C at water pressures of 3 to 5 kb.

2. At temperatures significantly lower than those of curve A (Fig. 4-5), the pair clinochlore-quartz become partially dehydrated to talc-cordierite. Fawcett and Yoder's curve (B in Fig. 4-5) representing this reaction is based mainly on syntheses from glasses. The temperature intervals of recorded reversals are very wide (500 to 650°C at 5 kb; 450 to 650°C at 2 kb). However it is not likely that the negative ΔG of the coupling reaction Enstatite + Forsterite + Spinel + Quartz + $H_2O \rightleftharpoons$ Talc + Cordierite would lower the stability temperature of chlorite by more than the 150° interval between curves A and B.

3. Ferrous chlorites appear to break down at temperatures significantly lower than do corresponding magnesian chlorites. Turnock (1960) has synthesized the ferrous aluminum chlorite daphnite at temperatures up to 565 to 590°C[1] at $P_{H_2O} = 2$ kb. Synthesis products alternative to daphnite at higher temperatures include mixtures of such phases as hematite, magnetite, hercynite, fayalite, and so on—some clearly metastable.

4. In the magnesian chlorite series the temperature of dehydration is higher for clinochlore than for less aluminous members approaching antigorite or for more aluminous chlorites closer to amesite.

Experimental studies on chlorites are still too imperfect to throw any light on the critical reactions in pelitic schists and greenschists over the lower span of temperatures within and beyond the greenschist facies. Geologic observations show that chlorite in such rocks is gradually eliminated in favor of recognized indices of higher grade: biotite, biotite-almandine, biotite-almandine-staurolite, in pelitic schists of regional metamorphism; biotite-cordierite and biotite-andalusite in hornfelses; hornblendic assemblages in amphibolites. Fawcett and Yoder's estimates of 575 to 625°C or alternatively 500 to 550°C as the upper limits of the greenschist facies at $P_{H_2O} = 2$ to 5 kb are unacceptable. They are based on data that at least are open to criticism, concerning a reaction (clinochlore + quartz $\rightleftharpoons$ talc + cordierite + H_2O) that is in no way diagnostic of the greenschist facies boundary.

The Stability Field of Cordierite

In progressive metamorphism cordierite becomes increasingly prominent in pelitic rocks as the result of successive reactions involving elimina-

---

[1] Depending on P_{O_2}: 565°C in the presence of a magnetite-hematite buffer; 590°C in the presence of magnetite-wüstite.

tion of chlorites and micas and more rarely (only in very aluminous rocks) pyrophyllite. These reactions have not been followed closely in the field, nor have they been investigated in the laboratory. Some simple ideal models that have been proposed are:

(1) $Mg_4Al_2(Al_2Si_2O_{10})(OH)_8 + 2Al_2Si_4O_{10}(OH)_2$
       Chlorite (amesite)   Pyrophyllite

$$\rightleftharpoons 2Mg_2Al_4Si_5O_{18} + 6H_2O$$
Cordierite

(2) $(Mg, Fe)_5Al(AlSi_3O_{10})(OH)_8 + KAl_2(AlSi_3O_{10})(OH)_2 + 2SiO_2$
       Chlorite   Muscovite   Quartz

$$\rightleftharpoons (Mg, Fe)_2Al_4Si_5O_{18} + K(Mg, Fe)_3(AlSi_3O_{10})(OH)_2 + 4H_2O$$
Cordierite   Biotite

(3) $2K(Mg, Fe)_3(AlSi_3O_{10})(OH)_2 + 6KAl_2(AlSiO_{10})(OH)_2 + 15SiO_2$
       Biotite   Muscovite

$$\rightleftharpoons 3(Mg, Fe)_2Al_4Si_5O_{18} + 8KAlSi_3O_8 + 8H_2O$$
Cordierite   K-feldspar

In natural pelitic assemblages (Chinner, 1959) cordierite plays a role that is inversely complementary to that of almandine. At relatively low pressures, as inferred from hornfels parageneses, cordierite is common, almandine relatively rare; in cordierite the ratio MgO/FeO is much higher than in coexisting almandine. At higher pressures, as inferred from granulites, cordierite is much less widely distributed in pelites than is almandine; in both coexisting minerals the ratio MgO/FeO is higher than in the low-pressure assemblages. In the medium- and high-grade pelitic schists of regional metamorphism (Barrovian type) thought to represen much the same pressure range as granulites, but a lower range of temperature, cordierite is absent, garnet ubiquitous. The geologic data thus suggest the influence of reactions of the type

(4) $(Fe, Mg)_3Al_2Si_3O_{12} + X + Y + \cdots \rightleftharpoons (Mg, Fe)_2Al_4Si_5O_{18}$
       Almandine   Cordierite

$$+ U + V + \cdots$$

where X, Y, U, V, etc., are associated phases such as quartz, kyanite, biotite, hypersthene, potash feldspar, and so on. Reactions such as (4) would tend to proceed from left to right with increasing temperature or with decreasing pressure.

From geologic reasoning, then, we deduce a high-temperature low-pressure field of stability of cordierite-bearing assemblages extending to fusion temperatures[1] (cf. Fig. 4-6). Its low-temperature boundary will be a composite line having a variable positive slope, and compounded of parts

---

[1] Shown by occurrence of cordierite in naturally partially fused rocks (buchites) and by laboratory experiment (Schreyer and Yoder, 1964, p. 303).

of equilibrium curves corresponding to complex reactions similar to (1) to (4) above. At low temperatures and pressures, the cordierite field of pelitic schists abuts on fields of mica-chlorite assemblages. At higher pressures

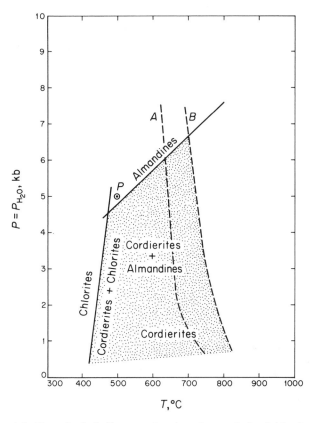

Fig. 4-6. Hypothetical diagram showing shape of the field of stability of cordierites (stippled) as inferred from geologic data. P is a point experimentally determined by *Schreyer and Yoder* (1964) for hydration and breakdown of magnesian cordierite to pyrophyllite and chlorite. A is the minimum melting curve of "granite." (*After N. L. Bowen and O. F. Tuttle,* 1958.) B is the melting curve of sanidine-quartz-water. (*After H. R. Shaw,* 1963.) Other lines entirely hypothetical.

and temperatures the adjoining fields are characterized by assemblages with garnet, biotite, and Al_2SiO_5 polymorphs.

Experimental exploration of the limits of the field of cordierite in pelitic rocks presents a difficult task indeed. To date we have only meager reliable data from such sources. Schreyer and Yoder (1964, p. 293) have constructed a curve which they believe to represent equilibrium (1) (up to $P_{H_2O} = 5$ kb) and a similar equilibrium involving Al_2SiO_5 instead of pyrophyllite (above $P_{H_2O} = 5$ kb). But most of their data are based on runs made with extremely unstable starting materials, and the recorded reaction products in most cases are clearly metastable. Moreover, recent work (e.g., Kerrick, 1967) suggests that even at low pressures, the cordierite-producing reactions may involve andalusite rather than pyrophyllite as the aluminous phase on the left-hand side of equation (1).*

Attempts by Schreyer and Yoder to break down cordierite by hydration reactions were for the most part unsuccessful. However, cordierite was successfully converted to pyrophyllite plus chlorite at $P_{H_2O} = 5$ kb and $T = 475$ to $500°C$. This assemblage, like many of the others, may perhaps prove to be metastable. Nevertheless the point 5 kb, $500°C$ must represent conditions under which magnesian cordierite is unstable at water pressure equal to load pressure. If, as Turnock (1960) has stated, ferrous chlorites break down at lower temperatures than do magnesian chlorites, then cordierites with a relatively high FeO/MgO ratio might form as stable phases at temperatures somewhat lower than $500°C$ at $P_{H_2O} = 5$ kb.

The provisional conclusion drawn from both geologic and experimental evidence is that at pressures of a few kilobars, cordierite assemblages of pelitic rocks cover a wide temperature range extending perhaps from $450°C$ to the temperatures of rock fusion. Garnet-cordierite assemblages become increasingly abundant within the chemical range of pelites with increasing pressure. At relatively high metamorphic pressures (guessed as 5 to 10 kb), cordierites are unstable and the magnesium of pelites is accommodated exclusively in almandine and biotite. The upper pressure limit of the cordierite field is likely to be a boundary with the positive relatively flat slope (perhaps 15 to 20 bars/deg) characteristic of most solid-solid reactions. It is emphasized that the only experimentally determined data of Fig. 4-6 are the point P and the fusion curves (A and B) of pelitic mixtures in the presence of excess water. These nevertheless place limits on the boundaries of the field of stability of cordierites in pelitic rocks. Otherwise, the boundaries are entirely hypothetical.

Chloritoid and Staurolite

In iron-rich aluminous pelitic shists, chloritoid and staurolite respectively are characteristic of the lower and higher grades of regional

---

*This is supported, within the experience of this writer, by the tendency for andalusite to appear in the outermost zones of contact aureoles in pelitic rocks where cordierite has not yet been formed.

metamorphism. Hoschek and Winkler (1965) record reversal of the simple equilibrium[1]

$$\text{Chloritoid} + \text{Andalusite} \rightleftharpoons \text{Staurolite} + \text{Quartz} + \text{Water}$$

at $P_{H_2O} = 4$ kb and $T = 540 \pm 15°C$. Elimination of chloritoid in favor of staurolite in metamorphism must usually be the result of more complex reactions involving micas. So staurolite-chloritoid-mica-quartz and staurolite-mica-qurtz assemblages may be assumed to record temperatures upward of 500°C at water pressures of a few kilobars (for instance, near X, Fig. 4-4). This is considerably below the upper temperatures at which Halferdahl (1961, p. 99) synthesized chloritoid from unstable starting materials.

REACTIONS IN SILICEOUS DOLOMITIC LIMESTONES

Within the range of metamorphic temperatures and pressures, the pairs dolomite-quartz and calcite-quartz tend to become unstable with increasing temperature. In a rock represented by some point in the calcite-dolomite-quartz triangle, progressive metamorphism leads to a series of step reactions, each involving partial elimination of CO_2. Such a series leads to progressive increase in the entropy of the system. For example, a possible sequence, starting from a mixture of equal parts of dolomite and calcite with a small amount of quartz (P in Fig. 4-7), might be

(1)   Elimination of quartz:

$$\text{Dolomite} + 2\ \text{Quartz} \rightarrow \text{Diopside} + 2CO_2$$

(2)   Elimination of diopside:

$$\text{Diopside} + 3\ \text{Dolomite} \rightarrow 4\ \text{Calcite} + 2\ \text{Forsterite} + 2CO_2$$

(3)   Elimination of dolomite:

$$\text{Dolomite} \rightarrow \text{Periclase} + \text{Calcite} + CO_2$$

The end product is the high-temperature assemblage calcite-forsterite-periclase. The sequence of reactions for other initial calcite-dolomite-quartz mixtures may be different. Thus the sequence for composition Q in Fig. 4-7 might be

(1)   Elimination of dolomite:

$$\text{Dolomite} + 2\ \text{Quartz} \rightarrow \text{Diopside} + 2\ CO_2$$

[1]They also record reversal of the equilibrium (probably metastable)

$$\text{Chloritoid} + \text{Pyrophyllite} \rightleftharpoons \text{Staurolite} + \text{Quartz} + \text{Water}$$

at a similar temperature at $P_{H_2O} = 8$ kb.

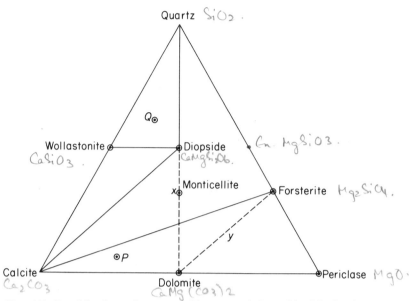

Fig. 4-7. Possible three-phase assemblages coexisting with CO_2 in the triangle calcite-dolomite-quartz at high temperatures (full lines). The broken lines x and y connect coexisting phases stable at lower temperatures (see text).

(2)   Elimination of calcite:

$$\text{Calcite} + \text{Quartz} \rightarrow \text{Wollastonite} + CO_2$$

The end product would be the assemblage wollastonite-diopside-quartz.

Clearly it is possible to imagine several alternative reaction sequences of increasing entropy for any one initial bulk composition. For example, an alternative sequence of two steps starting from P might be

(1)   Dolomite + Quartz → Calcite + Enstatite + CO_2
(2)   Enstatite + Dolomite → Calcite + Forsterite + CO_2

Some such reactions must however represent metastable equilibria. For example, as will be shown later, the equilibria

$$\text{Dolomite} + \text{Quartz} \rightleftharpoons \text{Calcite} + \text{Enstatite} + CO_2$$

and $$2 \text{ Dolomite} + \text{Quartz} \rightleftharpoons 2 \text{ Calcite} + \text{Forsterite} + 2 CO_2$$

are metastable in that for any given P_{CO_2}, their equilibrium temperatures lie beyond the field of stability of dolomite-quartz and within the stability field of diopside.

In nature, the situation is likely to be complicated by the presence of water as a constituent of the gas phase. This may lead to appearance of hydrous phases such as tremolite and talc as early products which later, as temperature rises, are eliminated in favor of anhydrous phases. Equilibria between carbonates, hydrous silicates and gas are controlled by temperature, pressure, and the respective fugacities[1] of H_2O and CO_2 in the gas phase. The fugacity of a gas component varies with the partial pressure of that component (in this case P_{CO_2} or P_{H_2O}) in the gas. It also expresses the departure from ideal mixing of the components, that is, the degree to which the two components may attract or repel each other. Greenwood (1963) has discussed this problem clearly, and has shown by experiment that over much of the range of metamorphic temperatures and pressures below 2 kb H_2O–CO_2 mixtures closely approach ideal behavior. This makes it possible to interpret the natural mineral assemblages in terms of T, P_{H_2O}, and P_{CO_2}; these are readily measured in the laboratory and are readily visualized in any given geologic situation.

It should be possible to list, in order of increasing temperature, a general sequence of actual reactions responsible for known mineral assemblages in metamorphosed siliceous dolomitic limestones. Such sequences have indeed been formulated. They are based on three independent approaches using three completely independent sets of data: geologic observations, experimental evaluation of appropriate reactions, and appraisal of reactions on the basis of standard thermochemical data.

Eskola (1922), on the basis of field and mineralogical observations in Scandinavia and North America, listed the sequence tremolite, diopside, wollastonite as indices of increasing temperature. Bowen (1940) formulated his now classic sequence of 13 possible steps, also based on geologic data. Tilley (1951) suggested minor revisions, the most important being inclusion of talc as the first silicate phase. The sequence of steps, so revised, leads to the successive appearance (each in rocks of appropriate limited composition) of talc, tremolite, forsterite, diopside, periclase, wollastonite, monticellite, akermanite, tilleyite, spurrite, rankinite, merwinite, larnite. The last six are relatively unimportant since they are confined to silica-deficient rocks low in magnesium and are stable only at maximum temperatures and very low pressures—those attributed to what we shall later call the sanidinite facies.

Direct Experiments in Absence of Water

Figure 4-8 shows experimentally determined curves for four simple decarbonation reactions not involving water.

Curve A.

$$CaCO_3 + SiO_2 \rightleftharpoons CaSiO_3 + CO_2$$
$$\text{Calcite} \qquad \text{Quartz} \qquad \text{Wollastonite}$$

[1] Discussed in Turner and Verhoogen (1960, pp. 23, 24).

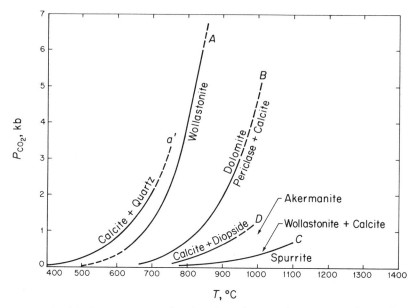

Fig. 4-8. Curves representing decarbonation reactions. A: experimentally determined curve of univariant equilibrium for $CaCO_3 + SiO_2 \rightleftharpoons CaSiO_3 + CO_2$. (*After R. I. Harker and O. F. Tuttle.*) a: calculated curve for the same reaction. (*After Danielsson as modified by A. J. Ellis and W. S. Fyfe.*) B: curve of maximum possible temperature of stability of dolomite, $CaMg(CO_3)_2 \rightarrow CaCO_3 + MgO + CO_2$. (*After R. I. Harker and O. F. Tuttle.*) C: curve of minimum possible temperature of stability of spurrite, $2CaSiO_3 + 3CaCO_3 \leftarrow 2Ca_2SiO_4 \cdot CaCO_3 + 2CO_2$. (*After O. F. Tuttle and R. I. Harker.*) D: Curve of univariant equilibrium for $CaCO_3 + CaMgSi_2O_6 \rightleftharpoons Ca_2MgSi_2O_7 + CO_2$. (*After L. S. Walter.*)

This was reversed over narrow temperature limits at values of P_{CO_2} ($= P_f$) ranging from 300 to 3000 bars by Harker and Tuttle (1956). Curve A is thus an experimentally established curve of univariant equilibrium.

Curve B.

$$CaMg(CO_3)_2 \rightleftharpoons CaCO_3 + MgO + CO_2$$

Dolomite   Calcite   Periclase

This curve, presented by Harker and Tuttle (1955) was not reversed. It represents the lower temperature limits at which dolomite was observed to break down to calcite + periclase. In other words it defines the maximum possible stability limits of dolomite.

Curve C. Curve C (Tuttle and Harker, 1957) represents the minimum possible stability temperature of spurrite, as determined by conversion of spurrite in the presence of CO_2, to wollastonite + calcite.

$$2CaSiO_3 + 3CaCO_3 \leftarrow 2Ca_2SiO_4 \cdot CaCO_3 + 2CO_2$$

Wollastonite   Calcite   Spurrite

The reaction was not reversed from left to right.

Curve D. Curve *D* is the equilibrium curve for

$$CaCO_3 + CaMgSi_2O_6 \rightleftharpoons Ca_2MgSi_2O_7 + CO_2$$

Calcite   Diopside   Akermanite

as determined by Walter (1963, pp. 491–493). It was reversed experimentally over small temperature intervals at P_{CO_2} approximately 100 and 700 bars. At intermediate points the reaction proceeds from left to right at temperatures slightly higher than those of curve *D*. Walter also investigated three other equilibria over the same temperature-pressure range.

(1) $CaMgSi_2O_6 + 3CaMgSiO_4 \rightleftharpoons Mg_2SiO_4 + 2Ca_2MgSi_2O_7$

Diopside   Monticellite   Forsterite   Akermanite

T_e 880°C at $P = 400$ bars

(2) $2CaCO_3 + Mg_2SiO_4 + CaMgSi_2O_6 \rightleftharpoons 3CaMgSiO_4 + 2CO_2$

Calcite   Forsterite   Diopside   Monticellite

(3) $CaCO_3 + Mg_2SiO_4 \rightleftharpoons CaMgSiO_4 + MgO + CO_2$

Calcite   Forsterite   Monticellite   Periclase

According to Walter (1963, p. 773), the equilibrium curves for reactions (2) and (3) coincide, with limits of experimental error, with each other and with curve *D* (the akermanite reaction). It is difficult to reconcile this conclusion with the occurrence of monticellite-forsterite-calcite in natural contact parageneses. Moreover at low pressures ΔS for the breakdown of monticellite-forsterite-calcite to monticellite-periclase by reaction (3), written as

$$CaCO_3 + Mg_2SiO_4 + CaMgSiO_4 \rightarrow 2CaMgSiO_4 + MgO + CO_2$$

Calcite   Forsterite   Monticellite   Monticellite   Periclase

must be large and positive. There must therefore be a considerable interval of temperature between the appearance of the left hand assemblage by reaction (2) and its elimination in favor of monticellite-periclase by reaction (3). Apart from this general argument, the standard *S* and ΔH data for the mineral phases in question cannot be reconciled with Walter's contention that monticellite can form at almost identical temperatures by reaction (2) or reaction (3) at any given value of P_{CO_2} (Turner, 1967, pp. 13, 14).

Direct Experiments in the Presence of Water

There is general agreement among geologists that at relatively low temperatures the first metamorphic minerals to appear in siliceous dolomites are talc and tremolite. Reactions leading to the appearance and subsequent elimination of these minerals are influenced by both P_{CO_2} and P_{H_2O}. The same may be said also regarding the stability fields of other hydrous magnesian compounds, notably brucite and the humites. Some of the fundamental equilibria between talc, tremolite, brucite, and calc-magnesian carbonates and anhydrous silicates have been explored by direct experiment. As a first approximation, these may be treated in terms of P_{CO_2} and P_{H_2O} as respective partial pressures of two components mixing ideally to give a gas at a fluid pressure $P_f = (P_{CO_2} + P_{H_2O})$. Equilibria

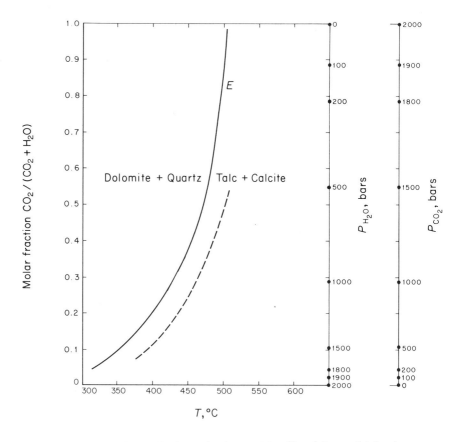

Fig. 4-9. Experimentally determined curve (E) of breakdown of dolomite-quartz presence of CO_2 and H_2O, $P_f = 2$ kb.

$$3CaMg(CO_3)_2 + 4SiO_2 + H_2O \rightarrow Mg_3Si_4O_{10}(OH)_2 + 3CaCO_3 + 3CO_2$$
$\quad$ Dolomite $\qquad$ Quartz $\qquad\qquad$ Talc $\qquad$ Calcite

(*After P. Metz and H. G. F. Winkler.*) The broken curve is the equilibrium curve calculated from thermochemical data.

may be represented as curves plotted against two rectangular coordinates, one of which is temperature, the other one of the pressure variables (the other being held constant). Alternatively, for some fixed value of P_f, temperature may be plotted against the molecular fraction $CO_2/(CO_2 + H_2O)$ in the gas (cf. Winkler, 1965, p. 29).*

Most of the experimental data on dolomite-silicate equilibria come from the work of Professor Winkler and his associates in Göttingen. Some equilibria were reversed, others not. The experimental method is such that demonstrated equilibria may prove to be metastable, especially where one

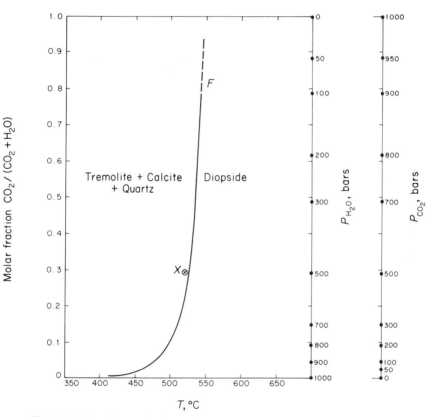

Fig. 4-10. Experimentally determined curve (F) of univariant equilibrium for

$$Ca_2Mg_5Si_8O_{22}(OH)_2 + 3CaCO_3 + 2SiO_2$$
$$\underset{\text{Tremolite}}{} \quad \underset{\text{Calcite}}{} \quad \underset{\text{Quartz}}{}$$
$$\rightleftharpoons 5CaMgSi_2O_6 + 3CO_2 + H_2O$$
$$\underset{\text{Diopside}}{}$$

(*After P. Metz and H. G. F. Winkler.*) Point X is an equilibrium point calculated from thermochemical data.

*The right hand scales of Figs. 4-9, 4-10 and 4-12 should refer to relative proportions of H_2O and CO_2 *by weight*—not (as shown) to partial pressures, except for terminal values.

of the reaction products is prone to nucleate and grow readily, as seems to be the case with talc (cf. Greenwood, 1963, p. 320). On the whole, there is very good agreement between experimentally based equilibrium curves and those drawn from thermochemical data (cf. Turner, 1967; Metz, 1967). Data relating to four experimentally explored equilibria are represented graphically in Figs. 4-9 to 4-13.

Curve E. Figure 4-9 (Metz and Winkler, 1963; Winkler, 1965, p. 29):

$$3CaMg(CO_3)_2 + 4SiO_2 + H_2O \rightarrow Mg_3Si_4O_{10}(OH)_2 + 3CaCO_3 + 3CO_2$$

Dolomite   Quartz   Talc   Calcite

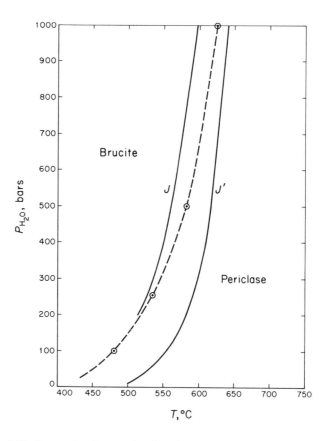

Fig. 4-11. Curves for the reaction $Mg(OH)_2 \rightleftharpoons MgO + H_2O$

Brucite   Periclase

J: experimentally determined. (*After W. S. Fyfe.*) *J'*: experimentally determined. (*After D. M. Roy and R. Roy.*) Broken curve, calculated approximately from thermochemical data. (MacDonald's more accurately calculated curve coincides almost exactly with *J*.)

The reaction was not reversed, but the curve represents the maximum temperatures at which dolomite-quartz could survive as a stable assemblage at the partial pressures of water indicated, the fluid pressure P_f being constant at 2 kb.

Curve F. Figure 4-10 (Metz and Winkler, 1964):

$$Ca_2Mg_5Si_8O_{22}(OH)_2 + 3CaCO_3 + 2SiO_2 \rightleftharpoons 5CaMgSi_2O_6 + 3CO_2 + H_2O$$

Tremolite   Calcite   Quartz   Diopside

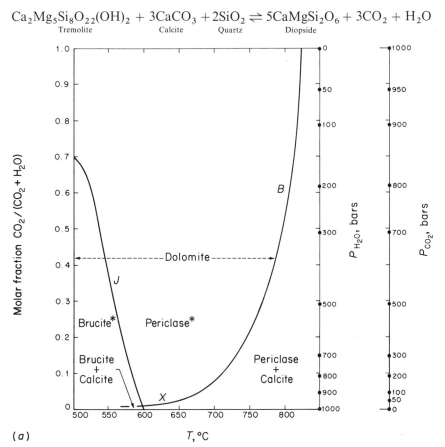

(*a*)

Fig. 4-12. Curve *J.* (*After W. S. Fyfe.*)

$$Mg(OH)_2 \rightleftharpoons MgO + H_2O$$

Brucite   Periclase

Curve *B.* (*After R. I. Harker and O. F. Tuttle.*)

$$CaMg(CO_3)_2 \rightleftharpoons CaCO_3 + MgO + CO_2$$

Dolomite   Calcite   Periclase

Both curves for constant $P_f = 1000$ bars, plotted in terms of molecular fraction $CO_2/(CO_2 + H_2O)$ (*cf. H. G. F. Winkler*). Asterisk (*) indicates metastable with calcite.

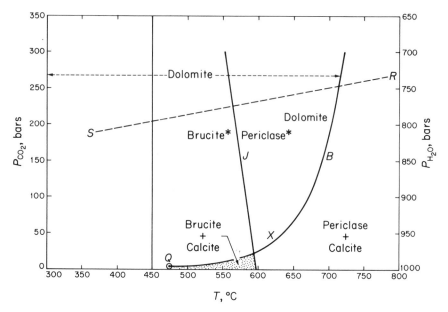

Fig. 4-13. Data of Fig. 4-12 plotted in terms of P_{H_2O} and P_{CO_2} (P_{H_2O} + P_{CO_2} = 1000 bars). Point Q is calculated from thermochemical data. Asterisk (*) indicates metastable with calcite.

Metz and Winkler record experimental reversal of the reaction within a few degrees at P_f = 1 kb and varying molecular ratios CO_2/H_2O.

Another possible reaction

$$Ca_2Mg_5Si_8O_{22}(OH)_2 + 11CaMg(CO_3)_2 \rightleftharpoons 8Mg_2SiO_4 + 13CaCO_3$$

$$\text{Tremolite} \qquad \text{Dolomite} \qquad \text{Forsterite} \qquad \text{Calcite}$$

$$+ 9CO_2 + H_2O$$

has been experimentally reversed by Metz (1967). Thermochemical data suggest that the equilibrium may be metastable—especially if $P_{CO_2} > P_{H_2O}$—in that the curve lies within the calculated stability field of calcite-dolomite-diopside.

Curve J. Figure 4-11 (Fyfe, 1958):

$$Mg(OH)_2 \rightleftharpoons MgO + H_2O$$

$$\text{Brucite} \qquad \text{Periclase}$$

Pseudomorphs of brucite after periclase are well known in some contact-metamorphosed dolomites (predazzites). The corresponding equilibrium has been explored by a number of workers (among them Bowen and Tuttle, 1949; Kennedy, 1956; Roy and Roy, 1957; Fyfe, 1958). The great discrepancies between their respective findings (an interval of 300° at $P_{H_2O} = 1$ kb) are due largely to experimental difficulties arising from rapid hydration of periclase during quenching from experimental conditions to room temperature and pressure. Fyfe's curve J, representing reversal of the reaction over 10° intervals, is preferred by this writer to that of Roy and Roy (shown in Fig. 4-11 as J'). Curve J is almost identical with one previously determined experimentally by Kennedy (1956) and with a curve computed by MacDonald (1955) from thermochemical data. (For comparison, the broken curve has now been calculated from thermochemical data slightly different from those used by MacDonald, and employing the simple approximations described in Chap. 3. It is of course less accurate than MacDonald's curve.)

The conditions under which brucite is likely to form from periclase during postmetamorphic cooling, or possibly from dolomite during low-temperature metamorphism, are illustrated in Figs. 4-12, 4-13. Postulated conditions are constant fluid pressure of 1 kb, the gas phase being a mixture (assumed to be ideal) of CO_2 and water vapor. Two modifying influences are neglected: the slight effect of total pressure, $P_f = 1$ kb, upon the Dolomite → Periclase reaction at low values of P_{CO_2} and possible melting of dolomite at high water pressures and temperatures somewhat above 600°C, near point X (Wyllie, 1965).

There is textural evidence in some contact-metamorphosed dolomites that brucite forms directly from dolomite without previous development of periclase. Clearly from Figs. 4-12 and 4-13 this is possible only if a very low concentration of CO_2 is maintained in an essentially aqueous pore fluid. One of the common associates of brucite of this nature is a hydrous magnesium silicate of the humite family (rather than the corresponding anhydrous silicate forsterite).

An interesting problem is posed by brucite pseudomorphs after periclase in a matrix of calcite in predazzites. It is hard to believe that the path of cooling of the calcite-periclase assemblage always leads directly from the stability field of calcite-periclase-vapor to that of calcite-brucite-vapor (stippled in Fig. 4-13). Anywhere above the line QX the stable assemblage is dolomite-vapor. However, once the temperature has dropped below that of curve J, brucite could form as a metastable phase even in contact with vapor containing a relatively high concentration of CO_2. This, it is now suggested, may well be the situation in which periclase becomes replaced by brucite in predazzite. In support of this contention are two facts well known to experimenters—the tendency for brucite to form very rapidly from periclase during quenching from high temperatures, and failure to induce the reaction

$$Periclase + Calcite + CO_2 \rightarrow Dolomite$$

during long runs in the dolomite stability field. Not uncommonly in predazzites, the brucite pseudomorphs are enclosed in late-formed rims of clear dolomite (Turner, 1965, p. 396). These could of course indicate great fluctuations in the respective concentrations of water and CO_2 in the vapor phase during the heating and cooling cycle. Alternatively they may represent cooling along a simple gradient (such as RS in Fig. 4-13) with early rapid crystallization of brucite at the expense of periclase, somewhere to the left of curve J, and subsequent conversion of the metastable brucite-calcite assemblage to stable dolomite during slow cooling toward S.

Thermodynamic Appraisal of Reactions

Metamorphic reactions in the triangle calcite-dolomite-quartz have been evaluated from time to time from standard entropy, enthalpy and volume data (cf. Chap. 3, pp. 97–104). The classic instance was Goldschmidt's (1912) calculation of the equilibrium curve for the wollastonite reaction

$$CaCO_3 + SiO_2 \rightleftharpoons CaSiO_3 + CO_2$$

$$\underset{\text{Calcite}}{} \quad \underset{\text{Quartz}}{} \quad \underset{\text{Wollastonite}}{}$$

This curve was long used to set limits upon possible temperatures and pressures of metamorphism. It provided an explanation for the fact (well known to geologists) that wollastonite, though common in contact marbles, is generally absent from marbles resulting from regional metamorphism. Goldschmidt's curve has since been revised in terms of newer thermal data. Danielsson's (1950) version (slightly modified by Ellis and Fyfe, 1956) is that shown in Fig. 4-8a.

Weeks (1956) calculated a sequence of reactions in the absence of water; this has been widely cited in general texts covering petrology and mineralogy (e.g., Turner and Verhoogen, 1960, p. 518; Deer, Howie, and Zussman, 1963, p. 67). More recently the reaction sequence, both in the presence and in the absence of water, has been reexamined along similar lines by Turner (1967). The conclusions expressed below are drawn from this last paper, to which the reader is referred for details of basic data, the simplifying assumptions used, and the validity of this general approach.

The method of calculation employs essentially the same simplifications and approximations as have been outlined in Chap. 3 (pp. 99–102). For any given pressure, the equilibrium temperature of any reaction is believed to be accurately estimated only within $\pm 40°$. Since the same data are used throughout, the maximum possible error in the difference in temperature between any two equilibria is thought also to be about 40°. Therefore temperature intervals greater than 40 or 50° between successive reaction steps are believed to be significant.

The calculated equilibrium curves to correspond with those determined experimentally (Figs. 4-8 to 4-13), well within the limits of possible

error of calculation and of experimental measurements. My own preference, and probably that of most readers, is for the experimentally determined curve, provided it represents a truly reversed equilibrium.

Decarbonation steps in absence of water. Following Bowen (1940)
and Weeks (1956), we may first consider possible steps of decarbonation in
the anhydrous system calcite-dolomite-quartz.[1] The earlier steps calculated
by Turner (1967) are summarized in Table 4-1. Corresponding equilibrium
curves are shown in Fig. 4-14, and the sequence of possible phase assemblages with advancing temperature at $P_{CO_2} = 1$ bar is illustrated in Fig.
4-15. These are several points of disagreement with the sequences of steps
proposed respectively by Bowen and by Weeks.

Table 4-1. Calculated stable equilibria in the triangle Calcite-Dolomite-Quartz.
$P_{CO_2} = 1$ bar. Water absent.

Equilib- rium curve		For reaction proceeding $\rightarrow$ at 25°C/mole CO_2			Equilibrium temperature, °C $\pm$ about 40°
		ΔS, cal/mole°	ΔH, kcal	ΔG, kcal	
K	$Do + 2SiO_2 \rightleftharpoons Di + 2CO_2$	39.75	18.75	6.90	200
A	$Ca + Qu \rightleftharpoons Wo + CO_2$	38.59	21.05	9.55	270
L	$Di + 3Do \rightleftharpoons 4Ca + 2Fo$ $+ 2CO_2$	45.5	29.55	16.4	380
M	$2Ca + Di + Fo \rightleftharpoons 3Mo$ $+ 2CO_2$	39.1	26.7	15.05	410
B	$Do \rightleftharpoons Ca + Per + CO_2$	42.62	31.7	19.00	470

The first step

$$\text{Dolomite} + 2\ \text{Quartz} \rightleftharpoons \text{Diopside} + 2CO_2$$

is the same as that given by Weeks; his curve of equilibrium is within
20° of curve K (Fig. 4-14).

Weeks' second step

$$2\ \text{Dolomite} + \text{Quartz} \rightleftharpoons \text{Forsterite} + 2\ \text{Calcite} + 2CO_2$$

---

[1] Bowen treated tremolite as if it were anhydrous; here the status of tremolite is
discussed in the section treating reactions in the presence of water. Weeks used ΔH (at
$T = 25$°C; $P = 1$ bar) per mole CO_2 as an index of relative stability of possible phase
assemblages resulting from various reactions of decarbonation.

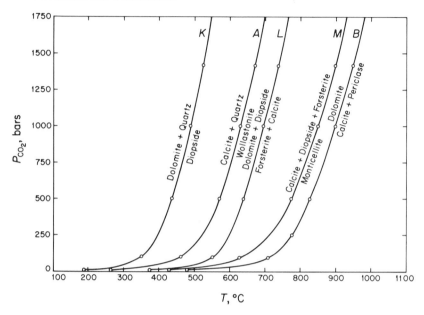

Fig. 4-14. Calculated curves of stable univariant equilibrium for reactions in triangle Calcite-Dolomite-Quartz; water absent. K: Dolomite + 2 Quartz $\rightleftharpoons$ Diopside + 2 CO_2. A: Calcite + Quartz $\rightleftharpoons$ Wollastonite + CO_2. L: Diopside + 3 Dolomite $\rightleftharpoons$ 4 Calcite + 2 Forsterite + 2 CO_2. M: 2 Calcite + Diopside + Forsterite $\rightleftharpoons$ 3 Monticellite + 2 CO_2. B: Dolomite $\rightleftharpoons$ Calcite + Periclase + CO_2. Lettering as in Fig. 4-8.

suggesting early appearance of forsterite, is here ruled out as representing a metastable equilibrium. It is situated well within the field in which diopside is more stable than the pair dolomite-quartz. Forsterite appears later from reaction L:

$$\text{Diopside} + 3 \text{ Dolomite} \rightleftharpoons 4 \text{ Calcite} + 2 \text{ Forsterite} + 2CO_2$$

In Figs. 4-14 and 4-15, wollastonite appears after diopside and before forsterite by reaction on curve A:

$$\text{Calcite} + \text{Quartz} \rightleftharpoons \text{Wollastonite} + CO_2$$

This is close to the corresponding calculated curves of Weeks and of Danielsson. The temperature interval of about 20° between the Danielsson curve (a in Fig. 4-8) and A in Fig. 4-14 reflects the margin of error here introduced by employing the approximations discussed in Chap. 3. Temperatures on curve A at P_{CO_2} = 500 to 1500 bars are some 40° lower than those on Harker and Tuttle's (1956a) experimentally determined curve (A in Fig. 4-8). Within limits of possible error there is no conflict.

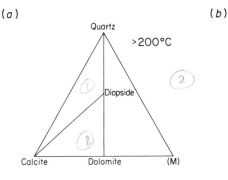

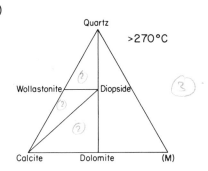

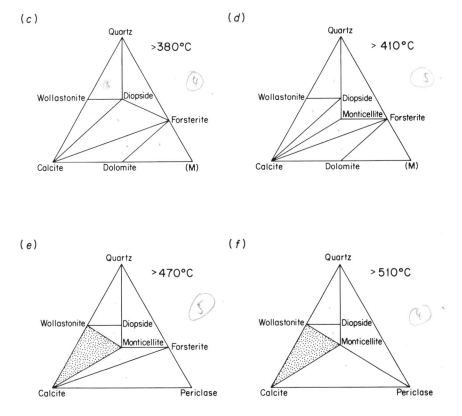

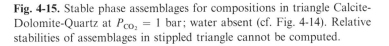

Fig. 4-15. Stable phase assemblages for compositions in triangle Calcite-Dolomite-Quartz at $P_{CO_2} = 1$ bar; water absent (cf. Fig. 4-14). Relative stabilities of assemblages in stippled triangle cannot be computed.

Weeks (1956*a*, fig. 4, *a*, *b*) shows virtually coincident univariant curves[1] for the alternative equilibria:

$$\text{Dolomite} + 2\ \text{Quartz} \rightleftharpoons \text{Diopside} + 2CO_2$$

and

$$\text{Dolomite} + \text{Quartz} \rightleftharpoons \text{Enstatite} + \text{Calcite} + CO_2$$

T_e of the enstatite equilibrium as calculated by this writer is at least 70° above that of the diopside equilibrium, and even the maximum admissible error in the ΔH and the ΔS values will not reduce the discrepancy to less than 50°. The enstatite equilibrium is regarded as metastable, and absence of the pair calcite-enstatite in metamorphic rocks is attributed to earlier elimination of quartz or dolomite to give diopside.

According to both Weeks' calculations and the sequence of curves M and B in Fig. 4-14, monticellite should appear by

$$2\ \text{Calcite} + \text{Diopside} + \text{Forsterite} \rightleftharpoons 3\ \text{Monticellite} + 2CO_2$$

before periclase:

$$\text{Dolomite} \rightleftharpoons \text{Calcite} + \text{Periclase} + CO_2$$

This conflicts with Bowen's sequence (periclase, wollastonite, monticellite) and with the views of many, perhaps most, geologists. Allowing for possible error in the thermochemical data, calculation still predicts that monticellite should appear at about the same temperature as periclase, or at somewhat higher temperatures. With an additional increase of 100° beyond the first appearance of monticellite on curve M, it is predicted that monticellite and periclase should again be generated simultaneously in silica-poor dolomites at the expense of the pair calcite-forsterite:

$$\text{Calcite} + \text{Forsterite} \rightleftharpoons \text{Monticellite} + \text{Periclase} + CO_2$$

Note that in such rocks (in the lowest triangles of Fig. 4-15) the assemblage calcite-forsterite-periclase should indeed appear (in accord with general geological opinion) before calcite-monticellite-periclase.

Inadequacy of thermochemical data makes it unprofitable to attempt any detailed evaluation of late steps in Bowen's sequence within the compositional field calcite-wollastonite-monticellite.

Decarbonation steps in presence of water. It is impossible to predict on thermochemical grounds whether, at equal low partial pressures of water and CO_2, the first silicate to form by reaction between dolomite

---

[1] The values of ΔH cited by Weeks for these reactions nevertheless suggest a considerably higher equilibrium temperature for the enstatite reaction.

and quartz should be tremolite or talc. The calculated order at $P_{H_2O} = P_{CO_2} = 1$ bar is

$$5 \text{ Dolomite} + 8 \text{ Quartz} + H_2O \rightleftharpoons \text{Tremolite} + 3 \text{ Calcite} + 7CO_2$$

at 180°C (Curve N, Fig. 4-16)

$$3 \text{ Dolomite} + 4 \text{ Quartz} + H_2O \rightleftharpoons \text{Talc} + 3 \text{ Calcite} + 3CO_2 \qquad \text{at 190°C}$$

The first equilibrium has therefore been classed *arbitrarily* as stable, the second as metastable. But the 10° temperature interval is not significant. Eventually talc, if initially the stable phase, must give way to tremolite:

$$2 \text{ Talc} + 3 \text{ Calcite} \rightleftharpoons \text{Tremolite} + \text{Dolomite} + H_2O + CO_2$$

The calculated temperature at $P_{H_2O} = P_{CO_2} = 1$ bar, again not significant, is 170°C. Where P_{CO_2} is small compared with P_{H_2O}—a possibility in permeable dolomites flushed with externally derived water at shallow depths— talc should be the first silicate to appear. This indeed has been observed in some aureoles (e.g., Tilley, 1948). However, it soon gives way to the tremolite-calcite assemblage that is so common in metamorphosed dolomitic limestones.

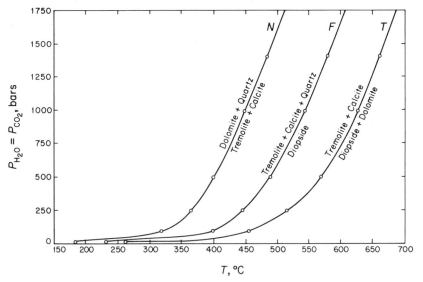

Fig. 4-16. Calculated curves of stable equilibrium for reactions in triangle Calcite-Dolomite-Quartz in presence of water. $P_{H_2O} = P_{CO_2}$. Tremolite is arbitrarily stated to be more stable than talc-calcite at temperatures to right of curve N. N: 5 Dolomite + 8 Quartz + $H_2O \rightleftharpoons$ Tremolite + 3 Calcite + 7CO_2. F: Tremolite + 3 Calcite + 2 Quartz $\rightleftharpoons$ 5 Diopside + 3CO_2 + H_2O. T: Tremolite + 3 Calcite $\rightleftharpoons$ Dolomite + 4 Diopside + CO_2 + H_2O.

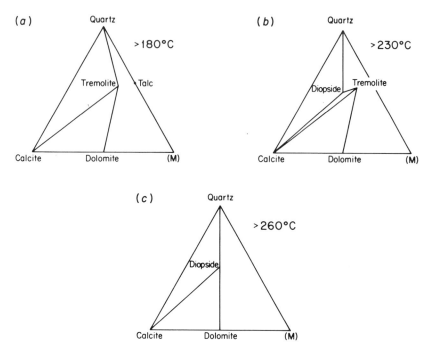

Fig. 4-17. Stable phase assemblages in the triangle calcite-dolomite-quartz at $P_{H_2O} = P_{CO_2} = 1$ bar (cf. Fig. 4-16).

Again there is good agreement between thermochemical prediction and direct experiment. Temperatures on the curve of Winkler and Metz (Fig. 4-9 *E*) for formation of calcite-talc from dolomite are only some 30 to 40° lower than those on the thermochemically calculated curve (broken line, Fig. 4-9). Although curve *E* represents a reaction that was not reversed, it is still slightly preferable to calculated curves for generation of talc or dolomite, for it represents the maximum temperatures at which dolomite-quartz can possibly remain stable in an aqueous environment.

After the pair tremolite-calcite becomes stable, whether at the expense of dolomite-quartz (Fig. 4-16 *N*) or by elimination of talc-quartz, two more steps should lead to the disappearance of hydrous silicates from the metamorphic assemblage (Figs. 4-16, 4-17; Table 4-2):

Curve *F*:

Tremolite + 3 Calcite + 2 Quartz $\rightleftharpoons$ 5 Diopside + 3CO$_2$ + H$_2$O

Curve *T*:

Tremolite + 3 Calcite $\rightleftharpoons$ Dolomite + 4 Diopside + CO$_2$ + H$_2$O

Table 4-2. Calculated stable equilibria (assuming tremolite stable with respect to talc-calcite) in the triangle Calcite-Dolomite-Quartz. $P_{H_2O} = P_{CO_2} = 1$ bar.

Equilib-rium curve		For reaction proceeding → at 25°/mole CO_2			Equilibrium temperature, °C ± about 40°
		ΔS, cal/mole°	ΔH, kcal	ΔG, kcal	
N	5Do + 8Qu + H$_2$O ⇌ Tr + 3Ca + 7CO$_2$	35.1	15.97	5.51	180
F	Tr + 3Ca + 2Qu ⇌ 5Di + 3CO$_2$ + H$_2$O	50.59	25.23	10.15	230
T	Tr + 3Ca ⇌ Do + 4Di + CO$_2$ + H$_2$O	72.27	38.2	16.66	260
	Thereafter sequence of equilibria is same as A to B, Table 4-1				

Thereafter the sequence of steps with further increase in temperature should be identical with that at the same values of P_{CO_2} in anhydrous rocks.

At partial pressures $P_{CO_2} = P_{H_2O} = 1$ bar, the calculated equilibrium temperature on curve T is 260°C. That for another possible reaction between calcite and tremolite

3 Tremolite + 5 Calcite ⇌ 11 Diopside + 2 Forsterite + 5CO$_2$ + 3H$_2$O

is 290°C. The 30° interval is probably significant; possible errors in ΔH and S values of all phases except forsterite and dolomite would affect both computations to much the same degree. For this reason, elimination of tremolite in favor of diopside-forsterite is tentatively considered to represent a metastable equilibrium under approximately equal partial pressures of water and CO_2. Nevertheless, as argued below, the tremolite-calcite-diopside-forsterite equilibrium may well be stable if P_{H_2O} is maintained at a high level compared with P_{CO_2}.

Reactions between calcite, dolomite, and silica, yielding phase assemblages containing only anhydrous silicates (diopside, wollastonite, forsterite) are only slightly affected by increase in P_{H_2O} at any constant value of P_{CO_2}. The stability field of tremolite, on the other hand, expands notably with increasing P_{H_2O} at constant P_{CO_2}. Figure 4-18 shows some thermochemically computed curves for the early significant decarbonation reactions under constant $P_{H_2O} = 1$ kb. The variables are P_{CO_2} and T. Several inferences may be drawn from the data of Fig. 4-18:

1. Even at very low values of P_{CO_2}, diopside will appear before wollastonite, but only in rocks whose compositions lie above the calcite-

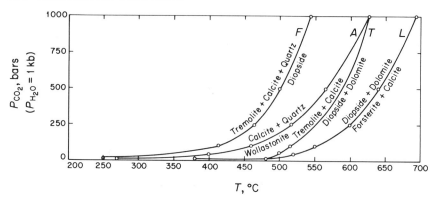

Fig. 4-18. Calculated equilibrium curves for decarbonation reactions at constant $P_{H_2O} = 1$ kb. F: Tremolite + 3 Calcite + 2 Quartz $\rightleftharpoons$ 5 Diopside + $3CO_2$ + H_2O. A: Calcite + Quartz $\rightleftharpoons$ Wollastonite + CO_2. L: Diopside + 3 Dolomite $\rightleftharpoons$ 4 Calcite + 2 Forsterite + $2CO_2$. T: Tremolite + 3 Calcite $\rightleftharpoons$ Dolomite + 4 Diopside + CO_2 + H_2O.

tremolite join. At no stage is the pair tremolite-wollastonite stable, for the computed temperature of the *metastable* equilibrium

$$Ca_2Mg_5Si_8O_{22}(OH)_2 + 3CaSiO_3 \rightleftharpoons 5CaMgSi_2O_6 + SiO_2 + H_2O$$
$$\underset{\text{Tremolite}}{} \quad \underset{\text{Wollastonite}}{} \quad \underset{\text{Diopside}}{} \quad \underset{\text{Quartz}}{}$$

at $P_{CO_2} = P_{H_2O} = 1$ bar is 70°C: still well within the limits of stability of the chemically equivalent pair dolomite-quartz.

2. At low pressures of CO_2 (up to about 200 to 300 bars), tremolite-bearing assemblages will continue to cover a wide range of rock composition (the triangle tremolite-calcite-dolomite in Fig. 4-19), while calcite-wollastonite-diopside is the most widespread assemblage in more calcareous rocks. The assemblage diopside-tremolite-calcite meantime is narrowly limited.

3. Described instances where forsterite-calcite-dolomite-and forsterite-calcite-tremolite appear in dolomitic rocks without previous development of diopside plus dolomite seem from purely thermochemical reasoning to represent reaction at high P_{H_2O} and very low P_{CO_2}. At $P_{H_2O} = 1000$ bars, this could occur at values of $P_{CO_2} = 1$ to 50 bars, at temperatures below 490°C (where curves L and T cross in Fig. 4-18). At such pressures the experimentally investigated equilibrium of Metz (1967):

3 Tremolite + 5 Calcite $\rightleftharpoons$ 11 Diopside + 2 Forsterite + $5CO_2$ + $3H_2O$

would become stable. In regional metamorphism at depth, a thoroughly recrystallized tremolite-calcite-marble is likely to have very low permeability to water vapor, present as the gas phase in adjoining rocks of other compositions. It is reasonable, then, to suppose that the gas phase within the

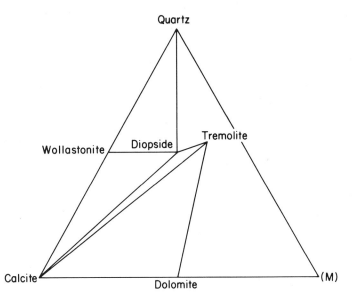

Fig. 4-19. Possibly stable phases in the triangle calcite-dolomite-quartz at $P_{H_2O} = 10 \times P_{CO_2}$ at temperatures slightly above those necessary for formation of wollastonite.

tremolite-calcite system at the time when the two solid phases react will be maintained at about the composition $5CO_2:3H_2O$ (above reaction) or $1CO_2:1H_2O$ (equilibrium T, Fig. 4-16). This implies partial pressures of water between one-half and one-quarter those of CO_2—conditions likely to cause tremolite to be eliminated in favor of diopside-dolomite, well before the appearance of forsterite. Clearly the relative permeability of dolomitic and calcitic marbles at high pressure and temperature must be significant in any discussion of the metamorphic mineral assemblages in calcareous rocks.

In conclusion, some computed values of temperature and pressure (at which metamorphic minerals might be expected to appear and then to be eliminated during progressive metamorphism of siliceous limestones and dolomites) are set out in Table 4-3. This is based strictly on thermo-chemical data as discussed above. Equilibrium temperatures determined by experimental reversal, where available, may be preferable to those of Table 4-3.

RELATIVE STABILITY OF CALCIUM-ALUMINUM SILICATES

At low grades of regional metamorphism the common calcium-aluminum silicates are first zeolites, especially laumontite, and then prehnite. At higher grades, these give way to lawsonite or pumpellyite, or

Table 4-3. Possible temperature gradients of progressive metamorphism consistent with Figs. 4-14, 4-16.

Index minerals		Limiting temperatures (°C) at P as below					
		P_{CO_2} (water absent)			$P_{H_2O} = P_{CO_2}$		
First appear	Disappear	500 bars	1000 bars	1400 bars	500 bars	1000 bars	1400 bars
Tremolite					400°	450°	480°
	Dolomite-quartz	440°	490°	520°	400°	450°	480°
Diopside		440°	490°	520°	490°	540°	580°
	Tremolite				570°	630°	670°
Wollastonite	Calcite-quartz	570°	630°	670°	570°	630°	670°
Forsterite	Dolomite-diopside	640°	700°	730°	640°	700°	730°
Monticellite	Calcite-diopside-forsterite	770°	850°	900°	770°	850°	900°
Periclase	Dolomite	830°	900°	950°	830°	900°	950°

to assemblages containing clinozoisite or zoisite. Ultimately all such hydrous silicates are eliminated in favor of calcic plagioclase or a combination of grossularite and anorthite. In most rocks the appearance and disappearance of these silicates is the result of complex coupled reactions. There are additional complications due to crystallization of plagioclase rather than anorthite (except in marbles), epidotes of variable iron content rather than clinozoisite, and replacement of Al by Fe^{3+} in "grossularite." Nevertheless, useful limits as to the significance of the metamorphic calcium-aluminum silicates, in terms of P_l, P_{H_2O}, and T, have already been set as a result of direct experimental investigation and thermochemical appraisal of certain ideal simple reactions. These will now be reviewed.

Predicted Stability Relations

Thermochemical data relating to many calcium-aluminum silicate minerals are scarce. For certain possible ideal equilibria, ΔV at 25°C and 1 bar is known fairly accurately. Approximate values of ΔS may be estimated, though within wider limits of error, from S data that have been determined for a few of the phases, supplemented by approximate S values of other phases based on the kind of reasoning set out in Chap. 3 (pp. 95–97). So it is possible to say something about relative slopes of equilibrium curves, always admitting the possibility that some of these equilibria may be metastable.

There is also a good deal of information regarding the natural appearance of many of the phases concerned in relation to geologically estimated relative temperatures and pressures. Combining the evidence drawn from both sources, Coombs (1960, pp. 346–348) set up a tentative diagram (Fig. 4-20) showing a predicted possible stability pattern of the metamorphic calcium-aluminum silicates in terms of relative temperature and pressure. Such a diagram is valuable in the same sense as Bowen's similarly predicted steps of metamorphism in siliceous dolomitic limestones. But it is a pattern only. The limits of stability of prehnite and of pumpellyite can only be guessed on the basis of relative degree of hydration and geologic data.

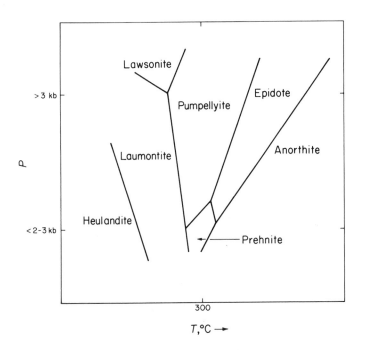

Fig. 4-20. Possible stability pattern of assemblages containing calcium-aluminum silicates in metamorphic rocks. (*After D. S. Coombs.*)

In Fig. 4-21 the broken curves *A*, *B*, and *C* represent thermochemically computed data for three simple equilibria.

Curve A (Crawford and Fyfe, 1965) sets minimum limits of pressure on generation of lawsonite from calcic zeolites in quartz-bearing rocks:

$$CaAl_2Si_4O_{12} \cdot 4H_2O \rightleftharpoons CaAl_2Si_2O_7(OH)_2 \cdot H_2O + 2SiO_2 + 2H_2O$$

Laumontite   Lawsonite   Quartz

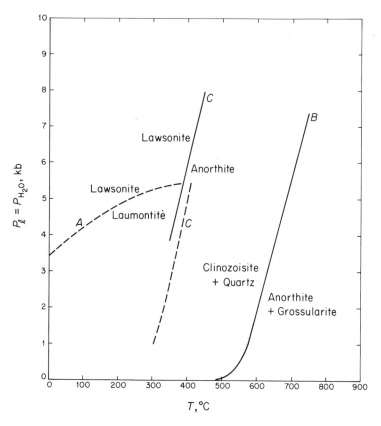

Fig. 4-21. Equilibrium curves for A: Laumontite $\rightleftharpoons$ Lawsonite + 2 Quartz + 2 Water. Calculated from thermochemical data. (*After W. A. Crawford and W. S. Fyfe.*) B: 4 Clinozoisite + Quartz $\rightleftharpoons$ 5 Anorthite + Grossularite + 2 Water. (*After M. J. Holdaway.*) C: Lawsonite $\rightleftharpoons$ Anorthite + 2 Water. Broken curve calculated from thermochemical data. (*After R. C. Newton and G. C. Kennedy.*) Full curve determined experimentally. (*After W. A. Crawford and W. S. Fyfe.*)

Because water is so loosely held in the zeolite structure, the dehydration reaction (left to right) actually involves a slight decrease in entropy ($\Delta S° = -5$ cal/deg). The volume change ΔV is high and negative—hence the flat slope of curve A. Clearly lawsonite is a sensitive index of P_{H_2O}.

Curve B (Holdaway, 1966) represents the predicted equilibrium curve for

$$4Ca_2Al_3Si_3O_{12}(OH) + SiO_2 \rightleftharpoons 5CaAl_2Si_2O_8 + Ca_3Al_2Si_3O_{12} + 2H_2O$$

Clinozoisite   Anorthite   Grossularite

This is a simplified version of a reaction that might lead to the formation of anorthite-grossularite in impure marbles at high grades of metamorphism, provided Holdaway's equilibrium is stable.

Curve C (Newton and Kennedy, 1963) is a thermochemically computed curve (broken curve *C*, Fig. 4-21) for the dehydration of lawsonite to anorthite:

$$CaAl_2Si_2O_7(OH)_2 \cdot H_2O \rightleftharpoons CaAl_2Si_2O_8 + 2H_2O$$

Lawsonite   Anorthite

Geologic evidence strongly suggests that, at pressures in the 3- to 5-kb range and temperatures around 400°C, clinozoisite-quartz in association with one of the many metamorphic aluminum-bearing silicates is more stable than anorthite. If so, curve *C*, although representing an equilibrium that may be stable, is not directly applicable to metamorphic rocks. Its value is that it sets maximum limits of temperature ($< 400°C$ at $P_{H_2O} = 4$ to 5 kb) for stable crystallization of lawsonite. A possible stable equilibrium representing in simplified form the transition from lawsonite-chlorite to clinozoisite-chlorite schists with increase in temperature might be

$$24CaAl_2Si_2O_7(OH)_2 \cdot H_2O + 5Mg_6(Si_4O_{10})(OH)_8$$

Lawsonite   Chlorite

$$\rightleftharpoons 12Ca_2Al_3Si_3O_{12}(OH) + 6Mg_5Al(AlSi_3O_{10})(OH)_8 + 14SiO_2 + 38H_2O$$

Clinozoisite   Chlorite   Quartz

We would expect such a reaction to occur at temperatures lower than those of curve *C* (whether thermochemically computed or determined by direct experiment).

Experimental Data

Upper limits of stability of lawsonite. The equilibrium

$$CaAl_2Si_2O_7(OH)_2 \cdot H_2O \rightleftharpoons CaAl_2Si_2O_8 + 2H_2O$$

Lawsonite   Anorthite

has been investigated independently by Newton and Kennedy (1963) and by Crawford and Fyfe (1965). The two sets of data are mutually consistent within the 4- to 5-kb range. Crawford and Fyfe's curve, representing reversal of the equilibrium across temperature intervals of 50°, is shown as the solid curve *C* in Fig. 4-21. This is in excellent agreement with the calculated curve of Newton and Kennedy. Obviously, lawsonite assemblages can be stable only at low metamorphic temperatures, perhaps only below 350°C, and high water pressures.

Upper limits of stability of clinozoisite-quartz. At high grades of regional metamorphism, the assemblage calcite-clinozoisite-quartz in impure marbles gives way to assemblages containing anorthite and grossularite (cf. Kennedy, 1949, pp. 49–53). Holdaway (1966) has reversed the corresponding equilibrium, using as starting materials a clinozoisite and a grossularite, in both of which the ratio Fe^{3+}/Al was about 0.15. So the reaction was complicated by change in this ratio in the two coexisting phases. Holdaway discussed his experiments in terms of a coupled reaction whose components are

$$4Ca_2Al_3Si_3O_{12}(OH) + SiO_2 \rightleftharpoons 5CaAl_2Si_2O_8 + Ca_3Al_2Si_3O_{12} + 2H_2O$$

Clinozoisite $\qquad$ Quartz $\qquad$ Anorthite $\qquad$ Grossularite

and

$$2Ca_2Fe_3Si_3O_{12}(OH) + 3Ca_3Al_2Si_3O_{12} \rightleftharpoons 2Ca_2Al_3Si_3O_{12}(OH)$$

Iron epidote $\qquad$ Grossularite $\qquad$ Clinozoisite

$$+ 3Ca_3Fe_2Si_3O_{12}$$

Andradite

The equilibrium curve is shown as B (solid) in Fig. 4-21. Again there is good agreement with thermochemical prediction. In metamorphic rocks of more complex composition, such as amphibolites and metagraywackes, elimination of epidote in favor of plagioclase is complicated by the higher Fe^{3+}/Al ratio of typical epidotes, and especially the relatively high albite content of the plagioclase phase. Moreover, grossularite is not usually present in the high-grade assemblages. All that can be said is that, in rocks of this kind, epidote will diminish in quantity, and ultimately will disappear at temperatures much lower than those of curve B.

RELATIVE STABILITY OF SODIUM-ALUMINUM SILICATES

In mineral assemblages crystallizing at low temperatures and comparatively low pressures characteristic of the transition from deep diagenesis to low-grade metamorphism, sodium is contained principally in the zeolite analcite. With the onset of metamorphism in the chlorite zone analcite gives way to albite

$$NaAlSi_2O_6 \cdot H_2O + SiO_2 \rightleftharpoons NaAlSi_3O_8 + H_2O$$

Analcite $\qquad$ Quartz $\qquad$ Albite

In rocks of higher grade (such as those in the almandine zone of Scotland), albite and clinozoisite enter into a complex reaction resulting in appearance of oligoclase (about An_{30}). In glaucophane schists and their associates, the anhydrous sodium-aluminum silicate in quartzose rocks is jadeite, which usually contains significant amounts of iron $Na(Al, Fe^{3+})Si_2O_6$. In eclogites and in some glaucophane schists, sodium is present almost entirely in omphacite, a pyroxene intermediate between jadeite and diopside. The mutual stability relations of analcite-quartz, albite, and jadeite-quartz are geologically significant. They have been explored both from the thermochemical angle and by direct experiment.

The Quartz-analcite-albite Equilibrium

One of the difficulties of investigating by direct experiment the equilibrium

$$NaAlSi_2O_6 \cdot H_2O + SiO_2 \rightleftharpoons NaAlSi_3O_8 + H_2O$$

Analcite   Quartz   Albite

lies in the ease with which metastable sodium zeolites (other than analcite) appear as products of synthesis from various possible starting materials. The most satisfactory data to date are those of Campbell and Fyfe (1965), whose tentative curve for the equilibrium is shown as A in Fig. 4-22.

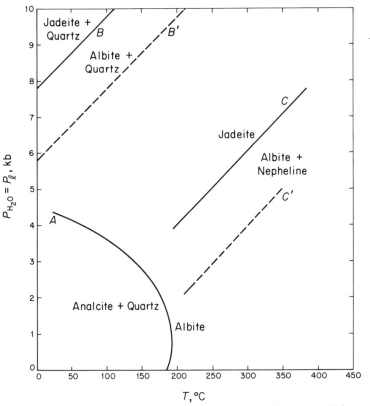

Fig. 4-22. Equilibrium curves for A: Analcite + Quartz $\rightleftharpoons$ Albite + Water. Experimentally determined at low pressure, and extrapolated from thermochemical data. (*After A. S. Campbell and W. S. Fyfe.*) B, B': Jadeite + Quartz $\rightleftharpoons$ Albite. B' thermochemically calculated; B corrected in relation to C. (*After W. S. Fyfe and G. W. Valpy.*) C, C': Jadeite $\rightleftharpoons$ Albite + Nepheline. C experimentally determined. (*After E. C. Robertson, F. Birch and G. J. F. MacDonald.*) C' thermochemically computed. (*After W. S. Fyfe and G. W. Valpy.*)

They record evidence of reversal in the presence of liquid water and vapor at about 190°C at low pressures. Starting at this point, they calculated the configuration of the equilibrium curve from standard entropy data. Values of $\Delta S°$ and $\Delta V°$ for the equilibrium (water in liquid state) are anomalous compared with other dehydration reactions (in which $\Delta V°$ is usually many times larger).

$$\Delta V° = 1.92 \text{ cm}^3 \qquad \Delta S° = 1.005 \text{ cal/mole}°$$

This is because of the low density of analcite and the loosely held condition of the water molecule within the open analcite structure. Consequently, at pressures ($P_{H_2O} = P_l$) of a few kilobars, the slope of the equilibrium curve is not only negative but surprisingly flat. At 100°C and pressures of a few kilobars, increase in water pressure actually brings about a reaction involving dehydration. Herein lies the answer to a question raised by Winkler (1965, p. 50). Assuming the stability of analcite-quartz at high pressures below 300°C, he concluded (mistakenly in this writer's opinion) that the transition from albite schists to quartz-jadeite assemblages (commonly associated with glaucophane schists) must occur at temperatures much higher than the 200 to 300°C range to which we have elsewhere assigned this reaction (e.g., Brown, Fyfe, and Turner, 1962).

Equilibria with Jadeite and Albite

Consider the equilibrium

$$\underset{\text{Jadeite}}{\text{NaAlSi}_2\text{O}_6} + \underset{\text{Quartz}}{\text{SiO}_2} \rightleftharpoons \underset{\text{Albite}}{\text{NaAlSi}_3\text{O}_8}$$

The reaction proceeds from left to right with marked increase in volume and in entropy. Values calculated from standard data (Chap. 3, pp. 95–96) are $\Delta V° = 16.54 \text{ cm}^3$; $\Delta S° = 8.4 \text{ cal/deg}$. The equilibrium curve must have a positive slope of about 20 bars/deg. Various writers have attempted to calculate the equilibrium curve from existing thermochemical data. Such a curve, calculated by Fyfe and Valpy (1959) is B' (broken line) in Fig. 4-22. These writers used the same data to compute the curve C' (broken line) for

$$\underset{\text{Jadeite}}{2\text{NaAlSi}_2\text{O}_6} \rightleftharpoons \underset{\text{Nepheline}}{\text{NaAlSiO}_4} + \underset{\text{Albite}}{\text{NaAlSi}_3\text{O}_8}$$

This second equilibrium was experimentally investigated by Robertson, Birch, and MacDonald (1957), who reversed the reaction over rather wide temperature intervals at pressures between 10 and 20 kb.[1] A curve drawn within their reversal limits and having a 20 bars/deg slope is shown as C

---

[1] Their more generally cited curve is based on additional data relating to syntheses from glass.

(solid line in Fig. 4-22). If this is accepted in preference to the computed curve C' (as we do here), then the computed curve B' must be similarly corrected (Fyfe and Valpy, 1959, p. 319). The solid curve B has been drawn by this writer to show this correction.

Although the quartz-jadeite-albite equilibrium as depicted in Fig. 4-22 cannot be regarded as precisely determined, it sets limits upon the stability fields of natural jadeite assemblages:

1. It is clear that the nearly pure jadeites associated with albite (but not quartz) in the silica-deficient environment afforded by serpentinite bodies can form stably at moderate to high metamorphic pressures over the temperature range 200 to 400°C.

2. Pure jadeite could form in stable association with quartz only at very low temperatures and very high pressures. Although the pressure limits at which natural ferriferous jadeites can coexist with quartz will be lower than those for ideal jadeite-quartz, it still follows that natural quartz-jadeite assemblages must indicate crystallization at very high metamorphic pressures in the 200 to 400°C range. A guess at such lower limits might be 7 to 10 kb.

3. It is likely that omphacite might be a stable phase in mineral assemblages in the high-pressure region, even at temperatures as low as 300 to 400°C.

EQUILIBRIA IN MAGNESIAN SCHISTS

Ultramafic bodies initially consisting principally of olivine, enstatite and diopside commonly become altered, during their cooling history, to serpentinites. Whether serpentinization involves extensive transfer of silica and magnesia, as well as obvious introduction of water, is immaterial to the present discussion. We assume the starting materials for later metamorphism to consist principally of serpentine minerals and brucite, serpentine minerals alone, or, much more rarely, the pair serpentine-talc.

Progressive metamorphism of serpentinites may be treated in the first instance as a series of dehydration steps in the system $MgO–SiO_2–H_2O$, starting from the equally hydrated ideal assemblages (listed in order of increasing silica content):

Antigorite-brucite
Antigorite
Antigorite-talc

The final anhydrous assemblages will be

Forsterite-enstatite
Enstatite-quartz

At intermediate steps the less hydrated silicate anthophyllite may be a possible constituent of the more siliceous assemblages. If calcium has not been entirely removed during serpentinization, it will be accommodated in all assemblages by tremolite—up to the high temperatures at which tremolite itself becomes dehydrated to diopside-enstatite.

Progressive metamorphism of magnesian schists involves the same equilibria investigated in connection with the problem of peridotite serpentinization. But the steps are in reverse order, and we are not faced with problems of compositional change other than steady expulsion of water at some constantly maintained value of P_{H_2O}. It is assumed that P_{H_2O} equals load pressure P_l; this is the condition under which most experiments have been conducted in the laboratory.

Thermodynamic evaluation of some equilibria has been attempted (Olsen, 1963; Greenwood, 1963; Page, 1967; Kitahara and Kennedy, 1966). However, there are no reliable thermochemical data for any of the crystalline varieties of serpentine—chrystotile, lizardite, or antigorite. These, unfortunately, are the dominant, and often the sole mineral phases in the starting material for metamorphism—serpentinized peridotite.

Experimental Data Relating to Earlier Steps of Dehydration

A sequence of possible dehydration steps has been investigated experimentally by Bowen and Tuttle (1949), Yoder (1952), and Kitahara et al. (1966). Their findings agree; and they have drawn univariant equilibrium curves for three steps of progressive dehydration (cf. Table 4-4) in the order

(1)
$$\underset{\text{Serpentine}}{Mg_6Si_4O_{10}(OH)_8} + \underset{\text{Brucite}}{2Mg(OH)_2} \rightleftharpoons \underset{\text{Olivine}}{4Mg_2SiO_4} + 6H_2O$$

(2)
$$\underset{\text{Serpentine}}{5Mg_6Si_4O_{10}(OH)_8} \rightleftharpoons \underset{\text{Olivine}}{12Mg_2SiO_4} + \underset{\text{Talc}}{2Mg_3Si_4O_{10}(OH)_2} + 18H_2O$$

(3)
$$\underset{\text{Forsterite}}{Mg_2SiO_4} + \underset{\text{Talc}}{Mg_3Si_4O_{10}(OH)_2} \rightleftharpoons \underset{\text{Enstatite}}{5MgSiO_3} + H_2O$$

Each step can indeed be represented as an equilibrium. In each one, entropy increases from left to right. But in the absence of thermochemical data for serpentine minerals, and in view of the recently demonstrated stability of anthophyllite at temperatures in the 600 to 800°C range (Greenwood, 1963), we have no proof that any of these equilibria is stable. In particular it is impossible to evaluate another equilibrium

$$\underset{\text{Serpentine}}{Mg_6Si_4O_{10}(OH)_8} \rightleftharpoons \underset{\text{Talc}}{Mg_3Si_4O_{10}(OH)_2} + \underset{\text{Brucite}}{3Mg(OH)_2}$$

for which ΔS must presumably be small.

Experimental work to date on equilibria (1) to (3) unfortunately has concentrated mainly on syntheses from glasses and oxide mixes.[1]

---

[1] The curves for steps (1) and (2) drawn for pressures up to 60 kb by Pistorius (1963) also were based on oxide mixes, using the squeezer technique.

Nevertheless, from the few observed points of observed reaction between mineral phases (synthetic or natural), it is possible to set limits upon the three steps of Bowen and Tuttle.

Step 1. Olivine was converted to serpentine and brucite by Bowen and Tuttle at P_{H_2O} about 1 kb and $T = 340°C$. The reverse reaction was observed by Kitahara et al. at $P_{H_2O} = 6$ kb and $T = 500°C$. Temperatures on Bowen and Tuttle's curve could be lowered 60° or raised 30°, without conflict with the above data. Raleigh and Paterson (1965) have provided significant evidence from a completely independent source, suggesting that dehydration of natural serpentinites at step 1 may indeed occur at between 300 and 350°C at $P_{H_2O} = 3.5$ kb (X, Fig. 4-23). They found that the ultimate strength of a brucite-bearing serpentinite under a confining pressure of 3 to 5 kb drops suddenly in this temperature range, with change from plastic to brittle behavior. This they attribute to the onset of the dehydration reaction.

Step 2. Serpentine has been converted to forsterite and talc at temperatures close to 500°C and $P_{H_2O} = 1$ to 3 kb. The reaction was reversed by Kitahara at 580°C and $P_{H_2O} = 10$ kb. These data set upper limits on the temperatures at which serpentine can exist as a stable phase. Steps 1 and 2 can be coupled to give the relation

$$\text{Serpentine} \rightleftharpoons \text{Talc} + 3 \text{ Brucite}$$

At 400 to 500°C, ΔG and ΔS for this reaction might well be very small, in which case steps 1 and 2 might almost coincide, instead of being separated by the generally accepted 80° interval postulated by Bowen and Tuttle. Raleigh and Paterson, however, have similar evidence to the above, confirming in this case the Bowen and Tuttle curve between 1 and 3 kb. At these pressures, the change from ductile to brittle behavior occurs near 500°C. Moreover, they identified microscopically visible new grainlets of olivine and talc in the specimens so affected.

Step 3. Bowen and Tuttle (1949, p. 445) record the conversion of enstatite to forsterite-talc at $T = 650°C$ and $P_{H_2O} = 1.6$ kb. The reverse reaction was observed by Kitahara et al. at $T = 750°C$ and $P_{H_2O} = 6$ kb; the same authors reversed the equilibrium at $T = 730°C$ and $P_{H_2O} = 10$ kb. The equilibrium, however, is metastable; for in this range of temperatures anthophyllite has been shown to be stable with respect to enstatite-quartz or enstatite-talc (Greenwood, 1963).

Experimental Data Relating to Advanced Steps of Dehydration

Contrary to the conclusions of Bowen and Tuttle (1949) and of Yoder (1952), Fyfe (1962) demonstrated the stability of anthophyllite-quartz with

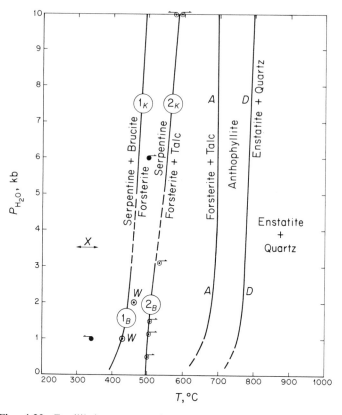

Fig. 4-23. Equilibrium curves determined experimentally for hydrous and anhydrous magnesian mineral phases: (1) Serpentine + 2 Brucite ⇌ 4 Forsterite + 6 H_2O. (1_B, *after N. L. Bowen and O. F. Tuttle*; 1_K *after S. Kitahara et al.*). Reactions starting from mineral phases shown by solid circles. (2) 5 Serpentine ⇌ 12 Forsterite + 2 Talc + $18H_2O$ (2_B, *after N. L. Bowen and O. F. Tuttle*; 2_K, *after S. Kitahara et al.*). Reactions starting from mineral phases shown by circled points. *W,W* are points of direct reversal obtained by C. M. Scarfe and P. S. Wyllie (1967). *A*: 9 Talc + 4 Forsterite ⇌ 5 Anthophyllite + $4H_2O$. (*After H. J. Greenwood.*) *D*: Anthophyllite ⇌ 7 Enstatite + Quartz + H_2O. (*After H. J. Greenwood.*)

respect to talc, and of anthophyllite with respect to quartz-enstatite, at $T = 670$ to 760°C and $P_{H_2O} = 2$ kb. His conclusions were confirmed and amplified in a detailed experimental and thermochemical treatment by Greenwood (1963)[1] of the successive equilibria

---

[1] This paper is recommended for its clarity and objectivity to petrologists having little first-hand experience with experimental evaluation of metamorphic equilibria.

A $9Mg_3Si_4O_{10}(OH)_2 + 4Mg_2SiO_4 \rightleftharpoons 5Mg_7Si_8O_{22}(OH)_2 + 4H_2O$
      Talc   Forsterite   Anthophyllite

B $Mg_7Si_8O_{22}(OH)_2 + Mg_2SiO_4 \rightleftharpoons 9MgSiO_3 + H_2O$
         Anthophyllite   Forsterite   Enstatite

C $Mg_3Si_4O_{10}(OH)_2 \rightleftharpoons 3Mg_7Si_8O_{22}(OH)_2 + 4SiO_2 + 4H_2O$
        Talc   Anthophyllite   Quartz

D $Mg_7Si_8O_{22}(OH)_2 \rightleftharpoons 7MgSiO_3 + SiO_2 + H_2O$
         Anthophyllite   Enstatite   Quartz

Greenwood reversed all his equilibria. In addition, he showed that other equilibria, which he also reversed, are metastable. Such are the later steps of Bowen and Tuttle and of Kitahara and Kennedy, leading to production of enstatite from talc assemblages (e.g., step 3 above).

The total temperature span of steps A to D in Greenwood's sequence at any given pressure is less than 100°C, for example, about 700 to 800°C at $P_{H_2O} = 10$ kb; 650 to 750°C at $P_{H_2O} = 1$ kb.

Petrologic Implications

Progressive metamorphism of serpentinites at some constant pressure, say $P_{H_2O} = 1$ kb, should lead to decreasingly hydrous mineral assemblages. The corresponding sequence of appearance of new and disappearance of earlier mineral phases for bulk compositions between $2MgO \cdot SiO_2$ and $3MgO \cdot 4SiO_2$ is tabulated in Table 4-4. Elimination of the amphibole anthophyllite in favor of the pyroxene enstatite provides an index of general conditions for the reaction

$$\text{Hornblende} \rightleftharpoons \text{Pyroxenes} + \text{Water}$$

in high-temperature metamorphism. There is close agreement between Greenwood's step D and Boyd's (1956) curve for the breakdown of tremolite at 850°C and $P_{H_2O} = 1$ kb.

$$Ca_2Mg_5Si_8O_{22}(OH)_2 \rightleftharpoons 2CaMgSi_2O_6 + 3MgSiO_3 + SiO_2 + H_2O$$
   Tremolite   Diopside   Enstatite   Quartz

Ferriferous amphiboles are expected to break down at lower temperatures which depend on prevailing values of P_{O_2} in rocks buffered by iron oxides. Decrease in P_{O_2} lowers the breakdown temperature; for this is a reducing reaction.

The sequence of steps in Table 4-4 poses a major problem regarding serpentinization of peridotite. In most serpentinites, the bulk composition of the rock at all stages lies between olivine and serpentine. If the end product includes talc, it may be somewhat more siliceous than serpentine, at least in the final state of serpentinite. With water available in sufficient

Table 4-4. Sequence of mineral assemblages in progressive metamorphism of serpentinites and soapstones (steps numbered as in text) at $P_{H_2O} = 1$ kb

Initial rock	Serpentinite		Soapstone	
Mg/Si	2	1.5	1	0.5
Phase compositions....	Fo	Serp.	En Ant.	Talc
Step — **T, °C**				

Step	T, °C			
1	<350	Serpentine-brucite	Serpentine-talc	Talc-quartz
2	350–500	Serpentine-forsterite	Serpentine-talc	Talc-quartz
A	500–650	Forsterite-talc		Talc-quartz
B	650	Forsterite-anthophyllite	Ant.-en.	Ant.-talc
C	750	Forsterite-enstatite	Ant.-en.	Ant.-talc / Ant.-quartz
D	>750	Forsterite-enstatite		Enstatite-quartz

quantity during cooling of the olivine-enstatite assemblage from about 1000°C, the steps of hydration should be

1. Conversion of enstatite to anthophyllite-forsterite (step *B*), closely followed by elimination of anthophyllite (step *A*). So, at perhaps 650 to 700°C, depending on the pressure conditions, the peridotite should now consist of primary olivine, together with pseudomorphs of forsterite-talc after enstatite. This assemblage of minerals should persist unchanged during a long cooling interval while temperatures drop from about 650 to 500°C.

2. Conversion of forsterite-talc pseudomorphs to serpentine minerals at about 500°C, followed by elimination of olivine in favor of serpentine-brucite at 300 to 350°C.

Most peridotites show no trace of the early talc-anthophyllite stages. Enstatite has often been directly pseudomorphed by serpentine. A recent detailed study of serpentinization by Page (1967) shows what is probably the normal sequence of reactions:

(1) Olivine + Enstatite + Water → Chrysolite + Lizardite + Magnetite

(2) Olivine + Water → Chrysolite + Lizardite + Brucite + Magnetite

The reactions are complicated by presence of iron in different states of oxidation in all the mineral phases, so that P_{O_2} (essentially that corresponding to a quartz-fayalite-magnetite buffer) must have had an important influence on the serpentinization process.

THE ARAGONITE ⇌ CALCITE INVERSION

Aragonite is the denser lower-entropy form of the two $CaCO_3$ polymorphs aragonite and calcite. The inversion curve may be assumed to have the usual positive slope of Solid ⇌ Solid reactions. It has been calculated from ΔS° and ΔV° of inversion as 15 ± 8 bars/deg (Chap. 3, p. 104).

The equilibrium curve that has been generally accepted for some time is shown in Fig. 4-24 as AD. It was determined in the low-temperature range, using relative solubility data, by Jamieson (1953). At higher temperatures and pressures (400 to 600°C, 9 to 13 kb) the equilibrium was reversed by Clark (1957) along a curve continuous with Jamieson's low-

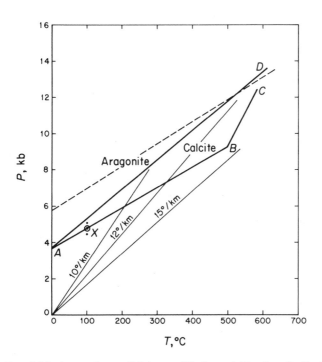

Fig. 4-24. Aragonite ⇌ Calcite equilibrium. (*AD after J. C. Jamieson and S. P. J. Clark; ABC after A. L. Boettcher and P. S. Wyllie; Broken line after G. Simmons and P. Bell.*) X is point of reversal by *W. A. Crawford and W. S. Fyfe.* Light lines are possible geothermal gradients.

temperature sector—at a slope of 15 bars/deg. Subsequently, Simmons and Bell (1963) modified the inversion curve on the basis of "squeezer" experiments, raising the value of the transition pressure at room temperature from 4 to 6 kb. Their curve was rejected in favor of the Jamieson-Clark curve on the basis of experimental reversal of the equilibrium by Crawford and Fyfe (1964) over the interval 4.2 to 4.5 bars at 100°C (X in Fig. 4-24).

The latest investigation of polymorphism in calcium carbonate is that of Boettcher and Wyllie (1967). Their curve (ABC in Fig. 4-24) is well within the limits of slope permitted by the entropy-volume data and is compatible with both the low-temperature data of Jamieson and the high-temperature reversals of Clark.[1] It passes precisely through Crawford and Fyfe's point of reversal X. For these reasons, the inversion curve given preference in this book is that of Boettcher and Wyllie (AB).

At temperatures of a few hundred degrees centigrade, the rate of inversion aragonite → calcite is so rapid that aragonite could not survive cooling under natural conditions along a geothermal temperature-depth gradient of 15°C/km (Brown, Fyfe, and Turner, 1962).[2] Not only temperature, but presence of pore water, greatly accelerates the inversion. However, at lower temperatures, 200 to 300°C, where geothermal gradients of only 10 to 12°C/km intersect the inversion curve, aragonite could survive unloading to surface conditions with little or no inversion to calcite. This explains the widespread occurrence of calcite in all calcareous metamorphic rocks except the glaucophane-schists and their associates. In these the surviving polymorph of $CaCO_3$ may be aragonite.

CONCLUSION

Anyone who has had the patience to read this chapter must have become aware of the new significance that has been given to the descriptive data of metamorphic mineralogy and petrography by the accumulated results of research in the laboratory on simple mineral equilibria at high temperature and pressure. In the course of time, the classic work of the earlier experimenters has been found faulty in some respects; it has been modified in the light of later and more precise data. The debt of the geologist to the pioneer workers in the Geophysical Laboratory, Washington, is obvious; they inaugurated a new era in metamorphic petrology. Today the geologist is fortunate in having at his disposal a surprisingly large

[1] Boettcher and Wyllie have taken into account the inversion of calcite I to calcite II which appears to be the stable form of calcite on the high-pressure high-temperature side of a triple point placed by them in the vicinity of 9 kb and 500°C.

[2] Our previous conclusion is slightly modified to the form here stated, to take into account the new inversion data of Boettcher and Wyllie.

amount of reasonably accurate experimental data, which he may use with some confidence to place limits upon the ranges of temperature and pressure expressed by common metamorphic mineral assemblages. Bowen's (1940, pp. 272–274) concept of the "petrogenic grid" of equilibrium curves relating to metamorphic reactions is abstract no longer. It is now an instrument— admittedly not yet as precise as it may ultimately become with further refinements—increasingly capable of effective use in calibrating temperature and pressure gradients of crystallization in metamorphic terranes.

In the following chapters, we review the nature of common metamorphic mineral assemblages and the various patterns of mutual associations of such assemblages in what are now known as metamorphic facies. To say something of the possible range of temperatures and pressures expressed by each facies, we fall back upon the experimental data reviewed in this chapter.

REFERENCES

Althaus, E.: Der Stabilitätsbereich des Pyrophyllits unter dem Einfluss von Säuren. I, *Contrib. Mineral. Petrol.*, vol. 13, pp. 31–50, 1966.

Aramaki, S., and R. Roy: A new polymorph of Al_2SiO_5 and further studies in the system Al_2O_3–SiO_2–H_2O, *Am. Mineralogist*, vol. 48, pp. 1322–1347, 1963.

Banno, S.: Petrologic studies on Sanbagawa crystalline schists in the Bessi-Ino district, central Sikoku, Japan, *J. Fac. Sci. Univ. Tokyo*, sec. 2, vol. 15, pp. 203–319, 1964.

Bell, P. M.: Aluminum silicate system: experimental determination of the triple point, *Science*, vol. 139, pp. 1055–1056, 1963.

Boettcher, A. L., and P. S. Wyllie: Revision of the calcite-aragonite transition, with location of a triple point between calcite I, calcite II, and aragonite, *Nature*, vol. 213, pp. 792–793, 1967.

Bowen, N. L.: Progressive metamorphism of siliceous limestone and dolomite, *J. Geol.*, vol. 48, pp. 225–274, 1940.

———, and O. F. Tuttle: The system MgO–SiO_2–H_2O, *Bull Geol. Soc. Am.*, vol. 60, pp. 439–460, 1949.

———, and———: Origin of granite in the light of experimental studies in the system $NaAlSi_3O_8$–$KAlSi_3O_8$–SiO_2–H_2O, *Geol. Soc. Am. Mem.*, 74, 1958.

Boyd, F. R.: Tremolite, *Carnegie Inst. Wash. Yearbook No. 53*, 1953–1954, pp. 109–110, 1954.

Brown, E. H.: The greenschist facies in part of eastern Otago, New Zealand, *Contrib. Mineral. Petrol.*, vol. 14, pp. 259–292, 1967.

Brown, W. H., W. S. Fyfe, and F. J. Turner: Aragonite in California glaucophane schists, and the kinetics of the aragonite-calcite transition, *J. Petrol.*, vol. 3, pp. 566–582, 1962.

Campbell, A. S., and W. S. Fyfe: Analcime-albite equilibria, *Am. J. Sci.*, vol. 263, pp. 807–816, 1965.

Carr, R. M., and W. S. Fyfe: Synthesis fields of some aluminium silicates, *Geochim. Cosmochim. Acta*, vol. 21, pp. 99–109, 1960.

Chinner, G. A.: Garnet-cordierite parageneses, *Carnegie Inst. Wash. Yearbook No. 58*, 1958–1959, pp. 112–113, 1959.

Clark, S. P. J.: A note on the calcite-aragonite equilibrium, *Am. Mineralogist*, vol. 42, pp. 564–566, 1957.

———: A redetermination of equilibrium relations between kyanite and sillimanite, *Am. J. Sci.*, vol. 259, pp. 641–650, 1961.

Coombs, D. S.: Lower grade mineral facies in New Zealand, *Rept. Inter. Geol. Cong., 21st Session, Norden*, vol. 13, pp. 339–351, 1960.

———, A. J. Ellis, W. S. Fyfe, and A. M. Taylor: The zeolite facies with comments on the interpretation of hydrothermal syntheses, *Geochim. Cosmochim. Acta*, vol. 17, pp. 53–107, 1959.

Crawford, W. A., and W. S. Fyfe: Calcite-aragonite equilibrium, *Science*, vol. 144, pp. 1569–1570, 1964.

———, and ———: Lawsonite equilibria, *Am. J. Sci.*, vol. 263, pp. 262–270, 1965.

Danielsson, A.: Das Calcit-Wollastonitgleichgewicht, *Geochim. Cosmochim. Acta*, vol. 1, pp. 55–69, 1950.

Deer, W. A., R. A. Howie, and J. Zussman, "Rock-forming Minerals," vol. 2, Wiley, New York, 1963.

Ellis, A. J., and W. S. Fyfe: A note on the calcite-wollastonite equilibrium, *Am. Mineralogist*, vol. 41, pp. 805–807, 1956.

Engel, A. E. J., and C. G. Engel: Progressive metamorphism and granitization of the major paragneiss northwest Adirondack Mountains, New York, Part II, *Bull. Geol. Soc. Am.*, vol. 71, pp. 1–58, 1960.

Ernst, W. G.: Significance of phengitic micas in low-grade schists, *Am. Mineralogist*, vol. 48, pp. 1357–1373, 1963.

Eskola, P.: On contact phenomena between gneiss and limestone in western Massachusetts, *J. Geol.*, vol. 30, pp. 265–294, 1922.

Eugster, H. P., and D. R. Wones: Stability relations of the ferruginous biotite, annite, *J. Petrol.*, vol. 3, pp. 82–125, 1962.

———, and H. S. Yoder: *Carnegie Inst. Wash. Yearbook No. 53*, 1953–1954, pp. 111–114, 1954.

———, and ———: *Carnegie Inst. Wash. Yearbook No. 54*, 1954–1955, pp. 124–129, 1955.

Evans, B. W.: Application of a reaction-rate method to the breakdown equilibria of muscovite and muscovite plus quartz, *Am. J. Sci.*, vol. 263, pp. 647–667, 1965.

Fawcett, J. J.: *Carnegie Inst. Wash. Yearbook No. 62*, 1962–1963, pp. 139–143, 1963.

———: *Carnegie Inst. Wash. Yearbook No. 63*, 1963–1964, pp. 136–137, 1964.

———, and H. S. Yoder: Phase relationships of chlorites in the system $MgO-Al_2O_3-SiO_2-H_2O$, *Am. Mineralogist*, vol. 51, pp. 353–380, 1966.

Fyfe, W. S.: A further attempt to determine the vapor pressure of brucite, *Am. J. Sci.*, vol. 256, pp. 729–732, 1958.

———: On the relative stability of talc, anthophyllite, and enstatite, *Am. J. Sci.*, vol. 260, pp. 460–466, 1962.

———, and F. J. Turner: Reappraisal of the metamorphic facies concept, *Contrib. Mineral. Petrol.*, vol. 12, pp. 354–364, 1966.

———, ———, and J. Verhoogen: Metamorphic reactions and metamorphic facies, *Geol. Soc. Am. Mem. 73*, 1958.

———, and G. W. Valpy: The analcime-jadeite phase boundary and some indirect deductions, *Am. J. Sci.*, vol. 257, pp. 316–320, 1959.

Goldschmidt, V. M.: Die Gesetze der Gesteinsmetamorphose mit Beispielen aus der Geologie des südlichen Norwegens, *Vidensk. Skr. I, Mat.-Naturv. Kl.*, no. 22, 1912.

Greenwood, H. J.: The synthesis and stability of anthophyllite, *J. Petrol.*, vol. 4, pp. 317–351, 1963.

———: Gas mixtures, *Carnegie Inst. Wash. Yearbook No. 62*, 1962–1963, pp. 137–139, 1963.

Halferdahl, L. B.: Chloritoid: its composition, X-ray and optical properties, stability, and occurrence, *J. Petrol.*, vol. 2, pp. 49–135, 1961.

Harker, R. I., and O. F. Tuttle: Studies in the system $CaO-MgO-CO_2$, Part 1, *Am. J. Sci.*, vol. 253, pp. 209–224, 1955.

———, and ———: Experimental data on the $P_{CO_2} - T$ curve for the reaction: calcite + quartz ⇌ wollastonite + carbondioxide, *Am. J. Sci.*, vol. 254, pp. 239–256, 1956.

Hemley, J. J.: Some mineralogical equilibria in the system $K_2O-Al_2O_3-SiO_2-H_2O$, *Am. J. Sci.*, vol. 257, pp. 241–270, 1959.

Holdaway, M. J.: Hydrothermal stability of clinozoisite plus quartz, *Am. J. Sci.*, vol. 264, pp. 643–667, 1966.

Hoschek, G., and H. G. F. Winkler: Bildung von Staurolith und Chloritoid bei der experimentellen Metamorphose, *Naturwissenschaft, Jahrg.* 52, pp. 1–2, 1965.

Hutton, C. O.: Metamorphism in the Lake Wakatipu region, western Otago, New Zealand, *New Zealand Dep. Sci. Ind. Res. Geol. Mem. 5*, 1940.

Jamieson, J. C.: Phase equilibrium in the system calcite-aragonite, *J. Chem. Phys.*, vol. 21, pp. 1385–1390, 1953.

Kennedy, G. C.: Pyrophyllite-sillimanite-mullite equilibrium relations to 20,000 bars and 800°C, *Bull. Geol. Soc. Am.*, vol. 66, p. 1584, 1955.

———: The brucite-periclase equilibrium, *Am. J. Sci.*, vol. 254, pp. 567–573, 1956.

Kennedy, W. Q.: Zones of progressive regional metamorphism in the Moine schists of the western Highlands of Scotland, *Geol. Mag.*, vol. 86, pp. 43–56, 1949.

Khitarov, N. I., et al.: Relations amongst andalusite, kyanite, and sillimanite, under conditions of moderate temperatures and pressures, *Geokhimiya*, vol. 3, pp. 219–228, 1963.

Kitahara, S., S. Takenouchi, and G. C. Kennedy: Phase relations in the system $MgO-SiO_2-H_2O$ at high temperatures and pressures, *Am. J. Sci.*, vol. 264, pp. 223–233, 1966.

MacDonald, G. J. F.: Gibbs free energy of water at elevated temperatures and pressures with applications to the brucite-periclase equilibrium, *J. Geol.*, vol. 63, pp. 244–252, 1955.

McNamara, M. J.: Biotite-chlorite equilibrium reactions in a carbonate-free system, *J. Petrol.*, vol. 7, pp. 404–413, 1966.

Metz, P.: Experimentelle Untersuchung und thermodynamische Berechnung von Gleichgewichtsreaktionen im System $CaO-MgO-SiO_2-CO_2-H_2O$, 1967. Abstract of paper presented at Annual Meeting, *Deut. Mineral. Ges.*, Munich, 1966.

————, and H. G. F. Winkler: Experimentelle Gesteinsmetamorphose, VII, Die Bildung von Talk aus kieseligem Dolomit, *Geochim. Cosmochim. Acta*, vol. 27, pp. 431–457, 1963.

————, and ————: Experimentelle Untersuchung der Diopsidbildung aus Tremolit, Calcit, und Quarz, *Naturwissenschaft*, Jahrg. 51, pt. 10, pp. 1–3, 1964.

Miyashiro, A.: Chlorite of crystalline schists, *J. Geol. Soc. Japan*, vol. 63, no. 736, pp. 1–8, 1957.

Nelson, B. W., and R. Roy: Synthesis of the chlorites, *Am. Mineralogist*, vol. 43, pp. 707–725, 1958.

Newton, R. C.: Kyanite-sillimanite equilibrium at 750°C, *Science*, vol. 151, pp. 1222–1225, 1966.

————, and G. C. Kennedy: Some equilibrium reactions in the join $CaAl_2Si_2O_8–H_2O$, *J. Geophys. Res.*, vol. 68, pp. 2967–2983, 1963.

Olsen, E.: Equilibrium calculations in the system Mg, Fe, Si, O, H, and Ni, *Am. J. Sci.*, vol. 261, pp. 943–956, 1963.

Page, N. J.: Serpentinization at Burrow Mountain, California, *Contrib. Mineral. Petrol.*, vol. 14, pp. 321–342, 1967.

Pistorius, C. W. F. T.: Some phase relations in the system $MgO–SiO_2–H_2O$, to high pressures and temperatures, *Neues Jahrb. Mineral Monatsh.*, pp. 283–293, 1963.

Raleigh, C. B., and M. S. Paterson: Experimental deformation of serpentinite and its tectonic implications, *J. Geophys. Res.*, vol. 70, pp. 3965–3985, 1965.

Ramberg, H.: Chemical thermodynamics in mineral studies, "Physics and Chemistry of the Earth," pp. 226–252, Pergamon Press, New York, 1964.

Robertson, E. C., F. Birch, and G. J. F. MacDonald: Experimental determination of jadeite stability relations to 25,000 bars, *Am. J. Sci.*, vol. 255, pp. 115–137, 1957.

Roy, D. M., and R. Roy: A redetermination of equilibria in the system $MgO–H_2O$, *Am. J. Sci.*, vol. 255, pp. 574–583, 1957.

Roy, R., and E. F. Osborn: The system $Al_2O_3–SiO_2–H_2O$, *Am. Mineralogist*, vol. 39, pp. 853–885, 1954.

Schreyer, W.: Zur Stabilität des Ferrocordierits, *Beitr. Mineral. Petrog.*, vol. 11, pp. 297–322, 1965.

Schreyer, W., and H. S. Yoder: *Carnegie Inst. Wash. Yearbook No. 60*, 1960–1961, pp. 149–152, 1961.

————, and ————: The system Mg–cordierite—H_2O and related rocks, *Neues Jahrb. Mineral. Abhandl.*, vol. 3, pp. 271–342, 1964.

Segnit, R. E., and G. C. Kennedy: Reactions and melting relations in the system muscovite-quartz at high pressures, *Am. J. Sci.*, vol. 259, pp. 280–287, 1961.

Shaw, H. R.: The four-phase curve sanidine-quartz-liquid-gas, *Am. Mineralogist*, vol. 48, pp. 883–896, 1963.

Simmons, G., and P. Bell: Calcite-aragonite equilibrium, *Science*, vol. 139, pp. 1197–1198, 1963.

Tilley, C. E.: On some mineralogical transformations in crystalline schists, *Mineral. Mag.*, vol. 21, pp. 34–46, 1926.

————: Earlier stages in metamorphism of siliceous dolomites, *Mineral. Mag.*, vol. 28, pp. 272–276, 1948.

————: A note on the progressive metamorphism of siliceous limestones and dolomites, *Geol. Mag.*, vol. 88, pp. 175–178, 1951.

Turner, F. J.: Note on the genesis of brucite in contact metamorphism of dolomite, *Beitr. Mineral. Petrog.*, vol. 11, pp. 393–397, 1965.

————: Thermodynamic appraisal of steps in progressive metamorphism of siliceous dolomitic limestone, *Neues Jahrb. Mineral. Monatsh.*, 1967, pp. 1–22, 1967(*a*).

————: Some limits of pressure in regional metamorphism as indicated by stability fields of some critical minerals, "Etages Tectoniques", Baconnière, Switzerland, pp. 79–83, 1967(*b*).

————, and J. Verhoogen: "Igneous and Metamorphic Petrology," McGraw-Hill, New York, 1960.

Turnock, A. C.: *Carnegie Inst. Wash. Yearbook No. 59*, 1959–1960, pp. 98–103, 1960.

Tuttle, O. F., and R. I. Harker: Synthesis of spurrite and the reaction Wollastonite + Calcite $\rightleftharpoons$ Spurrite + Carbon dioxide, *Am. J. Sci.*, vol. 255, pp. 226–234, 1957.

Velde, B.: Low-grade metamorphism of micas in pelitic rocks, *Carnegie Inst. Wash. Yearbook No. 63*, 1963–1964, pp. 142–147, 1964.

————: Upper limits of stability of muscovite, *Am. Mineral.*, vol. 51, pp. 924–929, 1966.

Walter, L. S.: Experimental studies on Bowen's decarbonation series, *Am. J. Sci.*, vol. 261, pp. 488–500, 773–779, 1963.

Weeks, W. F.: A thermochemical study of equilibrium relations during metamorphism of siliceous carbonate rocks, *J. Geol.*, vol. 64, pp. 245–270, 1956.

Weill, D.: Stability relations in the Al_2O_3–SiO_2 system calculated from solubilities in the Al_2O_3–SiO_2–Na_3AlF_6 system, *Geochim. Cosmochim. Acta*, vol. 30, pp. 223–227, 1966.

————, and W. S. Fyfe: A preliminary note on the relative stability of andalusite, kyanite, and sillimanite, *Am. Mineralogist*, vol. 46, pp. 1191–1195, 1961.

Winkler, H. G. F.: Das T-P Feld der Diagenese und niedrigtemperierten Metamorphose aufgrund von Mineralreaktionen, *Beitr. Mineral. Petrog.*, vol. 10, pp. 70–93, 1964.

————: "Petrogenesis of Metamorphic Rocks," Springer, New York, 1965.

Wones, D. R., and H. P. Eugster: Stability of biotite: experiment, theory, and application, *Am. Mineralogist*, vol. 50, pp. 1228–1272, 1965.

Wyllie, P. J.: Melting relations in the system CaO–MgO–CO_2–H_2O, with petrological implications, *J. Petrol.*, vol. 6, pp. 101–123, 1965.

Yoder, H. S.: The MgO–Al_2O_3–SiO_2–H_2O system and related metamorphic facies, *Am. J. Sci.*, Bowen vol., pp. 569–627, 1952.

————: Role of water in metamorphism, *Geol. Soc. Am. Spec. Paper 62*, pp. 505–524, 1955.

————, and H. P. Eugster: Phlogopite synthesis and stability range, *Geochim. Cosmochim. Acta*, vol. 6, pp. 157–185, 1954.

————, and ————: Synthetic and natural muscovites, *Geochim. Cosmochim. Acta*, vol. 8, pp. 225–280, 1955.

Graphic Representation
and Nomenclature
of Metamorphic Facies

GRAPHIC PRESENTATION OF MINERALOGICAL DATA
AS A FUNCTION OF ROCK COMPOSITION

Use of Triangular Phase Diagrams

The whole range of rock composition within any facies—from limestone to shale to basalt or sandstone—can be expressed in terms of perhaps a dozen principal phases. This number is surprisingly small. Omitted, of course, are accessory minerals such as zircon and apatite, and minerals confined to rocks of unusual chemical composition and limited extent, for example, fluorite and axinite in metasomatically affected limestones.

Now the definitive property of a facies is the constant and therefore predictable relation that exists between the observed combinations of mineral phases (mineral assemblages) and rock composition as expressed by chemical analysis. Five widely distributed minerals in high-grade

172

quartz-bearing rocks of what we shall call the amphibolite facies are kyanite, almandine, plagioclase, hornblende, and diopside. Rocks of a certain limited range of composition (for example, X in Fig. 5-1) can be expressed equally well in terms of several alternative combinations of these phases: plagioclase-hornblende, plagioclase-diopside-almandine, plagioclase-diopside-almandine-kyanite. The observed assemblage is always plagioclase-hornblende. Combinations such as Y in Fig. 5-1, somewhat richer in alumina, are represented, however, by plagioclase-hornblende-almandine: never by the chemically equivalent trio plagioclase-diopside-almandine. Kyanite is confined to pelitic rocks, and diopside to rocks relatively rich in lime and low in alumina. We have already seen that within any major facies there may be some latitude regarding correlation, but it is always within sharply defined narrow limits. Within the smaller units (the local subfacies), correlation is rigorous.

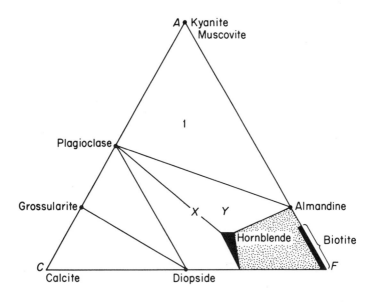

Fig. 5-1. *ACF* diagram for quartz-bearing assemblages of the kyanite zone, Scottish Highlands. Stippled field not recorded.

To express the correlation between mineralogy and chemical composition in any given facies or subfacies, Eskola introduced the now widely practised procedure of plotting mineral and rock compositions in terms of three chemical components. This treatment can completely express the range of possible variation only in the simplest of rock series. It may be done, for example, using CaO, MgO, and SiO_2 as variables, for metamorphosed siliceous dolomitic limestones, assuming CO_2 to be present as a pore fluid in all assemblages. However, it is possible, by judicious selection of variables and exclusion of phases present in all assemblages, to express by a triangular plot most of the essential variations for a wide range of rock composition in almost every facies. Plots in terms of four components give fuller information, but are more difficult to visualize. The usual procedure is to plot on triangular three-component diagrams. It may be necessary to limit the range of rock composition so plotted, or to plot the same data on two or three complementary diagrams having one or two components in common.

The *ACF* Diagram

Still in general use today are the two three-component diagrams introduced half-a-century ago by Eskola. Most generally applicable is the *ACF* diagram (Figs. 5-1, 5-2) depicting mineralogical and chemical

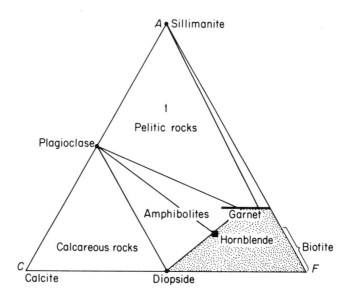

Fig. 5-2. *ACF* diagram for mineral assemblages in quartzo-feldspathic gneisses and associated amphibolites in an area of southwestern Quebec. (*Data from R. Kretz*, 1959, 1963.) Stippled field not recorded.

variation in terms of Al_2O_3, CaO, and (Mg, Fe)O. In any facies, the effect of variation in SiO_2 upon the possible mineral assemblages can be illustrated by comparing two *ACF* diagrams, one for rocks with excess SiO_2 crystallizing as free quartz (the most widely applicable case), and the other for rocks deficient in SiO_2. In the same way, special diagrams could be constructed for rocks with excess K_2O, deficient H_2O, and so on. The following rules for calculating the percentages of the components A, C, and F from a chemical analysis of the rock are given by Eskola (1939, p. 347):

> To correct for the accessories ilmenite, sphene, and magnetite, the percentages (by weight) of these minerals are first estimated by micrometric analysis as i, s, and m respectively. Then from the percentage of FeO (by weight) subtract 50% i and 30% m; likewise subtract 30% s from CaO and 70% m from Fe_2O_3. The percentages of the various oxides, corrected as above, are now calculated as molecular percentages, and CaO is then further corrected for calcite and apatite by subtracting molecular amounts equivalent to 3 P_2O_5 + CO_2. A, C, and F can now be reckoned as follows and are finally recalculated so that $A + C + F = 100$: $A = Al_2O_3 + Fe_2O_3 - (Na_2O + K_2O)$; $C = CaO$; $F = MgO + FeO + MnO$. Note that A is given by the total alumina and ferric iron, less the quantity that would be required to combine with total alkali as feldspar.

For calcareous rocks containing calcite or dolomite as principal phases, it is customary to omit the CO_2 correction. Clearly the ACF diagram is a somewhat crude representation of mineral paragenesis. There are many mineral phases in which mutual substitution of Mg^{2+} and Fe^{2+} is far from complete. The same applies to Al^{3+} and Fe^{3+}, as illustrated, for example, in their contrasted behavior in epidote minerals and plagioclase. Partition of such elements between coexisting phases may be highly significant as an index of grade of metamorphism. But this is completely obscured by plotting (Al, Fe)$_2O_3$ and (Mg, Fe)O as single components. In spite of such defects, the ACF plot is very useful in illustrating the gross features of correlation between mineralogical and chemical composition in the common mineral assemblages of most facies.

To complete the ACF diagram, tie lines are drawn between coexisting pairs of minerals. The fact that these ties do not cross in Figs. 5-1 and 5-2 further emphasizes the compositional correlation. All rocks whose compositions plot in a triangular field of these diagrams are found to be composed of the same three phases—those at the apices of the triangle in question. While this is true of Figs. 5-1 and 5-2, exceptions (where tie lines between associated phases do cross) are characteristic of some facies, especially those representing the lower grades of metamorphism. The significance of crossing ties will be discussed later.

The AKF Diagram

To express supplementary information regarding quartz-bearing micaceous assemblages containing a single calcic phase, such as plagioclase or epidote, Eskola introduced the AKF diagram. Such rocks are described as containing "excess Al_2O_3 and SiO_2." The analysis is recalculated so that

$$A = Al_2O_3 - (CaO + Na_2O + K_2O)$$
$$K = K_2O$$
$$F = FeO + MgO + MnO$$
$$A + K + F = 100$$

Figures 5-3 and 5-4 are *AKF* diagrams for pelitic rocks corresponding to triangle 1 in Figs. 5-1 and 5-2, respectively. They bring out the respective roles of micas and potash feldspar in the pelitic assemblages. Figure 5-3 is based on the observations of Francis (1964), who recorded in pelitic schists of the kyanite zone southwest of Inverness, Scotland, the following assemblages:

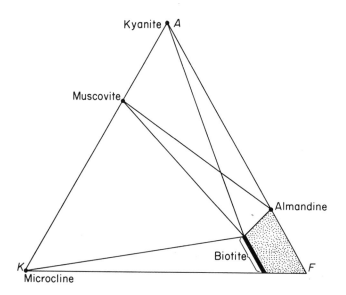

Fig. 5-3. *AKF* diagram for quartz-bearing pelitic rocks of the kyanite zone in Glen Urquhart, northeastern Scotland. Data (*from G. N. Francis, 1964*) corresponding to triangle 1 in Fig. 5-1. Stippled field not represented.

Kyanite-almandine-muscovite-biotite
Kyanite-muscovite-biotite
Almandine-muscovite-biotite
Microcline-muscovite-biotite

Quartz and plagioclase are additional phases in each assemblage. A higher grade of metamorphism from another region is illustrated in Fig. 5-4. In pelitic gneisses from a sector of southwestern Quebec, Kretz (1959; 1963) found muscovite absent. In its place appears the equivalent pair K-feldspar-

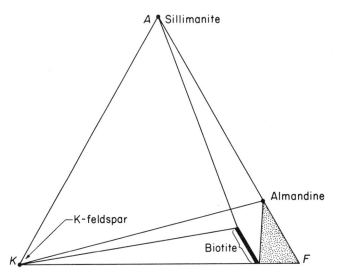

Fig. 5-4. *AKF* diagram for pelitic gneisses of triangle 1 in Fig. 5-2. (*Data from R. Kretz*, 1963.) Stippled field not recorded.

sillimanite. These minerals are typically associated with abundant almandine-rich garnet and biotite, as well as with the ubiquitous quartz and plagioclase.

In both Fig. 5-3 and Fig. 5-4, crossing tie lines correspond to the common occurrence of six-phase assemblages such as quartz-plagioclase-kyanite-almandine-muscovite-biotite or quartz-plagioclase-sillimanite-almandine-biotite-K-feldspar. To elucidate the significance of such assemblages we must turn to yet other projections, such as the *AFM* diagram described later.

Significance of Crossed Ties

It is impossible to apply the phase rule to a mineral assemblage, either as a test of equilibrium or as an index of variance, unless the compositions of all associated mineral phases are known. However, we know in a qualitative way that the phase rule limits the number of phases that can coexist in a heterogeneous system in equilibrium. We also know that the existence of each precise relation, which may be expressed by a chemical equation, between phases in any assemblage

$$A + B = C + D$$

reduces the variance of possible equilibrium by one. The absence of crossing ties in Figs. 5-1 and 5-2 implies the absence of any such relations. It suggests, but does not prove, that each phase assemblage represented by an individed triangle or by a tie may represent divariant equilibrium.

Turning now to the crossing ties of Figs. 5-3 and 5-4, three alternative explanations suggest themselves:

1. The six-phase assemblages represent disequilibrium.

2. They represent univariant equilibrium, e.g., a range of P and T on a conventional reaction curve (cf. Figs. 4-2 to 4-4).

3. They represent divariant equilibrium, in which case the crossing ties do not express any precise chemical equation. This could be true if the ratio MgO/FeO in the F component were markedly different in two coexisting phases such as garnet and biotite. Again, in manganiferous rocks, Mn may enter preferentially into one mafic mineral, such as garnet, rather than into others such as biotite or hornblende. This possibility can be explored in two ways. One is to plot mineral and rock compositions in terms of four components such as Al_2O_3, K_2O, FeO, and MgO. The other is to see if there is any regular relation between the MgO/FeO ratios of coexisting phases such as garnet and biotite, or biotite and hornblende.

Thompson's *AFM* Projection

Among the assemblages that seem to be most responsive to relatively small changes in pressure and temperature are those of pelitic schists. Except at the highest grades of metamorphism, these contain muscovite as the sole white-mica phase. To cover variation in muscovite schists of any subfacies, Thompson (1957) developed a projection based upon a tetrahedral plot of four components (Fig. 5-5):

$$A = Al_2O_3$$
$$B = K_2O$$
$$F = FeO$$
$$M = MgO$$
$$A + B + F + M = 100$$

Any muscovite-bearing assemblage can be represented graphically by projecting each pertinent point in the $ABFM$ tetrahedron upon the AFM plane (Fig. 5-7) by a straight line drawn through the muscovite point P. Every such assemblage contains muscovite and may contain quartz and/or plagioclase in addition to the phases connected by the lines in the AFM projection. Phases whose compositions lie in the tetrahedral sector $PAFM$ (Fig. 5-5) project within the AFM triangle itself in Fig. 5-7. Examples are almandine and staurolite. Others, such as the biotites, located in the pyramidal sector $PONFM$ plot in Fig. 5-7 below the FM join. Points in the tetrahedron $PBNO$ project above the A apex of the AFM triangle. Potash feldspar, in absence of sillimanite, plots at A. Note that the upward and downward continuations of any line drawn through A in Fig. 5-7 (e.g., the AM edge) meet at infinite distance.

Data for plotting biotite composititions on the AFM projection (given FeO, MgO, MnO, and Al_2O_3) are shown in the lower half of

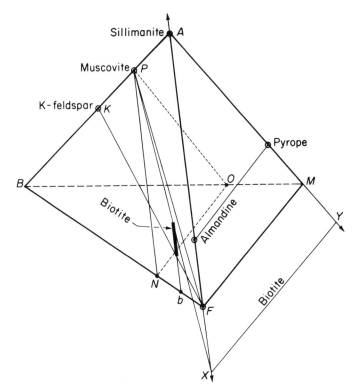

Fig. 5-5. The *ABFM* tetrahedron. (*After J. B. Thompson.*)

Fig. 5-6. Metamorphic biotites approximate compositions between $K(Mg, Fe, Mn)_3(AlSi_3O_{10})(OH)_2$ and $K(Mg, Fe, Mn)_{2\frac{1}{2}}Al_{\frac{1}{2}}(Al_{1\frac{1}{2}}Si_{2\frac{1}{2}}O_{10})$ $(OH)_2$. So $K_2O/(Al_2O_3 + MgO + FeO + MnO) = \frac{1}{7}$. On the *ABF* face of the fundamental tetrahedron (Fig. 5-5), these biotites plot on the solid bar on the join *Ab*, where $Fb/bB = \frac{1}{8}$. Corresponding *A* values on the *AFM* projection (Fig. 5-7) are -50 to -25.

The *AFM* projection is not practicable for plotting total-rock compositions. But it can express accurately the range of composition of coexisting mineral phases. Possible additional phase assemblages in quartz-muscovite schists (pelitic) from the muscovite-sillimanite zone of New Hampshire have been represented by Thompson (1957, p. 581) in the *AFM* projection here reproduced as Fig. 5-8.

To show partition of Fe^{2+}, Mg^{2+}, and Al^{3+} ions between coexisting biotites and garnets of rocks containing K-feldspar but no muscovite, a modified diagram *A'F'M'* may be drawn by projecting from the K-feldspar point *K* upon the *AFM* face of the tetrahedron (Fig. 5-5). Values of *A'* for

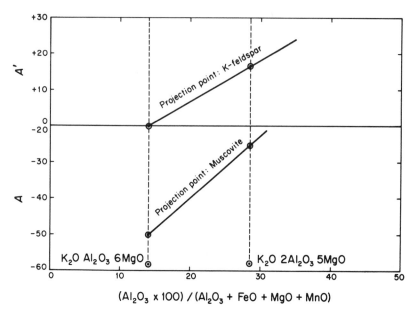

Fig. 5-6. Data for plotting biotite compositions on *AFM* (below) and *A'F'M'* (above) diagrams, given molecular proportions of Al_2O_3, FeO, MgO, MnO.

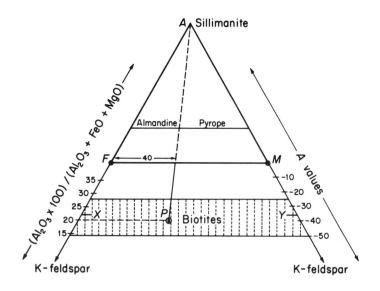

Fig. 5-7. Plots of biotite and garnet on AFM diagram (projection point: Muscovite).

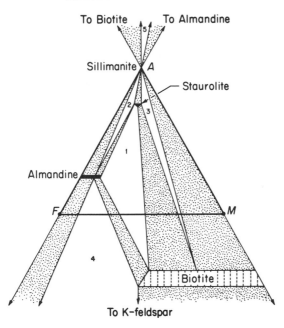

Fig. 5-8. *AFM* diagram for mineral phases and possible phase assemblages in quartz-muscovite schists of the muscovite-sillimanite zone, New Hampshire. (*After J. B. Thompson.*) Fields of two-phase assemblages stippled. Three-phase fields blank: (1) Almandine-staurolite-biotite; (2) Almandine-staurolite-sillimanite; (3) Sillimanite-staurolite-biotite; (4) Almandine-biotite-orthoclase; (5) Sillimanite-almandine-biotite.

biotite, based on this type of projection, are shown in the upper half of Fig. 5-6 and in Fig. 5-9. Figure 5-10 is an $A'F'M'$ plot of biotites and garnets (using analyses given by Kretz, 1959 and 1963) in quartzo-feldspathic gneisses from southwestern Quebec. This diagram amplifies the paragenesis depicted in more general terms in Figs. 5-2 and 5-4. All these rocks lack muscovite. Many contain K-feldspar. Quartz and plagioclase are additional phases in all assemblages. Some contain sillimanite, some hornblende; but these are mutually exclusive.

Figure 5-10 brings out two points consistent with, but not proving, equilibrium in the various assemblages:

1. Biotites in the assemblages biotite-garnet-sillimanite and biotite-garnet (above PQ) are relatively high in Al. Biotites of hornblende-bearing assemblages (whether or not these contain garnet or K-feldspar) are low in Al (below PQ in Fig. 5-10).

2. The ratio Mg/Fe in biotite is consistently higher than in associated garnet. The crossing of garnet-biotite ties is insignificant.

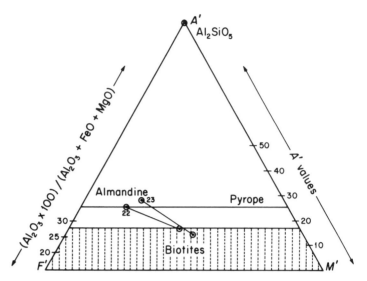

Fig. 5-9. Plots of biotite and garnet on $A'F'M'$ diagram (projection point: K-feldspar).

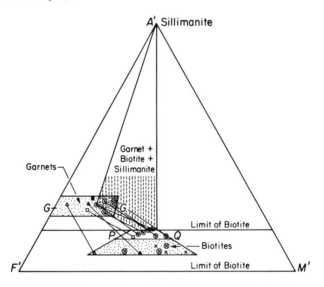

Fig. 5-10. $A'F'M'$ diagram for mineral phases associated with quartz and K-feldspar in gneisses from southwestern Quebec (cf. Figs. 5-2, 5-4). (*Data from R. Kretz,* 1959, 1963.) Circled dots: biotite-garnet-sillimanite. Open triangles: biotite-garnet-hornblende. Circled crosses: biotite-hornblende. Open square: biotite-garnet. Assemblages lacking K-feldspar are biotite-hornblende (crosses), garnet-biotite-hornblende (solid triangles), garnet-hornblende (solid square). *GG* is theoretical garnet composition.

Such relations may also be clearly expressed in a simpler manner by plotting some significant chemical parameter such as $Mg/(Mg + Fe + Mn)$ for two coexisting minerals. Figure 5-11 is an example of such a plot for biotite and garnet in the quartzo-feldspathic biotite-garnet sillimanite gneisses from Quebec (Kretz, 1963). These fall in the lower part of the garnet-biotite-sillimanite field of Fig. 5-10.

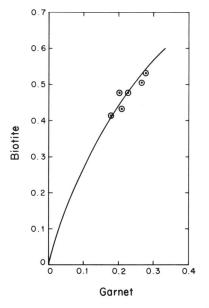

Fig. 5-11. Plot of $Mg/(Fe + Mg + Mn)$ in coexisting garnets and biotites of quartz-orthoclase-garnet-biotite-sillimanite gneisses from southwestern Quebec. (*After R. Kretz*, 1963, *p.* 12.) Compare with the circled points of Fig. 5-10.

Conclusion—With a Note on Equilibrium

Gross features of correlation between chemical and mineralogical composition of rocks belonging to a facies can usually be illustrated in terms of the *ACM* and *AKM* projections of Eskola. Where these have crossing tie lines, auxiliary diagrams such as the *AFM* projection may be necessary to bring out the correlation in greater detail. The fact that facies, and especially local subfacies, can be represented thus, suggests very strongly that the phase assemblages approximate divariant equilibrium. Equilibrium, however, can never be demonstrated certainly. All that can be said of Figs. 5-10 and 5-11 is that they are compatible with equilibrium. Moreover, since the chemical data refer to average compositions of mineral phases and rocks, there is still the possibility of small-scale disequilibrium. This, indeed, has already been demonstrated as a normal condition for the individual garnet crystals. These very often show strong compositional zoning, with Mn decreasing and Mg increasing from core to rim. Biotite crystals, on the other hand, tend to be homogeneous. In discussing prevalence of equilibrium, as with related problems of homogeneity in structure, it is essential to define the scale of the phenomenon under discussion.

SYNOPSIS OF CURRENTLY RECOGNIZED METAMORPHIC FACIES

Development of Nomenclatural Ideas

Using mineralogical criteria, Eskola (1920) first defined five metamorphic facies. He illustrated their main mineralogical characteristics in terms of *ACF* diagrams and outlined approximate pressure-temperature conditions for each facies, as inferred by him from their field occurrence.

Each facies was named after some rock-type (mineral assemblage) considered to be critical and diagnostic of the facies in question. Most of these diagnostic rocks approximate basaltic composition. This form of nomenclature is by no means ideal. The *hornfels facies*, for example, later was renamed the *pyroxene-hornfels* facies after its critical assemblage, diopside-hypersthene-plagioclase—characteristic of high-temperature hornfelses. But other pyroxene-bearing hornfelses (the common plagioclase-hornblende-diopside rocks) fall into another facies, which is now called the *hornblende-hornfels facies*. In spite of many such ambiguities most petrologists, to avoid further confusion, have retained Eskola's nomenclature with as little change as possible. This is the attitude adopted here, although some additions and further minor nomenclatural changes have been found unavoidable.

In his final statement, Eskola (1939, p. 344) listed eight metamorphic facies. These he correlated with temperature and pressure in the diagrammatic form reproduced here as Table 5-1.

As foreshadowed in an early critical essay by Becke (1921), there has been some divergence of opinion, and even confusion, as to the number of recognizable facies, their nomenclature and mutual relations, and their possible subdivision into units (subfacies) of more than local significance.

Table 5-1. Metamorphic facies in relation to temperature and pressure (diagrammatic). (*After Eskola, 1939, p. 344.*)

Pressure increasing ↓	Temperature increasing →			
				Sanidinite
	Greenschist	Epidote-amphibolite	Amphibolite	Pyroxene-hornfels
				Granulite
		Glaucophane-schist		Eclogite

The situation, as it then existed, was surveyed by Fyfe, Turner, and Verhoogen (1958, pp. 8-20). Some of the changes introduced there have found general acceptance; others have been deemed by competent petrologists to be inadequate or unnecessary. The position adopted in this book follows the lines laid down by a later reappraisal of the facies problem by Fyfe and Turner (1966). A dozen facies are now recognized. As far as possible the older nomenclature has been retained. Subfacies, while usually clearly recognizable in a particular region of progressive metamorphism, are considered to be of local rather than general significance.[1]

Any attempt to survey the nature and possible physical significance of the gamut of individual facies necessarily oversimplifies a complex phenomenon. Our earlier treatment of facies (Turner and Verhoogen, 1960, pp. 508-560) draws an admittedly artificial line between the facies of contact metamorphism and those of regional metamorphism. Equally open to criticism is the descriptive device of placing the facies of each series in an unduly simplified order of increasing metamorphic grade (temperature). In the chapters that follow there is no such implication—any more than in our earlier treatment, or in Eskola's purely diagrammatic arrangement (Table 5-1)—of simplicity in the general pattern of metamorphism.

Some of the most complete descriptions of individual facies refer to contact aureoles developed locally in otherwise unmetamorphosed rocks. Field conditions imply a considerable range of temperature at relatively low pressure (cf. pp. 255–258). It is not unwarranted to describe such parageneses as facies of contact metamorphism; their relative order on an ideal temperature gradient at some hypothetical pressure is abundantly clear. Many of the facies of regional metamorphism, on the other hand, illustrate the products of mineral reaction at much greater depths than those of the typical contact aureole. Such, almost certainly, are the rocks of the Barrovian zones in the Highlands of Scotland, and (probably at much lower temperatures) the glaucophane schists of California. It has become increasingly clear, however, that there are facies that reflect conditions of metamorphism intermediate between those of the shallow contact aureoles and those represented by Barrow's zones. This situation was expressed in schematic fashion by Fyfe, Turner, and Verhoogen (1958, p. 237, fig. 107). To meet it, Miyashiro (1961) introduced the useful concept of *facies series* to which we will return later.

Approach Adopted in This Book

The position adopted here regarding the status and nomenclature of metamorphic facies is essentially that stated by Fyfe and Turner (1966) but

---

[1] This in no way minimizes the importance of local subfacies as indices of local pressure-temperature gradients.

with one important modification. The facies that are generally recognized today on the basis of universally recurring critical mineral parageneses are eleven in number. They are (1) albite-epidote-hornfels, (2) hornblende-hornfels, (3) pyroxene-hornfels, (4) sanidinite, (5) zeolite, (6) prehnite-pumpellyite-metagraywacke (inadvertently not specifically named as such by Fyfe and Turner), (7) greenschist, (8) amphibolite, (9) granulite, (10) glaucophane-lawsonite-schist, and (11) eclogite. In the course of the present survey, this writer has become increasingly aware that parageneses transitional between those of some of the above facies not only are known, but are repeated (with minor variation) in many parts of the world and sometimes cover large areas. Such parageneses have, by definition, the full status of facies. To invent new names to cover these transitional facies would not only overtax and complicate unduly the current nomenclature scheme; but in addition it would result in falsely presenting a picture of sharp interfacies boundaries where none exist. This procedure would have all the faults that attended our earlier efforts to multiply and to sharply define universally applicable subfacies.

To meet this situation, it is proposed to recognize transitional facies, where such exist on a more than local basis, and to name them accordingly. In most areas of progressive regional metamorphism, the greenschist facies of the chlorite and biotite zones is clearly distinguishable from the amphibolite facies of the zones of almandine, staurolite and kyanite or sillimanite. But between the two, in some areas (e.g., the Scottish Highlands) covering much of the almandine zone, in others (e.g., New Hampshire-Vermont) overlapping the high-grade part of the biotite zone, are parageneses combining to some degree the critical characteristics of the other two. These have previously been termed (with considerable attendant confusion) the epidote-amphibolite or albite-epidote-amphibolite facies, or a high-grade subfacies of the greenschist facies. Here they will be described simply as the greenschist-amphibolite-transition facies. Similarly, the amphibolite-granulite-transition facies will be introduced to replace what we previously termed the hornblende-granulite subfacies of the granulite facies. Other transition facies can be introduced where necessary.

Figure 5-12 shows schematically a tentative correlation between facies and the simplest physical controls of metamorphism—temperature and pressure (cf. Fyfe and Turner, 1966). It anticipates conclusions that will emerge in the course of the chapters that follow. In due course we shall find it possible to place more precise limits upon the pressure-temperature fields suggested at this stage in Fig. 5-12. This preliminary presentation should serve, however, to remove from the descriptive survey any false impression that facies fall neatly into pigeon holes whose boundaries conveniently parallel the rectangular coordinates of temperature and pressure.

In a later chapter we shall discuss metamorphism in relation to

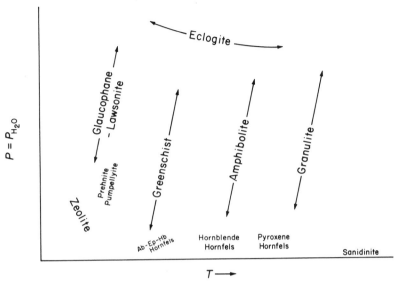

Fig. 5-12. Schematic relation of facies to temperature and pressure $(P_l = P_{H_2O})$. (*After W. S. Fyfe and F. J. Turner.*)

plutonism. It is appropriate at this point, however, to note that contact metamorphism may be induced at any depth by local elevation of temperature in the vicinity of intrusive bodies of magma. Depth, on the other hand, must be an important factor contributing to the physical conditions of all the variants of what we call regional metamorphism.

The individual facies of metamorphism will now be described in an arbitrary order as follows (cf. Fig. 5-12).

A. Facies of low pressure
   1. Albite-epidote-hornfels
   2. Hornblende-hornfels
   3. Pyroxene-hornfels
   4. Sanidinite
B. Facies of medium to high pressure
   5. Zeolite
   6. Prehnite-pumpellyite-metagraywacke
   7. Greenschist
   8. Amphibolite
   9. Granulite
C. Facies of very high pressure
   10. Glaucophane-lawsonite-schist
   11. Eclogite

Assuming constant or slightly increasing pressure, the facies in each of the three pressure categories have been numbered in order of increasing temperature. In the lower range of pressures, the low-temperature limits of facies 1 and 5 are conceived as temperatures at which the activation energies of metamorphic reactions are exceeded. At very high pressures induced by depth, temperatures corresponding to even a low thermal gradient, such as $10^\circ/km$, are thought to be high enough to activate rock-forming minerals to the point of metamorphism. So the low-temperature limit of facies 10 is visualized as the minimum temperature possible in the deepest levels of the earth's crust. At all pressures, the upper temperatures of metamorphism overlap the minimal temperatures of rock fusion.

In previous works, following the example of Eskola, we have attempted to define and describe the mineral paragenesis of each facies and subfacies in general terms. Each description was illustrated with a generalized *ACF* or *AKF* diagram. This procedure fails to bring out adequately the variation that exists within most facies. It tends to obscure real and sharp differences between the most prevalent parageneses of two "adjacent" facies—e.g., the hornblende-hornfels and the pyroxene-hornfels facies. On the other hand, there is a tendency to sharpen artificially what are actually gradual interfacial transitions.

In the next two chapters, therefore, we adopt a somewhat different approach. The parageneses of most facies are illustrated by particular examples, each with its own compositional diagrams (*ACF*, *AKF*, and so on). It must be understood that other cases are already known, or are likely to be recognized later, whose mineralogical characteristics overlap those of the described examples. Miyashiro (1961) has adopted a rather similar approach in setting up "facies series," each based on a type instance of progressive metamorphism.

REFERENCES

Becke, F.: Zur Faciesklassifikation der metamorphen Gesteine, *Tschermaks Mineral. Petrog. Mitt.*, vol. 35, pp. 215–230, 1921.

Eskola, P.: The mineral facies of rocks, *Norsk Geol. Tidsskr.*, vol. 6, pp. 143–194, 1920.

——: Die metamorphen Gesteine, "Die Entstehung der Gesteine" (T. F. W. Barth, C. W. Correns, P. Eskola), pp. 263–407, Springer, Berlin, 1939.

Francis, G. H.: Further petrological studies in Glen Urquhart, Inverness-shire, *Brit. Mus. (Nat. Hist.) Mineral. Bull.*, vol. 1, pp. 165–199, 1964.

Fyfe, W. S., and F. J. Turner: Reappraisal of the metamorphic facies concept, *Contrib. Mineral. Petrol.*, vol. 12, pp. 354–364, 1966.

——, ——, and J. Verhoogen: Metamorphic reactions and metamorphic facies, *Geol. Soc. Am. Mem.* 73, 1958.

Kretz, R.: Chemical study of garnet biotite and hornblende from gneisses of south-western Quebec, with emphasis on distribution of elements in coexisting minerals, *J. Geol.*, vol. 67, pp. 371–402, 1959.

———: Analysis of equilibrium in garnet-biotite-sillimanite gneisses from Quebec, *J. Petrol.*, vol. 5, pp. 1–20, 1964.

Miyashiro, A.: Evolution of metamorphic belts, *J. Petrol.*, vol. 2, pp. 277–311, 1961.

Thompson, J. B.: The graphical analysis of mineral assemblages in pelitic schists, *Am. Mineralogist*, vol. 42, pp. 842–858, 1957.

Turner, F. J., and J. Verhoogen: "Igneous and Metamorphic Petrology," 2d ed., McGraw-Hill, New York, 1960.

Review of
Metamorphic Facies
I: Facies of Low Pressure[1]

ALBITE-EPIDOTE-HORNFELS FACIES

This facies was introduced (Turner, 1948, p. 90; Fyfe, Turner, and Verhoogen, 1958, pp. 203-205) to cover mineral assemblages that sometimes appear in the outer fringes of contact aureoles at temperatures too low for development of hornblende-plagioclase assemblages in basic rocks. Recrystallization and reaction in such rocks tends to be imperfect. Associated with newly formed minerals, there are generally unstable relict phases inherited from the premetamorphic condition. For this reason the mineralogy of the albite-epidote-hornfels facies is known imperfectly. Neither is there any detailed record of mineral assemblages covering a wide range of rock composition in any one locality.

[1]Chapters 6 and 7 constitute a revised and amplified version of material in Fyfe, Turner, and Verhoogen (1958, pp. 199–239) and in Turner and Verhoogen (1960, pp. 508–560), presented, however, from a different approach. Literature cited in Chaps. 6 and 7 is mainly from publications not cited in our earlier books.

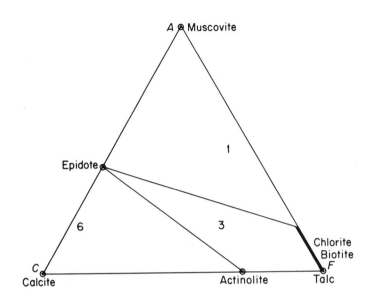

Fig. 6-1. Albite-epidote-hornfels facies. *ACF* diagram for rocks with excess SiO_2 and K_2O. Quartz, albite, and microcline are possible additional phases.

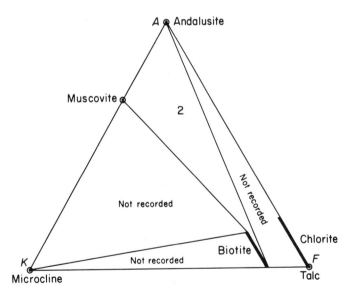

Fig. 6-2. Albite-epidote-hornfels facies. *AKF* diagram for rocks with excess SiO_2 and Al_2O_3 (triangle 1 of Fig. 6-1). Quartz, epidote, and albite are possible additional phases.

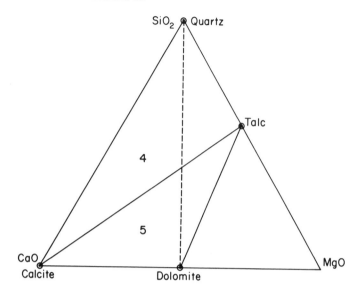

Fig. 6-3. Albite-epidote-hornfels facies. Phase assemblages in derivatives of siliceous limestone and dolomite (to left of broken line).

For the above reasons, we must be content to list a number of individually recorded assemblages (e.g., DeBooy, 1954, pp. 27, 28; Kanisawa, 1964, pp. 185-189) from outside the zone of hornblende-plagioclase hornfelses (hornblende-hornfels facies). The status of the calcareous assemblages is inferred from their occurrence in the outer parts of some aureoles and from experimental evidence regarding the expectable order of development of silicates from reactions between quartz and dolomite. Figures 6-1 to 6-3, which show probable relations between mineralogical data and rock composition, are subject to the same qualifications.

    A. Pelitic assemblages
        1. Quartz-muscovite-biotite(-chlorite)
        2. Quartz-muscovite-biotite-andalusite
    B. Basic assemblage
        3. Albite-epidote-actinolite-chlorite-quartz[1]
    C. Calcareous assemblages
        4. Calcite-quartz-talc
        5. Calcite-dolomite-talc
        6. Calcite-epidote

Whether tremolite-bearing assemblages may also develop (at somewhat

---

[1] Kanisawa records plagioclase of composition An_{10} to An_{24} in hornblende-plagioclase-epidote hornfels of this facies.

higher temperatures or lower values of P_{H_2O} than those which favor appearance of talc) is uncertain. Certainly assemblages with tremolite rather than talc are commonly found at a higher grade of metamorphism in the hornblende-hornfels facies.

Most of the assemblages listed above are also typical of the greenschist facies. One exception is quartz-mica-andalusite. The common greenschist mineral stilpnomelane is absent; so too are almandine-rich garnets which appear in small amounts at the higher grades within the greenschist facies.

HORNBLENDE-HORNFELS FACIES

Preliminary Definition

The mineralogical characteristics of the hornblende-hornfels facies are as follows: The typical assemblage of basic hornfelses is hornblende-plagioclase; diopside may also be present, but seldom almandine or epidote. Muscovite-biotite-quartz is ubiquitous in pelitic rocks; andalusite and/or cordierite appear mainly in rocks lacking potash feldspar. Sillimanite, but not kyanite, may take the place of andalusite in the more aluminous pelitic assemblages; pyrophyllite has not been recorded. Rocks formed from siliceous limestones and dolomite typically consist of combinations of calcite (or dolomite), tremolite, and diopside. After considering some individual hornblende-hornfels parageneses in detail, we shall find it necessary to amplify this definition in some respects.

Field Occurrence

The hornblende-hornfels facies embraces the majority of the rocks that have been described from clear-cut contact aureoles. They may pass outward, with decreasing metamorphic grade, into those imperfectly reconstituted rocks whose newly formed mineral assemblages we have assigned to the albite-epidote-hornfels facies. In some aureoles, they are seen to pass inward with increasing grade into rocks whose mineral assemblages define the pyroxene-hornfels facies. Such are the classic low-pressure Oslo aureoles (Goldschmidt, 1911) and the high-temperature zones adjacent to major basic plutons such as those of the Bushveld (cf. pp. 15–16) and Stillwater complexes. Elsewhere, the hornblende-hornfels facies continues to the intrusive contact. It is often represented also by mineral assemblages of completely enclosed pendants and xenoliths, especially in shallow plutons such as those of the Sierra Nevada of California.

Regional metamorphism does not necessarily imply great depth and high pressure. It has become increasingly clear from work in the Pyrenees (e.g., Zwart, 1962) and in northeastern Scotland (e.g., Read, 1952), that the

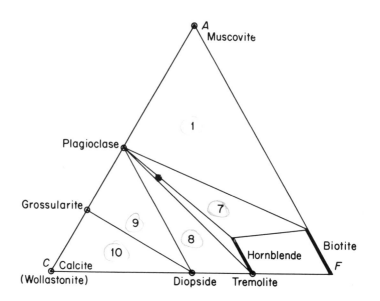

Fig. 6-4. Hornblende-hornfels facies, Orijärvi, Finland. *ACF* diagram for rocks with excess SiO_2 and K_2O. Quartz and microcline are possible additional phases.

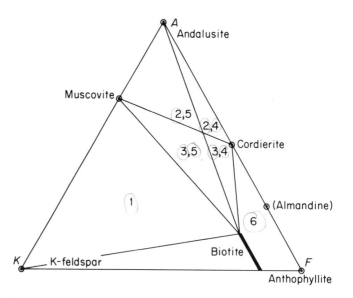

Fig. 6-5. Hornblende-hornfels facies, Orijärvi, Finland. *AKF* diagram for rocks with excess SiO_2 and Al_2O_3 (triangle 1 of Fig. 6-4). Quartz and plagioclase are possible additional phases.

194

mineral paragenesis of the hornblende-hornfels facies is developed, presumably at rather low pressures, in some areas at medium and high grades of what has been called regional metamorphism. The prevailing metamorphic rocks in such zones may even be termed hornfelses on textural grounds. Clearly there can be no sharp division, along a gradient of increasing pressure, between the hornblende-hornfels facies and the amphibolite facies as represented by rocks of medium to high grade in Barrow's zones of Scotland or the Alpine schists of southern New Zealand.

Orijärvi District, Finland

Eskola's concept of metamorphic facies sprang from his comprehensive study of contact metamorphism and local magnesia metasomatism in the vicinity of Precambrian granitic plutons in the Orijärvi region of Finland (Eskola, 1915; Fyfe, Turner, and Verhoogen, 1958, pp. 8, 206). On the paragenesis at Orijärvi he based his amphibolite facies. Today, the latter term is generally restricted to cover the amphibolites and associated rocks formed at higher pressures, mainly by regional metamorphism. The assemblages at Orijärvi typify the hornblende-hornfels facies as defined by Fyfe, Turner, and Verhoogen (1958, pp. 201, 206). Their essential character is illustrated in Figs. 6-4 and 6-5. The commoner assemblages, numbered according to the triangular fields of these diagrams are:

A. Pelitic
  1. Quartz-muscovite-biotite (-plagioclase-microcline)
  2. Quartz-muscovite-cordierite-andalusite (-plagioclase)
  3. Quartz-muscovite-biotite-cordierite (-plagioclase)
  4. Quartz-biotite-cordierite-andalusite
  5. Quartz-muscovite-biotite-andalusite
B. Quartzo-feldspathic
  1. Quartz-plagioclase-microcline-muscovite-biotite
  7. Quartz-plagioclase-microcline-biotite-hornblende
C. Calcareous
  9. Diopside-grossularite (-quartz-plagioclase)
  10. Grossularite-diopside-calcite-quartz or
      Grossularite-diopside-wollastonite
D. Basic
  7. Plagioclase-hornblende (-biotite-quartz)
  8. Plagioclase-hornblende-diopside (-quartz)
E. Magnesian
  6. (a) Cordierite-anthophyllite (-biotite)
     (b) Cordierite-anthophyllite-almandine (-biotite)

The magnesian hornfelses of Orijärvi are products of magnesia-iron metasomatism concurrent with metamorphism. Nevertheless their present mineral composition is broadly consistent with approximate equilibrium

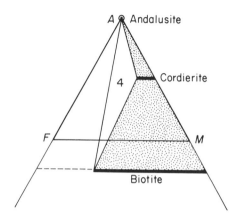

Fig. 6-6. Hornblende-hornfels facies, Orijärvi, Finland. Schematic AFM diagram for magnesian assemblages projected from the Muscovite point. Quartz and muscovite are possible additional phases. Stippled areas represent two-phase assemblages.

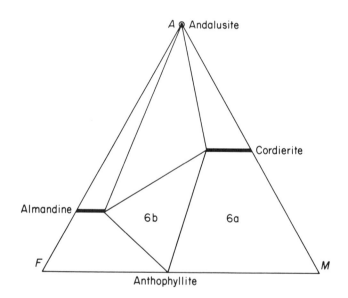

Fig. 6-7. Hornblende-hornfels facies, Orijärvi, Finland. *AFM* diagram for magnesian assemblages lacking muscovite. Quartz and biotite are possible additional phases.

within each of the principal mineral assemblages. Different degrees of mutual substitution of Fe^{2+} and Mg^{2+} are shown by the constituent mineral phases: cordierite, anthophyllite, biotite, and almandine (Eskola,

1915, p. 122). Eskola's data on compositions of the individual minerals are incomplete; in fact, there are no available analyses of the Orijärvi biotites. Still there is enough to illustrate in a rather crude fashion the phase relations in muscovite-bearing assemblages (Fig. 6-6) and in those with biotite as the sole possible mica phase (Fig. 6-7).

Tôno Aureole, Japan

Outermost zone. A Jurassic granodiorite pluton, 30 km in diameter, near Tôno in the northeastern part of the island of Honsyu, has developed a zoned contact aureole in the surrounding Paleozoic sediments and associated basic volcanics. Mineralogical aspects of metamorphism have been described in detail by Seki (1957) and by Seki and Yamasaki (1957).

In the outermost zones of the aureole, pelitic assemblages include various combinations of quartz, muscovite, biotite, andalusite, and albite-oligoclase. Intercalated volcanics consist principally of chlorite, sodic plagioclase, epidote, and actinolite. Tremolite has developed in calcareous rocks. The mineral assemblages suggest the albite-epidote-hornfels rather than the typical hornblende-hornfels facies.

Inner zones. Rocks of distinctly higher metamorphic grade border the western margin of the pluton and extend from a few hundred meters to over 1 km from the exposed contact. The mineral assemblages are more complex than in the outer zone. With the exception of an unusually iron-rich aluminous ferroanthophyllite (Seki and Yamasaki, 1957), the constituent minerals have not been analysed. But full data for refractive indices of coexisting biotites, cordierites, anthophyllites and garnets make it possible to construct the essential features of AFM and $A'F'M'$ diagrams to illustrate the main features of the paragenesis. Pelitic rocks on the whole are unusually rich in iron and high in aluminum.

Throughout the inner aureole, basic hornfelses are always represented by the hornblende-plagioclase (An_{73} to An_{72}) assemblage, diagnostic of the hornblende-hornfels facies. But there are two concentric inner zones characterized by distinctive mineralogical criteria that stamp them as mutually distinct local subfacies:

1. A cordierite-almandine zone immediately following the outermost zone of andalusite-mica hornfelses. Characteristic features of pelitic rocks are abundance of cordierite, andalusite, and anthophyllite. Calcareous rocks include the assemblages calcite-epidote-plagioclase-diopside and calcite-diopside-quartz.

2. A sillimanite zone, developed within a few hundred yards of the plutonic contact and comprising the innermost portion of the aureole. Pelitic hornfelses contain sillimanite, not andalusite; anthophyllite is absent; microcline appears in some rocks. In calcareous assemblages of appropriate composition, wollastonite and grossularite are present just

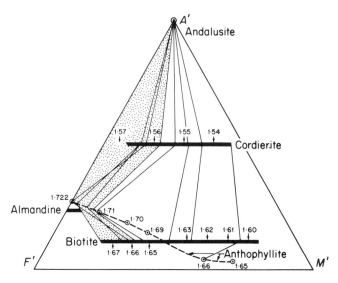

Fig. 6-8. Hornblende-hornfels facies, Tôno aureole, Japan (cordierite-almandine zone). $A'F'M'$ diagram for pelitic hornfelses lacking muscovite. Quartz and plagioclase are possible additional phases; garnet is present in all assemblages of stippled area. Mineral compositions are inferred from γ refractive index values as shown (Al content of magnesian anthophyllites is uncertain).

as in corresponding rocks at Orijärvi (cf. triangles 9 and 10, Fig. 6-4).

Pelitic rocks in the cordierite-almandine zone include all the quartz-mica-andalusite-cordierite combinations found at Orijärvi (assemblages 1 to 5, p. 195). In addition, however, there are all possible five- and six-phase combinations of quartz, muscovite, biotite, andalusite, cordierite, anthophyllite, and almandine. These are illustrated in $A'F'M'$ and AFM diagrams (Figs. 6-8 and 6-9) based on the optical data of Seki (1957, p. 332), and of Yamasaki (1957)[1] for anthophyllite and associated minerals. It would seem that there is a tendency, in any given assemblage, for the ratio FeO/MgO to decrease in the order almandine > anthophyllite > biotite ≳ cordierite. Almandine, as usual, appears only in rocks whose FeO/MgO ratio is high (stippled area of Figs. 6-8 and 6-9). Typical assemblages consist of four or five phases, e.g., quartz-almandine-muscovite-biotite, quartz-almandine-andalusite-anthophyllite-cordierite. Six- and seven-phase assemblages with anthophyllite, garnet, and muscovite are shown by ties in the stippled area of Fig. 6-9. The corresponding assemblage without muscovite (quartz-almandine-andalusite-biotite-anthophyllite-cordierite) is represent-

---

[1]Values of γ refractive indices, from which compositions of associated minerals have been inferred, are shown for each mineral—1.54 to 1.57 for cordierite, and so on.

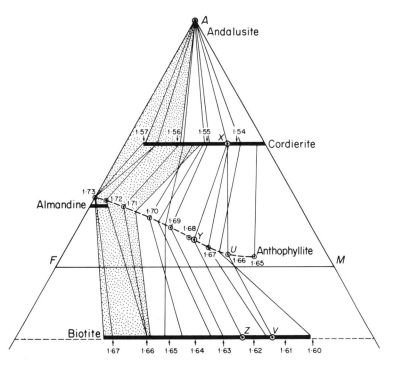

Fig. 6-9. Hornblende-hornfels facies, Tòno aureole, Japan (cordierite-almandine zone). *AFM* diagram for pelitic hornfelses containing muscovite. Quartz and plagioclase are possible additional phases; garnet is present in all assemblages of stippled area. Mineral compositions are inferred from γ refractive index values as shown.

ed in the stippled part of Fig. 6-8.

The simpler four-phase assemblages of the cordierite-almandine zone (e.g., quartz-muscovite-cordierite-biotite and quartz-muscovite-biotite-andalusite) conform to the limits imposed by the phase rule on systems in divariant equilibrium. Some of the more complex assemblages are more consistent with either univariant equilibrium or disequilibrium. Take, for example, quartz-muscovite-biotite-anthophyllite-andalusite-cordierite, as represented by the zigzag ties $AXYZ$ and $AXUV$ in Fig. 6-9. The six solid phases can be related theoretically by the equation

(1) $6KAl_2(AlSi_3O_{10})(OH)_2 + 2Mg_{6\frac{1}{2}}Al_{\frac{1}{2}}(Al_{\frac{1}{2}}Si_{7\frac{1}{2}}O_{22})(OH)_2$
  Muscovite   Anthophyllite

$+ Mg_2Al_4Si_5O_{18}$
  Cordierite

$\rightleftharpoons 6KMg_{2\frac{1}{2}}Al_{\frac{1}{2}}(Al_{1\frac{1}{2}}Si_{2\frac{1}{2}}O_{10})(OH)_2 + 6Al_2SiO_5 + 17SiO_2 + 2H_2O$
  Biotite   Andalusite   Quartz

For biotites Z to V, anthophyllites Y to U, and cordierite X (Fig. 6-9), the Mg/Fe ratio on both sides of the equation also balances within limits of error of calculation. So the six-phase assemblages represented by the ties $AXYZ$—$AXUV$ are consistent with univariant equilibrium. But univariant equilibrium requires that for any given value of P_{H_2O}, each of the coexisting phases—biotite, anthophyllite, cordierite, and garnet—must have a unique composition. Clearly, this is not so for the minerals shown in Fig. 6-9. Either they represent a finite though not necessarily large range of temperature or P_{H_2O}, or there is a significant departure from equilibrium.

Other pelitic assemblages in the cordierite-almandine zone do show unmistakable signs of internal disequilibrium. Such are spinel-corundum-biotite-muscovite-quartz and assemblages containing spinel, corundum, cordierite, and quartz. Not only is the phase assemblage itself inconsistent with equilibrium, but there is textural evidence of reaction between the constituent phases (Seki, 1957, pp. 329, 330).

In the sillimanite zone of the Tôno aureole, the pelitic assemblages are much simpler. The Al_2SiO_5 polymorph is sillimanite. There are the usual three- and four-phase combinations of quartz, biotite, muscovite, sillimanite, and cordierite (and in iron-rich rocks, almandine) just as in Fig. 6-5. Anthophyllite is completely lacking,[1] and in rocks relatively rich in FeO and MgO, cordierite (and/or almandine) is associated with both biotite and muscovite (cf. Fig. 6-10). Microcline appears in sillimanite-, cordierite-, or almandine-bearing assemblages, with one or both micas. In the AKF diagram (Fig. 6-10) there are many crossing ties. Again there is strong indication of either disequilibrium or univariant equilibrium expressed by equations such as

(2) $4KMg_{2\frac{1}{2}}Al_{\frac{1}{2}}(Al_{1\frac{1}{2}}Si_{2\frac{1}{2}}O_{10})(OH)_2 + KAl_2(AlSi_3O_{10})(OH)_2$
     Biotite   Muscovite

$+ 7Al_2SiO_5 + 20SiO_2 \rightleftharpoons 5KAlSi_3O_8 + 5Mg_2Al_4Si_5O_{18} + 5H_2O$
   Sillimanite   Quartz   Microcline   Cordierite

Figure 6-11 is an AFM plot showing the compositions (inferred from the γ refractive index) of coexisting biotites, cordierites, and (in the stippled area) almandines in muscovite-bearing rocks of the sillimanite zone.

Sierra Nevada, California

General setting. The Sierra Nevada batholith of California is a composite granodioritic body consisting of hundreds of independently emplaced plutons. Its exposed area is approximately 600×80–100 km (Fig. 6-12). Emplacement of the component plutons along the western

---

[1]The reaction leading to elimination of anthophyllite is perhaps that expressed in equation (1) above.

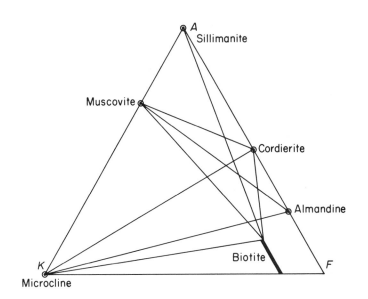

Fig. 6-10. Hornblende-hornfels facies, Tòno aureole, Japan (sillimanite zone). *AKF* diagram for pelitic quartz-bearing assemblages. Quartz and plagioclase are possible additional phases.

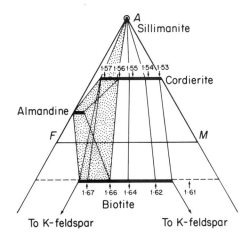

Fig. 6-11. Hornblende-hornfels facies, Tòno aureole, Japan (sillimanite zone). *AFM* diagram (schematic) for pelitic assemblages. Muscovite, quartz, and biotite are possible additional phases; garnet may be present in assemblages of the stippled area. Numbers refer to γ refractive indices.

margin has been dated radiometrically as upper Jurassic (Curtis, Evernden, and Lipson, 1958). Along the main axis of the batholith the date of intrusion was upper Cretaceous.

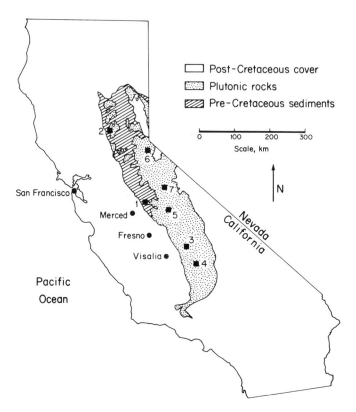

Fig. 6-12. Map of Sierra Nevada batholith (stippled). (*After G. N. Curtis.*) Locations referred to in text: (1) Indian Gulch contact; (2) Bidwell Bar contact; (3) Visalia pendant; (4) Isabella pendant; (5) Twin Lakes pendant; (6) Ebbett Pass pendant; (7) May Lake pendant.

The invaded rocks along the western border of the batholith are Paleozoic and Mesozoic metasediments and metavolcanics bearing the imprint of lowest-grade regional metamorphism. Remnant masses of similar rocks, commonly several kilometers long, occur as roof pendants and as septa separating individual plutons, scattered along the axis of the batholith. These are enclosed in the younger plutonic bodies. Opinion differs as to the depth of cover at the time of intrusion at the presently exposed level. The maximum stratigraphic thicknesses of sections of

Paleozoic and Mesozoic metasediments preserved in roof pendants are each about 10 km (Bateman et al., 1963, pp. 5, 6). From the chemical composition of the more siliceous plutonic rocks, Bateman et al. have inferred water pressures of around 5 kb, such as might develop under a cover upward of 15 km in thickness. Loomis (1966, p. 243) estimates the thickness of cover as about 8 km.

Contact metamorphism at the western margin. Contact effects of the older intrusions along the western border of the batholith are illustrated by the observations of Best (1963, pp. 114-120) in the Indian Gulch quadrangle (1 in Fig. 6-12). Here there is an outer zone in which basic metavolcanics have recrystallized to the assemblage quartz-albite-epidote-hornblende. Associated pelites are graphitic muscovite-biotite phyllites with large andalusite porphyroblasts. This is the albite-epidote-hornfels facies of contact metamorphism. Nearer the contact the grade of metamorphism rises and the assemblages are those of the hornblende-hornfels facies: hornblende-plagioclase-sphene, and quartz-plagioclase-biotite-muscovite with andalusite, almandine, or cordierite. This is essentially the Orijärvi paragenesis, except that magnesian and calcareous assemblages are lacking.

At the contact with an outlying pluton at Bidwell Bar (2 in Fig. 6-12), the development of the hornblende-plagioclase assemblage in basic volcanics has been studied in more detail by Compton (1958). The parent rock outside the aureole is metabasalt ("greenstone") consisting of actinolite-albite-epidote-chlorite. In the outer part of the aureole this gives way to the first contact assemblage: hornblende-oligoclase (An_{26}), with minor epidote. Nearer the contact, epidote disappears completely; the final assemblage is hornblende-andesine (An_{38}), sometimes with minor diopside-hedenbergite. At the onset of metamorphism the Al_2O_3 content of the amphibole changes abruptly from $4\frac{1}{2}$ percent in the greenstone actinolite, to between 10 and 11 percent in the hornblendes of the two hornfels assemblages.[1] At the same time Fe_2O_3 increases from less than 1 percent in the actinolites, to 5 to 7 percent in hornblendes.

Contact metamorphism in pendants. In the axial roof pendants, the metavolcanic assemblage wherever present is—with a single recorded exception (Loomis, 1966)—hornblende-plagioclase (-diopside). So the pendant assemblages, like those on the western flanks of the older plutons, belong to the hornblende-hornfels facies. But, as first realized by Rose (1958), the associated pelitic and calcareous assemblages in some pendants

---

[1]This important change can be detected optically. In actinolite outside the aureole, $\gamma = 1.645$, $2V_x = 77$ to $80°$; in hornblendes within the aureole, $\gamma = 1.670$ to 1.680, $2V_x = 64$ to $69°$.

include some that are generally regarded as marking a higher metamorphic grade—that of the pyroxene-hornfels facies. Such are

Calcite-forsterite
Calcite-forsterite-periclase (now transformed to brucite)
Biotite-andalusite-microcline-quartz
Biotite-cordierite-andalusite-microcline-quartz

In other pendants none of these high-grade assemblages is present. The paragenesis of the Sierran pendants is illustrated below by reference to specific examples.

(a) Northeast of Visalia (3 in Fig. 6-12) is an enclosed strip of metasediments and metavolcanics 50 km by 2 to 8 km, the mineralogy of which was recorded by Durrell (1940). The principal assemblages (cf. Fig. 6-13) are as follows:

A. Pelitic
    1. Quartz-biotite-andalusite-muscovite-orthoclase-plagioclase. Potash feldspar appears to be replacing muscovite.
    2. Quartz-orthoclase-cordierite-biotite-sillimanite (or andalusite). Almandine is present in some rocks.

B. Calcareous (cf. also simpler assemblages, Fig. 6-13b)
    3. Calcite-wollastonite-diopside (-plagioclase)
    4. Calcite-wollastonite-diopside-grossularite
    5. Calcite-diopside-grossularite (-plagioclase)
    6. Quartz-wollastonite-diopside (-grossularite)
    7. Quartz-wollastonite-diopside (-plagioclase or zoisite)
    8. Quartz-diopside-labradorite-hornblende
    9. Calcite-forsterite, with minor but not obviously secondary brucite and talc

Vesuvianite and/or clinozoisite may appear in assemblages 4 and 7. The absence of tremolite is striking and bears out the relatively high metamorphic grade indicated by association of microcline with andalusite and cordierite in pelitic hornfelses.

C. Basic
    10. Hornblende-plagioclase (andesine or labradorite)
    11. Hornblende-plagioclase-diopside
    12. Hornblende-bytownite-almandine

D. Magnesian; deficient in silica
    13. Enstatite-forsterite-chlorite[1]-spinel. This is metamorphosed serpentinite.
    14. Hornblende-hypersthene-spinel

(b) In an extensive pendant near Isabella (4 in Fig. 6-12) the rocks are mainly pelitic. There are some associated basic and calcareous assem-

[1] Approximately $Mg_{5\frac{1}{4}}Al_{\frac{1}{4}}(Al_{\frac{1}{4}}Si_{3\frac{1}{4}}O_{10})(OH)_8$.

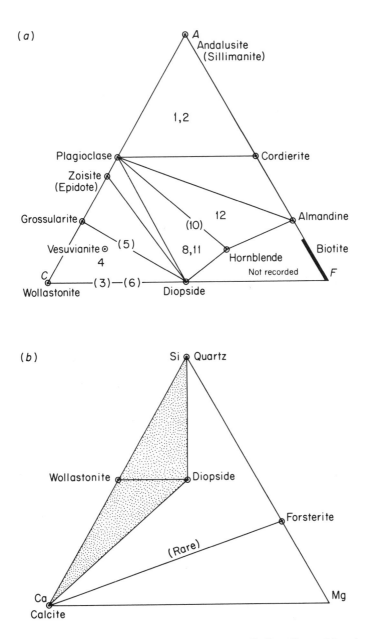

Fig. 6-13. Hornblende-hornfels facies, near Visalia, Sierra Nevada, California. (*a*) *ACF* diagram. Quartz and plagioclase are possible additional phases. K-feldspar may occur (sometimes with muscovite) in assemblages of triangle 1, 2. (*b*) Simple assemblages (stippled triangles and ties) in marbles.

blages typical of the hornblende-hornfels facies. Best and Weiss (1964) have recognized four zones of progressive metamorphism of pelitic rocks, the grade increasing from deep within the pendant toward the exposed contacts with the enclosing granodiorite. Typical assemblages in order of increasing grade, are:

1. Quartz-muscovite-chlorite-hematite.[1] This is the preintrusive regional metamorphic assemblage.
2. Quartz-muscovite-biotite-andalusite-ilmenite.[1]
3. Quartz-biotite-andalusite (sillimanite)-oligoclase-microcline-ilmenite.
4. Quartz-biotite-sillimanite-cordierite-plagioclase ($An_{20}-An_{37}$)-microcline-ilmenite. Almandine may also be present or may occur to the exclusion of cordierite.

Increase in metamorphic grade is here accompanied by decreasing oxidation of iron. In assemblage 2, ilmenite appears in place of hematite and remains the sole iron-oxide phase to the highest grade of metamorphism. In biotites the oxidation ratio (molecular)

$$\frac{2FeO_3 \times 100}{2Fe_2O_3 + FeO}$$

decreases from 17.8 in assemblage 2 to 11.0 in assemblage 3 to between 1.9 and 4.2 in assemblages 4. Figure 6-14 is an $A'F'M'$ plot of coexisting analysed biotites, cordierites, and garnets in three high-grade quartz-ilmenite-bearing assemblages of type 4 above:

Biotite-sillimanite-almandine-perthite-plagioclase (An_{25}) (stippled triangle a)
Biotite-sillimanite-cordierite-perthite-plagioclase ($An_{21}-An_{30}$) (stippled triangle b)
Biotite-andalusite-cordierite-almandine-plagioclase ($An_{24}-An_{37}$) (quadrilateral c bounded by broken lines)

(c) Calcareous rocks, mainly derivatives of limestone rather than dolomite, are widely distributed in roof pendants of the High Sierra. Such, for example, are the groups of pendants, each typically not more than 1 to 3 km in length, at Twin Lakes (Chesterman, 1942), Ebbett Pass (Parker, 1959), and May Lake (Rose, 1958). These are respectively numbered 5, 6, and 7 in Fig. 6-12. The calcareous assemblages (Fig. 6-15) for the most part are those considered to be typical of higher grades in the hornblende-hornfels facies. Each area has the following additional peculiar characteristics.

At Twin Lakes the pelitic assemblage is quartz-biotite-muscovite-feldspar. Hornblendic assemblages are not widely developed, but pargasite

---

[1]Composition of accompanying feldspars not recorded.

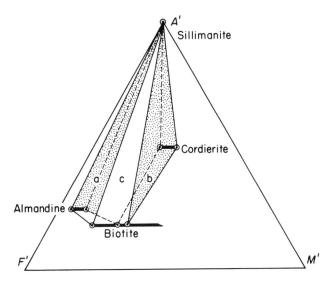

Fig. 6-14. Hornblende-hornfels facies, Isabella pendant, Sierra Nevada, California. $A'F'M'$ diagram for high-grade pelitic assemblages. Quartz, ilmenite, microcline, and plagioclase are possible additional phases.

or tremolite appears in some calcareous rocks, and there are skarns rich in hornblende and epidote. Calcite marble and dolomitic marble are widespread. Some of the simple parageneses recorded at individual localities are shown in Fig. 6-15a to c. The diopside-calcite assemblage is common. Tremolite is present only locally; in one locality (cf. Fig. 6-15b) the tremolite-calcite pair is closely associated with diopside-calcite and wollastonite-calcite. Silica-deficient calcareous rocks consist of multiphase combinations of calcite, spinel, clinohumite, pargasite, vesuvianite, bytownite, clintonite, and brucite (coarse individual tables). Locally, dolomite has been converted to calcite-periclase-forsterite (Fig. 6-15d); periclase is now completely replaced by brucite, and forsterite has been partly converted to antigorite. Assemblages in calc-silicate hornfelses and skarns are shown in Fig. 6-15c.

At Ebbett Pass (Fig. 6-16) the quartzo-feldspathic assemblages are

1. Quartz-plagioclase-biotite-muscovite (-microcline)
2. Quartz-plagioclase-hornblende (-microcline)
3. Quartz-plagioclase-diopside (-scapolite)

Scapolite is widespread in calcareous assemblages with grossularite, diopside, and in some cases vesuvianite. Some variation in metamorphic grade is indicated by limitation of the low-grade assemblage calcite-tremolite-quartz (Fig. 6-15a) to part of one pendant, and localization of

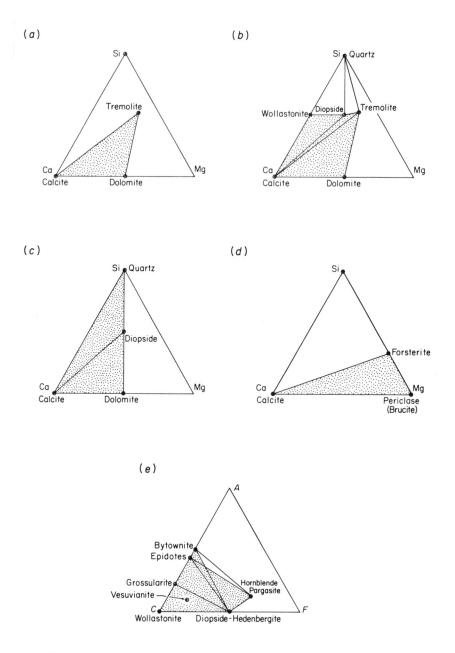

Fig. 6-15. Hornblende-hornfels facies, Twin Lakes pendants, Sierra Nevada, California. Observed assemblages.(stippled triangles and ties) at individual localities. (*a*) to (*d*) in marbles; (*e*) in calcsilicate hornfelses and skarns (quartz and phlogopite are possible additional phases).

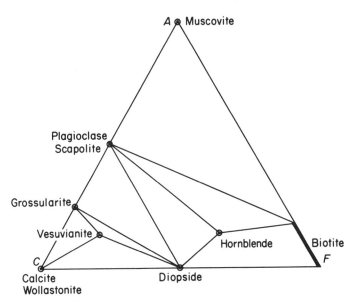

Fig. 6-16. Hornblende-hornfels facies, Ebbett Pass pendant, Sierra Nevada, California. Assemblages in rocks with excess SiO_2 and K_2O. Quartz and (less often) microcline are possible additional phases.

the high-grade wollastonite-bearing assemblages (Fig. 6-15e) in another.

At May Lake, tremolite-bearing rocks are absent, and rocks with wollastonite and diopside (Fig. 6-15e) widespread. Calcite-chondrodite-spinel and calcite-clinohumite-brucite are present; but in the latter assemblage there is no textural evidence that brucite was preceded by periclase. While the metabasaltic assemblage is hornblende-plagioclase-biotite, pelitic rocks consist of cordierite-andalusite-biotite-microcline-quartz. It was from this association that Rose (1958) concluded that "the andalusite-cordierite-microcline assemblage can form in the amphibolite[1] facies, and the transition between this and the assemblage muscovite-biotite-quartz occurs well below the upper limit of the amphibolite[1] facies."

Santa Rosa Aureoles, Nevada

In the Santa Rosa Range, northern Nevada, upper Triassic meta-sediments were invaded in late Cretaceous time by a number of steep-sided cross-cutting granodiorite and tonalite plutons. One of these is the Santa Rosa stock, whose elliptical outcrop covers an area of 90 km². The invaded Triassic rocks, previously affected by minimum-grade regional meta-

[1] Here termed the hornblende-hornfels facies.

morphism (greenschist facies), have been completely reconstituted under the thermal influence of the Santa Rosa stock within 1 to 2 km of the plutonic contacts. The effects of contact metamorphism adjacent to the Santa Rosa plutons have been documented in unusual detail by Compton (1960). He estimates cover at the time of metamorphism as between 3 and 8 km thick, with 3 km ($P_l = 1$ kb) as the most probable value.

The mineral paragenesis in the outer and intermediate zones of the aureole is mostly normal for the hornblende-hornfels facies (Fig. 6-17). The ubiquitous basic mineral assemblage is hornblende-plagioclase. In the purer calcareous rocks, calcite-quartz is stable. Pelitic rocks show a prolific development of aluminum silicates reflecting a generally high content of Al_2O_3. They consist of the following combinations:

1. Cordierite-biotite
2. Cordierite-andalusite-biotite   } Plus quartz-muscovite-
3. Staurolite-andalusite-biotite   plagioclase
4. Andalusite-biotite

Cordierite and staurolite are mutually exclusive. The many chemical analyses that are available reveal no obvious correlation between the occurrence of these phases and the chemical composition of the total rock. The absence of andalusite in assemblage 1 has been shown by Compton to be due to relatively high CaO and low Al_2O_3 compared with assemblage 2. Consequently, plagioclase has crystallized in greater quantity and andalusite has been suppressed. Mean *AFM* values calculated from Compton's data are 20, 40, 20 for cordierite-biotite, and 42, 35, 22 for cordierite-andalusite assemblages.

Close to the contacts, staurolite no longer appears. At the same time muscovite, and to a lesser extent biotite, begin to break down toward the ideal high-temperature assemblage, quartz-plagioclase-microcline-cordierite-sillimanite. In this inner zone wollastonite appears in place of calcite-quartz in calcareous rocks relatively low in alumina. The paragenesis approximates that of Fig. 6-13a.

Significant changes in the oxidation ratio $(2Fe_2O_3 \times 100)/(2Fe_2O_3 + FeO)$ accompany progressive metamorphism in the Santa Rosa aureoles.[1] The mean value in the regional schists beyond the aureole is 17.6 (these rocks contain graphite as well as ores). It rises to 24 (and simultaneously graphite is eliminated) in the outer zone of the aureole and then falls in the inner zone to 12. Possibly high values favor crystallization of staurolite; for this mineral is not found in the inner aureole, and the value for staurolite-andalusite assemblages is somewhat higher than that for cordierite-andalusite assemblages (24 versus 16 as computed from Compton's table 4). Analyses of staurolite listed by Deer, Howie, and

---

[1] Values calculated from Compton (1960, p. 1403, table 3).

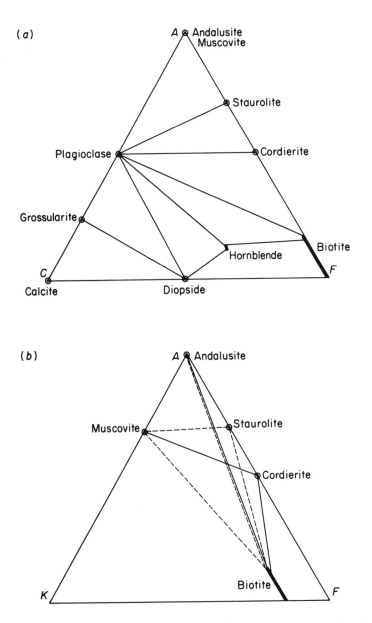

Fig. 6-17. Hornblende-hornfels facies, Santa Rosa stocks, Nevada (intermediate zone of aureole). (*a*) *ACF* diagram for rocks with excess SiO₂ and deficient in K₂O. Quartz is a possible additional phase. (*b*) *AKF* diagram for rocks with excess SiO₂ and Al₂O₃. Quartz and plagioclase are possible additional phases. Broken lines show staurolite-bearing assemblages.

Zussman (1962, pp. 154-155) show consistently a high oxidation ratio (17 to 35).

Suian District, Korea

An interesting zoned paragenesis of contact metamorphism in the aureole of the Suian granodiorite, Korea, has been described by Watanabe (1943). The intrusive body is a stock 100 km^2 in the area of outcrop, cutting Proterozoic and Paleozoic sediments, mainly dolomites and limestones. The aureole in places is 1 km in width. The following sequence of assemblages, developed in siliceous and pure dolomites, marks a series of zones of progressive contact metamorphism:

1. From 1000 to 500 m from the contact:
   Dolomite-tremolite-calcite
2. Between 500 and 200 m from the contact:
   Dolomite-forsterite-calcite
   Diopside-forsterite
3. From 200 to 50 m from the contact, the assemblages of zone 2 have been affected by boron-fluorine metasomatism giving, in addition to dolomite and forsterite, such minerals as clinohumite, chondrodite, kotoite and ludwigite.
4. At distances of 50 m or less from the contact:
   Calcite-brucite (pseudomorphous after periclase)
   Calcite-forsterite (clinohumite)-brucite

Associated pelitic rocks of zone 1 are spotted biotite phyllites. These pass into biotite hornfels (zone 2) and ultimately, in zone 4 into high-grade assemblages such as andalusite-cordierite-biotite-orthoclase-quartz and silica-deficient andalusite-corundum-spinel-orthoclase. Hornfelses derived from basic igneous rock consist of hornblende-plagioclase (-biotite) even in the zone of brucite-forsterite marble.

The Suian aureole is one of the few instances in which forsterite has been recorded developing directly from calcite-tremolite in a contact aureole. This, too, is another instance of the assemblage calcite-forsterite-periclase being formed prior to the breakdown of plagioclase-hornblende in associated basic hornfelses.

Calc-magnesian Skarns, Skye, Scotland

In the Broadford area of Skye, the Beinn an Dubhaich granite boss, several square kilometers in cross section, has developed a contact aureole in Cambrian dolomitic limestone and dolomite (Harker, 1904, pp. 141-151). In the outer part of the aureole, up to over 1 km from the contact, Tilley (1948) has recorded the successive development (with advancing grade) of the assemblages shown in Fig. 6-18a to c. The starting materials in every case were dolomite and silica, the latter in the form of chert nodules and

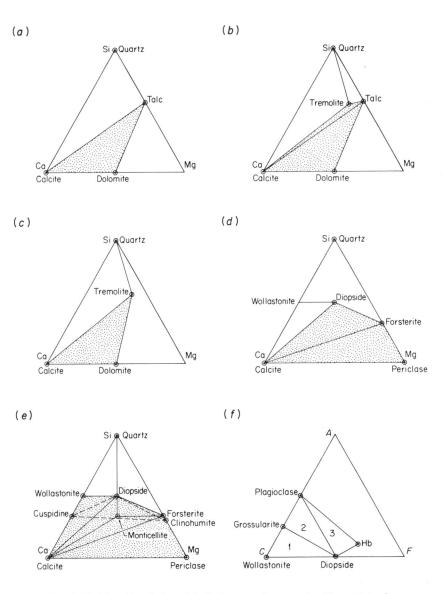

Fig. 6-18. Hornblende-hornfels facies, granite aureole, Skye (*Data from C. E. Tilley*, 1951.) (*a*) to (*c*) Successive stages in metamorphism of dolomite, outer zone of aureole. (*d*) High-grade dolomite assemblages, inner zone of aureole. (*e*) Skarn assemblages, inner aureole (phase assemblages in compositional triangle quartz-diopside-forsterite are not present). (*f*) Silica-saturated assemblages of skarns (1, 2) and associated metadiabase (3). Stippled areas in all diagrams are silica-deficient assemblages.

sponge forms. Critical assemblages of the three early stages of metamorphism are

1. Talc-calcite-quartz
2. Tremolite-talc-calcite
3. Tremolite-calcite-dolomite

The high-grade assemblages in the inner aureole (Tilley, 1951, pp. 623-624) are those of Fig. 6-18d. Although Tilley lists the order of appearance as talc, tremolite, forsterite, diopside, this writer can find no evidence in the literature as to whether elimination of tremolite was by reaction with dolomite to give calcite-forsterite, or by reaction with calcite to give diopside-dolomite. The first alternative is implied by Tilley's sequence of steps. The second is more consistent with thermochemical data.

Close to the granite contacts, reaction between flint nodules and enclosing dolomite has been accompanied by outward diffusion of Si and inward diffusion of Mg and Ca. Each nodule, plus a peripheral envelope of dolomite, has thus been converted into a compositionally zoned aggregate. The assemblages are those on the quartz-dolomite join of Fig. 6-18d, from within outward:

Quartz-diopside
Diopside
Diopside-forsterite
Forsterite-calcite

At various points along the granite contact, zoned skarns have developed by outward diffusion of Si, Al, Fe from the granitic magma. This seems to have been effected by the continuous outward flow of an aqueous gas carrying fluorine and boron as additional components. The outward sequence (a few inches in total width) from the granite contact may be represented in its simplest form as follows: (This neglects magnetite and a number of special fluorine- and boron-bearing phases locally introduced at a later stage.)

Grossularite-wollastonite or hedenbergite-plagioclase
Dark clinopyroxene
Light clinopyroxene (poorer in Al and Fe)
Clinopyroxene-monticellite (-spinel)
Forsterite (-clinohumite-spinel)
Calcite-forsterite

The skarn paragenesis conforms in its simpler and principal aspects to that represented for silica-deficient assemblages in Fig. 6-18e (stippled) and for quartz-bearing assemblages (inner skarn zones) in Fig. 6-18f. The presence of the "high-grade" phases monticellite, periclase, and cuspidine—minerals commonly considered to represent very high metamorphic temperatures (sanidinite facies)—is strong evidence that P_{H_2O} was consistently maintained at a level high enough to reduce P_{CO_2} to low values.

Where primarily zoned chert replacements occur in the skarn zone, the sequence of assemblages has been modified by inward migration of Ca to such as the following (again from within outward):

Quartz

Quartz-wollastonite

Wollastonite

Cuspidine-diopside-calcite

Diopside

Forsterite (-clinohumite)

Diopside-cuspidine-clinohumite-magnetite

Quartz-wollastonite

Wollastonite

Cuspidine-diopside

Monticellite (calcite)

Contact Metamorphism of Siliceous Dolomite, Granite Peak, Montana

The Granite Peak stock of Lewis and Clark County, Montana, is one of a series of late Cretaceous or early Tertiary granitic plutons intruded into initially unmetamorphosed later Precambrian sediments. The Marysville stock, whose aureole was described in Chap. 1, belongs to the same group of intrusions. In composition the Granite Peak stock is essentially granitic. Its outcrop is about $2\frac{1}{2}$ km in diameter. Where it cuts the Helena dolomite formation, there is a contact aureole whose maximum width of outcrop is 1 km; but field evidence suggests a dipping contact, so that the true width of the aureole may be only 300 m. The aureole has been described by Melson (1966) from whose publication the above details and those relating to metamorphic paragenesis have been taken.

The Helena dolomite is banded on the scale of a hand specimen. Alternating beds, a centimeter or two in thickness, are of two main kinds: dolomite-calcite-quartz with minor "illite" and chlorite; and argillaceous assemblages containing abundant "illite," detrital micas, clay minerals, quartz, and some carbonates. Metamorphism was essentially isochemical. Reactions at the first stages, as represented today by assemblages on the fringe of the aureole, are thought to have been controlled by partial pressures of water and CO_2 that varied from bed to bed as dictated by the relative proportions of clay minerals and carbonates.

The carbonate-quartz beds in the aureole have been converted to three- and four-phase assemblages that are combinations of quartz, dolomite, calcite, tremolite, diopside, wollastonite. Minor sphene and clinozoisite are ubiquitous, K-feldspar and/or phlogopite less frequent. Various combinations of these phases with phologopite, K-feldspar, plagioclase, and (at highest grades) cordierite appear in the accompanying pelitic beds.

In the purer carbonate-quartz layers the silicate phases appear, as

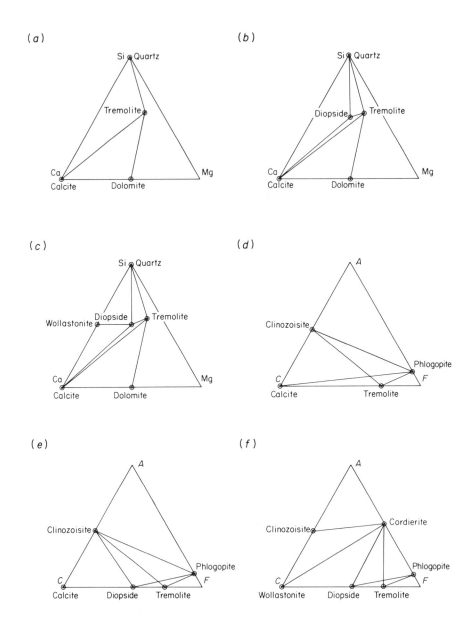

Fig. 6-19. Hornblende-hornfels facies, Granite Peak aureole, Montana. (*After W. G. Melson.*) (*a*) to (*c*) Assemblages in the triangle Calcite-Dolomite-Silica. (*d*) to (*f*) *ACF* diagrams for carbonate and agillaceous rocks with excess silica. Quartz and plagioclase are additional phases (K-feldspar in all but the tremolite assemblages of *f*). (*a*): transition zone; (*b*), (*d*), (*e*): outer zone; (*c*), (*f*): inner zone.

216

the contact is approached, in the order tremolite, diopside, wollastonite. In the more argillaceous bands there are parallel reactions leading to the appearance of phlogopite in the outer aureole (by reactions involving illite and chlorite) and cordierite in the innermost zone. Corresponding phase diagrams are shown in Fig. 6-19. The approximate distances of the corresponding zonal boundaries from the outcrop of the contact (as plotted on the map) are as follows:

a. Transition zone, a few meters wide
    1. Tremolite-calcite-quartz
b. Outer contact zone, 600 to 100 m
    1. Tremolite-diopside-quartz
    2. Tremolite-calcite-quartz
    3. Diopside-calcite-quartz
c. Inner contact zone, 100 to 0 m
    1. Tremolite-diopside-quartz
    2. Diopside-calcite-wollastonite
    3. Diopside-wollastonite-quartz

Melson (1966, p. 417) visualizes two parallel reaction sequences respectively controlling the mineralogy of carbonate-quartz and argillaceous beds:

Transition zones
a. Dolomite-quartz-H_2O → Tremolite-calcite-CO_2
b. Illite-calcite-quartz → Tremolite-K-feldspar-clinozoisite-H_2O-CO_2
Outer zone (outer portion):
a. Tremolite-quartz-calcite → Diopside-CO_2-H_2O
b. Dolomite-quartz → Diopside-CO_2 (in initially anhydrous beds)
c. Illite-calcite-quartz → Tremolite-phlogopite-clinozoisite-H_2O-CO_2
Outer zone (inner portion):
a. Tremolite- K-feldspar → Diopside-phlogopite-quartz
b. Calcite-phlogopite-quartz → Diopside-K-feldspar-H_2O-CO_2
Inner zone:
a. Calcite-quartz → Wollastonite-CO_2
b. Clinozoisite-diopside-quartz → Wollastonite-cordierite-H_2O.

Most of the assemblages described conform to the requirements of the phase rule for divariant equilibrium as discussed in Chap. 2. Occasional four-phase mineral assemblages in metamorphosed carbonate-quartz bands, notably tremolite-calcite-diopside-quartz, are consistent with univariant equilibrium.[1] They are here interpreted in this way; for local assemblages corresponding to some point on a curve of univariant

[1] Melson (1966, p. 413) treats the problem in an unnecessarily complicated way by assigning various degrees of mobility to participating components according to Korzhinski's approach, currently fashionable among some petrologists.

equilibrium (in this case Tremolite + 2 Quartz + 3 Calcite ⇌ 5 Diopside + H_2O + 3 CO_2) are to be expected in an aureole of progressive metamorphism involving steady outward flow of CO_2 and water.

For reasons set out in a later section of this chapter, dealing with temperature-pressure gradients in contact aureoles, the whole sequence of mineral assemblages in the Granite Peak aureole is assigned (not in complete agreement with Melson's conclusions) to the hornblende-hornfels facies ($P = 1$ to $1\frac{1}{2}$ kb; $T = 400$ to $650°$; cf. Fig. 6-35).

Hornblende-Hornfels Facies in Regional Metamorphism

Ryoke metamorphic belt, Japan. The hornblende-hornfels facies is represented on a grand scale by some of the metamorphic belts of Japan. The best known of these is the Ryoke belt, 50 km wide, extending 1000 km or more along the southwestern border of the principal islands of Honsyu, Sikoku, and Kyusyu (Fig. 6-20). Among many accounts of these rocks, reference is made particularly to those of Miyashiro (1958) and Suwa (1961). Metamorphism in the Ryoke belt is believed to have occurred in the middle Cretaceous. The belt is the site of many granitic intrusions; but the current view is that these have no direct relation to the pattern of progressive metamorphism, which is truly regional. Amphibolites are abundant throughout the whole belt and the amphibolite assemblages are the principal basis for recognition and mapping of four zones of progressive metamorphism. The essential mineral assemblages, as far as it is possible to generalize for so vast an area, are summarized in Table 6-1. They are typical in every respect of the hornblende-hornfels facies (albite-epidote-hornfels facies in zone 1). Transition to the pyroxene-hornfels (or possibly the granulite) facies is shown by local rare occurrence of higher-grade amphibolites consisting of bytownite-hornblende(brown)-cummingtonite (-diopside-hypersthene-olivine-spinel).

Additional details providing a useful clue as to possible pressure-temperature conditions in the fourth zone in a portion of the Abukuma region are given by Miyashiro (1958, pp. 243, 246, 267):

1. At the highest grade of metamorphism, muscovite has been eliminated in favor of sillimanite-K-feldspar.

2. The marble beds are only 1 to 10 m thick and are enclosed in semipelitic gneiss. Therefore internal partial pressure of water could have been maintained at a high level relative to P_{CO_2} during decarbonation reactions. The common assemblage here is calcite-wollastonite-diopside-grossularite, with calcite greatly predominant. Rarely, dolomite is also present; then the metamorphic assemblage is some combination of the phases calcite-dolomite-tremolite-diopside-forsterite-phlogopite-graphite. These calcareous assemblages indicate reactions at high P_{H_2O}/P_{CO_2} (cf. Figs. 4-18, 4-19).

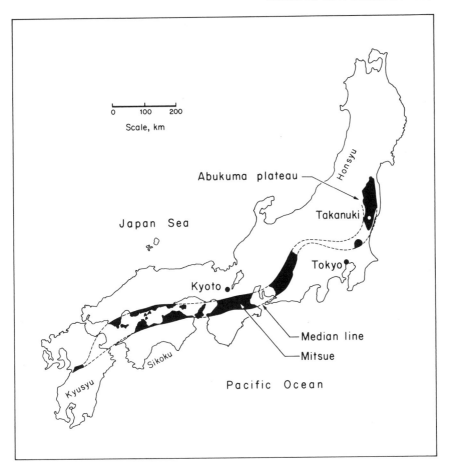

Fig. 6-20. The Ryoke metamorphic belt of Japan, showing areas studied intensively by *A. Miyashiro* (Abukuma) and by *K. Suwa* (Mitsue).

3. The oxidation ratio both in biotites and in hornblendes drops markedly with increasing metamorphic grade.

In the Mitzue region of the Ryoke belt (Suwa, 1961) metamorphism occurs mainly in the third and fourth zones. The andalusite → sillimanite transition occurs in the lower-grade part of zone 4. Small amounts of muscovite persist throughout. The appearance of cordierite and K-feldspar in abundance is thought by both writers to be due to reaction between muscovite, biotite, and quartz; evidently at temperatures lower than those of the muscovite-quartz ⇌ sillimanite-orthoclase equilibrium.

Table 6-1. Mineral assemblages of Ryoke metamorphic belt, Japan. Grade increasing, zone 1 → zone 4 (after A. Myashiro and K. Suwa)

Zone	1	2	3	4
Pelitic assemblages	Quartz-albite-biotite-chlorite Rare muscovite, spessartite-almandine ($Mn/Fe = 1$)	Quartz-andesine-biotite (-muscovite) Rare K-feldspar, andalusite, almandine ($Mn/Fe = 0.8 - 0.5$),	Quartz-andesine-biotite (-muscovite-almandine-K-feldspar) Rare andalusite, cordierite (Mn/Fe in garnet $= 0.2$)	Quartz-andesine-K-feldspar-biotite (-sillimanite-almandine) Rare cordierite
Basic assemblages	Albite-chlorite-actinolite-epidote (-calcite) Rare quartz, biotite	Andesine-hornblende (-epidote-sphene-chlorite) Rare diopside, biotite, quartz	Labradorite-hornblende (-diopside) Rare cummingtonite, biotite, quartz	Bytownite-hornblende-diopside (-cummingtonite) Rare quartz
Calcareous assemblages	Calcite-actinolite-quartz Rare K-feldspar, epidote	Diopside-epidote (-calcite-quartz-hornblende-sphene) Same assemblage with grossularite instead of epidote Rare K-feldspar	Diopside-grossularite (-calcite-hornblende-sphene) Rare quartz, K-feldspar	Diopside-grossularite-wollastonite (-hornblende-sphene) Rare calcite, K-feldspar

Hercynian metamorphism, Pyrenees and northern Portugal. The hornblende-hornfels facies is developed on a regional scale in Paleozoic sediments affected by Hercynian metamorphism in the central Pyrenees, as described by Zwart (1962; 1963). In one area, in the vicinity of Bosost, concentric zones, with the grade of metamorphism rising inward, occupy a thermal high approximately 10 × 5 km. Granitic rocks, usually strongly gneissic, are liberally developed in the central high-grade zone. The Aston and Hospitalet massifs some 50 miles east of Bosost are more deeply eroded complexes of a similar kind. Here a granite-gneiss and migmatite body some 30 km in diameter is bordered by metasediments mineralogically similar to those of the Bosost area and showing the same pattern of concentric zoning. The metamorphic rocks extend for many kilometers beyond the granitic gneiss boundary. In both regions the zones mapped by Zwart are based on the successive development in quartz-bearing pelitic rocks of the assemblages

1. Biotite-muscovite
2. Biotite-staurolite-andalusite-cordierite (less often garnet)
3. Biotite-cordierite-sillimanite

Rocks in zones 2 and 3 are porphyroblastic. Zwart relates porphyroblastic growth of each index mineral to some limited range of time within a prolonged sequence of deformational events recorded in each rock by cleavages, foliations, lineations, and rotation axes. From this study he concludes that the higher-grade rocks are polymetamorphic. As well as the "stable" minerals after which the zones are named, the rock may include unstable relict minerals representing the preceding equilibria either as undestroyed biotite-muscovite matrix or as rotated and partially destroyed porphyroblasts. Whether the reader accepts this ingenious correlation between crystallization and deformation or not, multiphase assemblages such as quartz-muscovite-biotite-cordierite-sillimanite-staurolite in zone 3 are unlikely to represent equilibrium. Zwart's sequence of three- to five-phase assemblages is, on the other hand, consistent with the requirements of divariant equilibrium, provided the associated "relict" minerals are neglected.

On stratigraphic and tectonic grounds, Zwart estimates the thickness of cover at the culmination of metamorphism as not greater than 5 km, corresponding to load pressures of less than 1 to 2 kb. He interprets the granitic gneisses and migmatites as products of granitization at a focus of thermal culmination. Alternatively it seems possible that intrusions of granitic magma may have been the primary cause of metamorphism.

In northern Portugal a similar pattern of Hercynian regional metamorphism had been recognized by Brink (1960). Here there is a broad zone of low-grade syntectonic metamorphism in lower Paleozoic sediments. More local, but still regional, are three zones concentric about contacts with posttectonic intrusive granitic plutons, whose index minerals, in order of increasing grade, are (1) biotite, (2) andalusite, and (3) sillimanite. In the Vila Real district the corresponding pelitic assemblages are

1. Quartz-biotite-muscovite (albite)
2. Quartz-biotite-muscovite-andalusite (albite-oligoclase)
3. Quartz-muscovite-sillimanite, localized very close to the contacts

Elsewhere, in the Viseu district, the zones are wider and staurolite occurs in the andalusite zone. Brink (1960, especially pp. 41-44, 129-131) recognizes an affinity with the Buchan type of metamorphism (described below), and emphasizes the close connection between the higher grades (zones 2, 3) and intrusion of granitic plutons.

Transition from hornblende-hornfels to amphibolite facies. In northeastern Scotland along the northern coast of Aberdeenshire and Banffshire (cf. Fig. 1-10) the pattern of progressive regional metamorphism of Dalradian sediments differs in several respects from that in Barrow's classic Dalradian zones some 80 to 100 km south. The two patterns are today distinguished as the *Buchan* (northern) and *Barrovian* (southern) types of regional metamorphism. Details of the Buchan pattern are obscured by paucity of outcrop, except along the coastal section, and by posttectonic effects in the vicinity of "Newer Granite" plutons. There is also the possibility, suggested by Chinner (1966), that the presence of sillimanite (sometimes with microcline) in andalusite- or kyanite-bearing assemblages is the result of a late thermal overprint closely following the principal metamorphic episode reflected in the Buchan pattern.

In spite of such uncertainties, some of the pelitic assemblages, as described by Harker (1932, pp. 230-235), Read (1952), and Chinner (1966, pp. 163-164), show transitional features between the respective parageneses of the hornblende-hornfels and the amphibolite facies. Many rocks show little or no evidence of internal deformation.[1] Texturally they resemble hornfelses of contact aureoles. Typical metamorphic assemblages in order of increasing grade are:

1. Muscovite-biotite-quartz (-oligoclase)
2. In Chinner's andalusite zone
   (a) Andalusite-cordierite-staurolite-biotite-muscovite-quartz-oligoclase
   (b) Andalusite-almandine-biotite-muscovite-quartz-oligoclase
3. In Chinner's kyanite zone, Kyanite (-andalusite)-almandine-biotite-muscovite-quartz-oligoclase.

Assemblages 2 and 3 collectively span a field transition from the hornblende-hornfels to the amphibolite facies. This is marked by development of

---

[1] For this reason Harker (1932) invoked "deficient shearing stress" as an essential factor in metamorphism of the Buchan type.

almandine and kyanite at maximum grades at the expense of cordierite and andalusite in the lower grades of metamorphism.

Calcareous assemblages of the transition zone include calcite-diopside-phlogopite and calcite-diopside-actinolite-epidote-quartz.

The same transitional facies is probably represented in some contact aureoles, e.g., the inner zone of the aureole surrounding the main Donegal granite, northwest Ireland (Chap. 1, pp. 10–11). Here kyanite appears in association with andalusite or sillimanite, and almandine and staurolite are unusually prevalent in pelitic hornfelses.

Review of Mineralogical Characteristics of the Hornblende-hornfels Facies

We are now in a position to review and amplify the definition of the facies given at the outset of this discussion (p. 193).

1. The principal phases in derivatives of basic rocks are invariably hornblende and plagioclase. The latter may have any composition between albite and anorthite; An_{25} to An_{40} is a common range, but such plagioclase, in contrast with that of the amphibolite facies, is not accompanied by epidote minerals.

2. Pelitic rocks seldom contain chlorite except as a retrogressive phase replacing biotite or cordierite. On entering the hornblende-hornfels facies, pelitic rocks immediately crystallize to biotite, muscovite, and an aluminous phase. Potash feldspar appears only in rocks low in Al_2O_3 and lacking aluminous minerals other than micas.

3. The typical aluminous phases in pelitic rocks are andalusite and cordierite. Almandine and staurolite, though not so widespread as cordierite, are nevertheless found in some rocks having a high ratio of FeO/MgO. They are indices of rock composition rather than (as was once thought) pressure or nonhydrostatic stress.

4. Andalusite is highly characteristic of this facies. Where temperatures may be inferred to be higher than normal—e.g., in proximity to igneous contacts—the place of andalusite may be taken by sillimanite. So widespread and characteristic is andalusite that it may be used as a pressure index, limiting the probable pressure field of the hornblende-hornfels facies to less than about 3 kb (cf. Fig. 4-1).

5. The characteristic mineral assemblages in marbles derived from siliceous dolomites and limestones are

Quartz-calcite-tremolite Calcite-dolomite-tremolite	cf. Fig. 4-17a
Quartz-diopside-calcite Calcite-diopside-tremolite	cf. Fig. 4-17b
Calcite-diopside-dolomite	cf. Fig. 4-17c

Where higher temperature or lower P_{CO_2} than normal may be inferred, we find such high-grade assemblages as

Calcite-wollastonite-diopside ⎫
Wollastonite-diopside-quartz ⎬ cf. Fig. 4-15b

Much more rarely these are accompanied by local development of

Calcite-diopside-forsterite ⎫
Calcite-forsterite-periclase (brucite) ⎬ cf. Fig. 4-15c, e.

Unusually high temperature may be inferred from proximity to plutonic contacts. Low values of P_{CO_2} are likely to be induced near contacts where water vapor continuously expelled from the crystallizing magma maintains P_{H_2O} at a high percentage of the total fluid pressure P_f. By the same mechanism, temperatures could be raised locally to above-average values. There is rather widespread direct evidence of the efficacy of magmatic gas in causing appearance of "high-temperature" minerals of this kind within the hornblende-hornfels facies. Thus wollastonite is commonly concentrated along joints. Forsterite and brucite (after periclase) appear in association with minerals carrying F, B, or OH—chondrodite, clinohumite, brucite, kotoite, scapolite. In the dolomitic skarns of Skye, the presence of monticellite and cuspidine reflects exceptionally low partial pressures of CO_2 in an environment where basic rocks were converted to plagioclase-hornblende-diopside. Persistence of the pervading aqueous phase during subsequent cooling is expressed in most such rocks by late crystallization of brucite, serpentine minerals and clintonite.

6. It has become increasingly clear that at maximum temperatures and low pressures within the hornblende-hornfels facies, muscovite-quartz breaks down to Al_2SiO_5 and K-feldspar. There is also evidence that biotite is beginning to react with quartz to give cordierite-bearing assemblages and that the stability temperature of staurolite has been exceeded (as in the Santa Rosa aureoles). Until recently (e.g., Turner and Verhoogen, 1960, p. 513), such assemblages as quartz-microcline-andalusite (or sillimanite)-cordierite were thought to be confined to the pyroxene-hornfels facies. Where they are associated with hornblende-plagioclase, they are here considered to mark the transition between the two facies (cf. Rose, 1958). Direct breakdown of muscovite-quartz to andalusite rather than to sillimanite suggests low values of load pressure, probably no greater than 1 to 3 kb.

7. Long recognized as a typical phase in magnesian assemblages of the hornblende-hornfels facies is anthophyllite (or cummingtonite). In classic examples from Orijärvi (Eskola, 1939, p. 353; Floyd, 1965, p. 236) and from Cornwall (Tilley, 1935; Floyd, 1965, p. 236) the molecular ratios MgO/FeO and $(MgO + FeO)/(Al_2O_3 + Fe_2O_3)$ are constantly high (respectively, 1.2–2 and 2–3). The oxidation ratio is uniformly low (commonly only 2–3). Contrasting sharply with these rocks are anthophyllite-

cordierite-biotite-andalusite assemblages from the Japanese Tôno aureole. Analyses cited by Seki (1957, p. 326) give MgO/FeO ratios as low as 0.4 and (MgO + FeO)/(Al$_2$O$_3$ + Fe$_2$O$_3$) only 0.5–0.6. Oxidation ratios in these rocks may be high (40 or more). In other aureoles such as those of the Sierra Nevada (California) and Santa Rosa (Nevada), anthophyllite is unknown in metasediments having similar A, C, F values to those of anthophyllite-bearing rocks elsewhere. The critical conditions—rock composition, P_{H_2O}, P_{O_2}, T, and so on—that determine the presence or absence of anthophyllite, are still unknown. However, it occurs chiefly in the hornblende-hornfels facies; and it is completely lacking in the pyroxene-hornfels facies.

PYROXENE-HORNFELS FACIES

Definition

The mineralogical characteristics of the pyroxene-hornfels facies are
1. Association of sillimanite (or andalusite) and cordierite with K-feldspar in pelitic rocks.
2. Absence of muscovite and more restricted occurrence of biotite than in the hornblende-hornfels facies.
3. Presence of diopside-hypersthene and absence of amphiboles in basic hornfelses.
4. Presence of wollastonite in calcic assemblages and of calcite-forsterite-periclase and calcite-forsterite-diopside in silica-poor dolomitic marbles.
5. Almandine garnet when present has a high Fe^{2+}/Mg ratio compared with that of granulite-facies assemblages. The typical magnesian phase is cordierite. Staurolite is unknown in the pyroxene-hornfels facies.

Field Occurrence

Rocks of this facies occur in the inner zones of contact aureoles. Favorable conditions are shallow depth of cover and high temperature (as inferred from proximity to plutonic contacts, particularly where the intrusive rock is basic or semibasic in composition). Mineralogically similar rocks in areas of regional metamorphism have distinctive features that place them in a low-pressure division of the granulite facies rather than in the pyroxene-hornfels facies proper.

Oslo Region, Norway

Goldschmidt's (1911) account of contact metamorphism in the Oslo district is one of the classics of petrology. The aureoles are developed round small plutons of essexite, sodic syenites, and granites where these cut Paleozoic pelitic, arenaceous, and calcareous sediments. In most aureoles the assemblages of the pyroxene-hornfels facies are confined to an inner zone which is flanked on the outside by rocks of the hornblende-hornfels facies. From stratigraphic evidence Goldschmidt computed the load pressure at the time of metamorphism as between 400 and 1000 bars. The Oslo paragenesis is of special interest in that it is the type of Eskola's original hornfels facies (now the pyroxene-hornfels facies). Goldschmidt recognized 10 principal assemblages (cf. Fig. 6-21a) any of which may contain both quartz and potash feldspar:

A. Pelitic and quartzo-feldspathic
    1. Quartz-orthoclase-andalusite-cordierite (-biotite)
    2. Quartz-orthoclase-plagioclase-andalusite-cordierite (-biotite)
    3. Quartz-orthoclase-plagioclase-cordierite (-biotite)
    4. Quartz-orthoclase-plagioclase-cordierite-hypersthene
B. Calcareous
    8. Plagioclase-diopside-grossularite
    9. Diopside-grossularite (-vesuvianite)
    10. Diopside-grossularite-wollastonite (-vesuvianite)

It has been generally assumed, following Goldschmidt (1911), that grossularite-quartz is stable in the pyroxene-hornfels facies. This combination is common enough in calcareous assemblages of the hornblende-hornfels facies. Moreover, such assemblages as grossularite-diopside-wollastonite and grossularite-diopside-plagioclase have been recorded in association with high-grade marbles (calcite-forsterite-diopside, calcite-forsterite-periclase) in the inner zones of some aureoles (e.g. Osborne, 1932). But most such rocks contain calcite and lack quartz. And although the grade of contact metamorphism is high, these grossularite-bearing assemblages are rarely, if ever, found in close association with the diagnostic basic assemblage plagioclase-diopside-hypersthene. Further ambiguity arises from the variable andradite content of metamorphic grossularite and the albite content of even the more calcic plagioclases. Anorthite-wollastonite, the chemically equivalent assemblage to grossularite-quartz, has long been considered characteristic of the sanidinite facies. Experimental reversal of the equilibrium

$$\text{Grossularite} + \text{Quartz} \rightleftharpoons \text{Anorthite} + \text{Wollastonite}$$

by Newton (1966) at $T = 600°C$, $P = 2\text{kb}$ supports the possibility that in the pyroxene-hornfels facies, the stable assemblage of *pure phases* is anorthite-wollastonite, not grossularite-quartz. Andesine-wollastonite-diopside has been recorded in association with grossularite-plagioclase assemblages in high-grade hornfelses of uncertain facies (Osborne, 1932, pp. 223-224; Harker, 1932, p. 94).

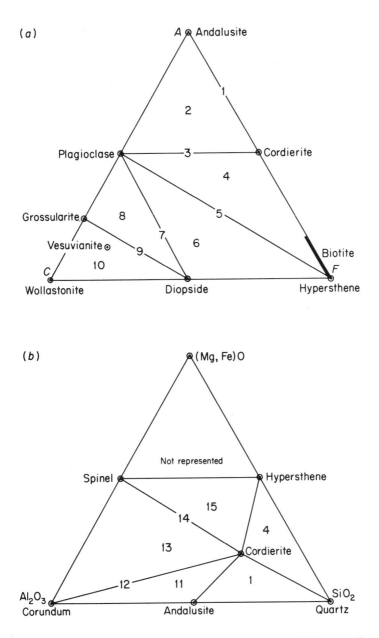

Fig. 6-21. Pyroxene-hornfels facies. (*a*) Oslo, Norway: *ACF* diagram for assemblages with excess SiO_2 and K_2O: quartz and potash feldspar are possible additional phases. (*b*) Comrie, Scotland: three-phase assemblages in aluminous rocks; orthoclase, biotite, and plagioclase are possible additional phases.

C. Basic

5. Plagioclase-hypersthene (-quartz)
6. Plagioclase-diopside-hypersthene (-quartz)
7. Plagioclase-diopside (-quartz)

Comrie Aureole, Scotland

In Chapter 1 (page 6) we saw how, in the vicinity of Comrie (Perthshire), the Carn Chois diorite pluton has imposed a zoned contact aureole on the adjacent low-grade phyllites and slates of the Dalradian series. Tilley's (1924) account of the mineralogy and chemistry of the resulting hornfelses in the innermost zone of the aureole is still one of the clearest discussions of high-grade contact metamorphism.

The dominant mineral assemblages are pelitic and semipelitic types carrying quartz and feldspar. They duplicate precisely corresponding assemblages in the Oslo aureoles (1 to 5 and 7 in Fig. 6-21a). Again the polymorph of Al_2SiO_5 is andalusite, and again muscovite has been eliminated in favor of andalusite-orthoclase. Basic igneous assemblages in the outer zone consist of hornblende-plagioclase-biotite (hornblende-hornfels facies). Within about 150-200 meters of the contact, this assemblage gives way to the typical assemblage of the pyroxene-hornfels facies—diopside-hypersthene-plagioclase.

There is also an interesting series of aluminous silica-deficient hornfelses in which corundum and spinel appear in place of, or associated with, andalusite and cordierite. These rocks generally contain orthoclase, plagioclase, biotite and magnetite as well. Recorded assemblages (cf. Fig. 6-21b) include

11. Andalusite-cordierite-corundum
12. Corundum-cordierite
13. Corundum-cordierite-spinel. This is the commonest assemblage
14. Cordierite-spinel
15. Cordierite-spinel-hypersthene

The high-temperature paragenesis of the Comrie aureole represents temperatures and pressures outside the stability fields not only of muscovite-quartz but of muscovite alone. Tilley finds clear evidence that biotite too is beginning to break down to assemblages with cordierite, cordierite-hypersthene or spinel-magnetite-cordierite. The recorded products (hercynite spinel and magnetite) agree with experimental findings (Chap. 4, pp. 123–125) that ferrous biotites, approaching annite, are likely to decompose at rather high metamorphic temperatures to give sanidine, magnetite and simple ferrous silicates (fayalite under experimental conditions; hypersthene and cordierite in the Comrie assemblages). Since oxidation of Fe^{2+} to Fe^{3+} is involved in most such reactions, they must be sensitive not only to temperature and water pressure but also to P_{O_2}. Presumably assemblages containing hercynite-magnetite-ilmenite in addition to biotite, cordierite, and orthoclase must have been internally buffered to some constant P_{O_2} at any given temperature. Simplified possible versions of the complex break-down reactions involving dehydration of biotite at temperatures outside the stability field of muscovite are

(1) $K_2Fe_6^{2+}(Al_2Si_6O_{20})(OH)_4 + O_2 \rightarrow 2KAlSi_3O_8 + 2Fe_3O_4 + 2H_2O$

     Biotite (annite)   Orthoclase   Magnetite

(2) $K_2Mg_2Fe_3^{2+}Al(Al_3Si_5O_{20})(OH)_4 + 6Al_2SiO_5 \rightarrow 2KAlSi_3O_8$

     Biotite   Andalusite   Orthoclase

$$+ Al_3Mg_2(Si_5AlO_{18}) + 2Al_2O_3 + 3FeAl_2O_4 + 2H_2O$$

          Cordierite   Corundum   Hercynite

Lochnagar Aureole, Scotland

In the Oslo and Comrie aureoles almandine is a notable absentee; and at one time it was thought that absence of garnets of this composition is characteristic of the pyroxene-hornfels facies. More recently it has come to be recognized that almandine is not uncommon in high-grade contact-metamorphic assemblages, but that it is restricted to rocks with a relatively high FeO/MgO ratio (Turner and Verhoogen, 1960, p. 522). The role of almandine in relation to the more widespread cordierite-biotite pair in pelitic assemblages of the pyroxene-hornfels facies has been clearly documented by Chinner's (1962) account of the Lochnagar aureole in the Highlands of Scotland. The Lochnagar pluton is essentially granodio-ritic. It is one of many posttectonic late Caledonian intrusions, and it has developed an aureole, up to 3 km in width, in Dalradian metasediments that had previously reached an advanced grade of regional metamorphism. The initial pelitic assemblage thus was quartz-oligoclase-biotite-almandine-sillimanite (-magnetite-hematite), with a high oxidation ratio (probably > 40).

In the innermost part of the aureole, amphibolites have recrystallized to the typical pyroxene-hornfels assemblage plagioclase-diopside-hypers-thene. Siliceous marbles are represented by calcite-wollastonite assemblages. Pelitic rocks duplicate the quartz-bearing and silica-deficient assemblages of the Comrie aureole, except that the Al_2SiO_5 polymorph is sillimanite; they invariably contain biotite, cordierite, and K-feldspar in association with any of the two- and three-phase associations shown in Figure 6-22a. Iron-oxide phases other than spinel (hercynite) have been eliminated during metamorphism. The oxidation ratio in the completely recrystallized hornfels is invariably low (< 2), showing that metamorphism involved reactions of reduction. Silica-deficient assemblages include combinations of potash feldspar, corundum, and spinel.

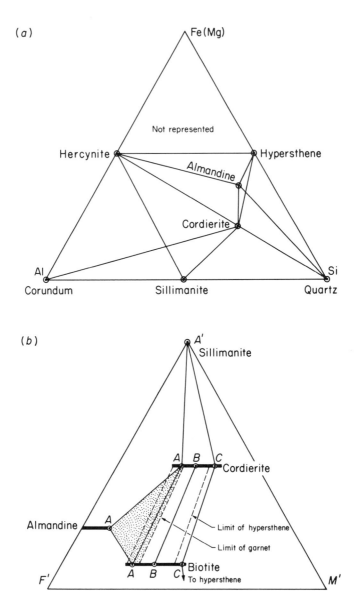

(a)

Fe(Mg)

Not represented

Hercynite — Hypersthene

Almandine

Cordierite

Al — Si
Corundum   Sillimanite   Quartz

(b)

A′
Sillimanite

A B C
Cordierite

Almandine   A

Limit of hypersthene

Limit of garnet

Biotite
A   B   C
To hypersthene

F′   M′

Fig. 6-22. Pyroxene-hornfels facies, Lochnagar aureole, Scotland. (*a*)
Coexisting phases in pelitic hornfelses; orthoclase and biotite can be
present in all assemblages. (*b*) $A'F'M'$ diagram for phase assemblages
coexisting with orthoclase (and other minerals). Circled points are
analysed minerals. Broken ties show compositions of phases estimated
from refractive indices. Stippled area shows limits of composition field
for garnetiferous assemblages.

230

Figure 6-22*b* is an $A'F'M'$ plot of coexisting analysed cordierites, biotites, and garnet (Chinner, 1962, p. 323). The stippled field is that in which garnet, cordierite, and biotite (compositions A) are mutually associated with quartz, orthoclase, and plagioclase. Cordierite and biotite C are mutually associated with hypersthene in a silica-deficient assemblage. Refractive index data (broken ties in Fig. 6-22*b*) show that in all assemblages, quartz-bearing or silica-deficient, the respective ratios of MgO/FeO in biotite vary uniformly in the manner indicated by the ties between analysed phases in Fig. 6-22. With decrease in the ratio MgO/FeO the compositional sequence of assemblages is

Biotite-cordierite-hypersthene-spinel
Biotite-cordierite-quartz
Biotite-cordierite-quartz-garnet

The composition field of garnetiferous rocks is much more limited than that of the garnet-bearing high-grade schists outside the aureole. Rocks in the outer part of the aureole whose MgO/FeO ratio exceeds that of the stippled field of Fig. 6-22 show clear textural evidence of reaction between garnet and surrounding minerals. Garnet may be seen in all stages of replacement by cordierite, orthoclase, and biotite, wherever it is in contact with biotite, quartz, and sillimanite. The kind of reaction that is suggested by Chinner is one of dehydration and reduction . It might perhaps be expressed thus:

$$4K_2(Mg_{2\frac{1}{2}}Fe^{2+}_{2\frac{1}{2}}Fe^{3+}_{\frac{1}{2}}Al_{\frac{1}{2}})(Al_3Si_5O_{20})(OH)_4 + \begin{cases} 8Fe_3Al_2Si_3O_{12} \\ \\ 2Mg_3Al_2Si_3O_{12} \end{cases}$$

Biotite, Garnet

$$+ 27Al_2SiO_5 + 47SiO_2 + H_2 \rightarrow 4KAlSi_3O_8 +$$

Sillimanite, Quartz, Orthoclase

$$2K_2MgFe^{2+}_5(Al_2Si_6O_{20})(OH)_4 + \begin{cases} 13Fe_2Al_3(AlSi_5O_{18}) \\ \\ 7Mg_2Al_3(AlSi_5O_{18}) \end{cases} + 5H_2O$$

Biotite, Cordierite

Basic Assemblages of Pyroxene-hornfels Facies

A characteristic mineral assemblage of the pyroxene-hornfels facies in the Oslo and Comrie aureoles is plagioclase-diopside-hypersthene (-quartz). This and silica-deficient assemblages of rather similar composition have been described in detail from other aureoles and from xenolithic blocks that have been subjected to unusually high temperature by total immersion in granitic magmas.

The aureole of the Tertiary Cuillin gabbro on the Scottish island of Skye illustrates the effects of contact metamorphism on a series of alkali basaltic lavas including some picritic types. Within 200 to 400 m of the gabbro contact these have been converted—probably with slight addition

of silica—to three types of hornfels (Almond, 1964):
Plagioclase-clinopyroxene-olivine
Plagioclase-clinopyroxene-hypersthene
Plagioclase-hypersthene

Opaque ores are present in all three assemblages. Plagioclase is An_{50} to An_{65}. Compositions of coexisting pyroxenes and olivines are uniform (tie line A, Fig. 6-23).

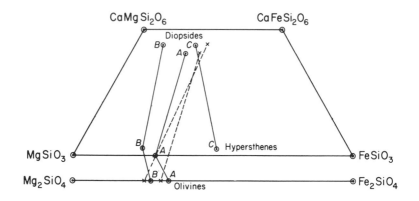

Fig. 6-23. Pyroxene-hornfels facies. Coexisting pyroxenes and olivines in basic hornfelses: A, B: Hebridean province, Scotland; C: Oslo. Broken lines show coexisting pyroxene and olivine in basic lavas from which was derived hornfels A. [*Data from I. D. Muir and C. F. Tilley* (*B*, *C*) *and from D. C. Almond* (*A*).]

The above is one of many examples of the formation of two-pyroxene hornfelses from basaltic lavas in aureoles generated by gabbro intrusions in the Hebridean Tertiary igneous province. According to MacGregor (1931) the usual assemblage is clinopyroxene-labradorite-olivine-magnetite; biotite and/or hypersthene may also be present. MacGregor records the composition of the olivine phase as being near to fayalite in many rocks. Basic assemblages very deficient in silica recorded by Thomas (1930, pp. 237, 308, 316) from the Ardnamurchan aureoles, include
Spinel-anorthite-hypersthene-olivine
Spinel-anorthite-diopside-olivine
Anorthite-hypersthene-diopside-olivine

Compositions of coexisting pyroxenes and olivines in several basic assemblages of the pyroxene-hornfels facies from the Hebridean province have been recorded by Muir and Tilley (1958). These are shown as tie lines in Fig. 6-23. The tie CC (Muir and Tilley, 1958, pp. 404, 405, OO') represents the pair diopside-hypersthene in a basic hornfels from the Olso area. In the two olivine-bearing hornfelses from Scotland (*A, B,* Fig. 6-23) the orthopyroxene is more magnesian than the associated olivine. As pointed out by Almond (1964, p. 425) this relation is that predicted on experimental grounds by Bowen and Schairer (1935, p. 213) for equilibrium at low pressures.

Silica-deficient Calcareous Assemblages in Pyroxene-hornfels Facies

Among the many accounts of contact metamorphism of slightly impure calcite and dolomite marbles, few record unequivocally the simultaneous appearance of plagioclase-diopside-hypersthene in associated basic rocks. So we are frequently in doubt as to whether the familiar silica-deficient assemblages in marbles should be assigned to the pyroxene-hornfels or to the hornblende-hornfels facies. The assemblages shown in Fig. 6-24 are those most widely developed in the innermost zones of relatively shallow aureoles, especially in the vicinity of dioritic rather than granitic plutons. With K_2O and Al_2O_3 as additional components, there appear such primary assemblages as the following [recorded by Joplin (1935) from a contact between dolomitic limestones and a dioritic pluton at Ben Bullen, Australia]

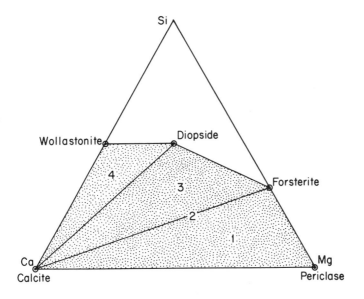

Fig. 6-24. Pyroxene-hornfels facies. Simple silica-deficient assemblages (stippled) in the triangle Calcite-Dolomite-Silica.

1. Calcite-periclase-forsterite-spinel
2a. Calcite-forsterite-spinel
2b. Calcite-forsterite-spinel-phlogopite
3. Calcite-forsterite-diopside-phlogopite

As is usual in high-grade magnesian assemblages, periclase has been partially or completely replaced by pseudomorphs of brucite; in some rocks forsterite shows partial replacement by serpentine.[1] These changes are an expectable consequence of reaction with gas (P_{H_2O} high compared with P_{CO_2}) during postmetamorphic cooling. The brucite pseudomorphs in the Ben Bullen marbles, as has also been observed elsewhere (Turner, 1965, p. 396), are rimmed with clear dolomite. The reaction sequence with falling temperature has been

(1) $$MgO + H_2O \rightarrow Mg(OH)_2$$
                Periclase   Brucite

(2) $$Mg(OH)_2 + CaCO_3 + CO_2 \rightarrow CaMg(CO_3)_2 + H_2O$$
         Brucite   Calcite   Dolomite

At the high temperatures reasonably assumed for the pyroxene-hornfels facies, there is no reason why minerals such as monticellite, and even melilite and spurrite, should not appear in slightly siliceous dolomites and marbles. From thermochemical and experimental data, these extreme steps in Bowen's reaction sequence can be predicted as likely to occur at temperatures scarcely higher than that of the periclase reaction (Turner, 1967). The necessary condition (as also for formation of periclase) is that the partial pressure of CO_2 be maintained continuously at a low level (perhaps no more than 50 bars) by free influx of water from the cooling pluton. In the innermost zone of the contact aureole of the Cuillin gabbro, Skye, plagioclase-hypersthene-diopside (-olivine) hornfelses derived from basic lavas are locally associated with marbles containing rankinite and spurrite. There is no reason to assign these assemblages to the sanidinite rather than to the pyroxene-hornfels facies. The significant inference is that metamorphism took place at high temperature (perhaps no more than 700°C) and under conditions such that, whatever the total fluid pressure may have been, P_{CO_2} never exceeded a few tens of bars. To what facies the assemblage is assigned is immaterial.

Metasomatic Calc-magnesian Assemblages, Crestmore, California

One of the clearest available accounts of high-grade metamorphism and metasomatism of slightly impure dolomites and limestones is Burnham's (1960) discussion of the complex paragenesis at Crestmore, California. Here there were two episodes of metamorphism. First, masses

---

[1] "Serpentine" replacing forsterite in marble is usually an aggregate of serpentine plus brucite.

of limestone around 100 m thick were engulfed in a quartz-diorite pluton and converted to nearly pure calcite marble and to periclase (brucite) marble. The mineral assemblages where silica was locally available.conform to those of Fig. 6-24. Subsequently the marbles so formed were invaded by a pipe of quartz-monzonite porphyry. Aqueous fluids from the porphyry magma introduced silica, alumina, magnesia, and iron into what is now a zoned silicated aureole 15 m in width. The influx of water was sufficiently rapid to maintain P_{CO_2} at a low level. In consequence "high-temperature" minerals such as monticellite, merwinite and spurrite, as well as a number of hydrous silicates (clinohumite, xanthophyllite) appear in various combinations in the aureole. The latter is roughly zoned, the sequence (with decreasing proximity to the contact) being

1. Grossularite-wollastonite-diopside
2. Vesuvianite
3. Monticellite with various combinations of clinohumite, forsterite, melilite, spurrite, tilleyite, spinel, etc.
4. Marble and brucite-marble

The zones of the aureole express a metasomatically imposed composition gradient rather than a gradient in temperature or pressure conditions. Each zone has developed at the expense of the assemblage now represented in the zone immediately outside it. The principal assemblages along a traverse from the marble into and across the monticellite zone approximate the following sequence, which can be represented in terms of the CaO–MgO–SiO$_2$ Al$_2$O$_3$ tetrahedron. These are shown in Fig. 6-26, on the CaO–MgO–SiO$_2$ triangle, omitting the coexisting aluminous phases (italicized below)

1. Calcite-periclase (brucite)-clinohumite-*spinel*
2. Calcite-clinohumite-forsterite-*spinel*
3. Calcite-forsterite-*spinel* (*-xanthophyllite*)
4. Calcite-forsterite-monticellite (*-xanthophyllite*)
5. Calcite-monticellite-*melilite* (*xanthophyllite*)
6. Calcite-monticellite-spurrite (or tilleyite)-*melilite*
7. Monticellite-spurrite-merwinite-*melilite*

This sequence, starting from brucite-marble *P*, is represented in Fig. 6-26 by analysed rocks lying along the line *PM*. The same sequence of assemblages has developed where the starting material is pure marble. Changes in bulk composition per unit volume are shown in Fig. 6-25.

With full attainment of assemblage 7, carbonate phases have been eliminated. Further metasomatism in the vesuvianite and grossularite zones approximates the sequence:

7a. *Vesuvianite*-monticellite-spurrite-merwinite-*melilite*
8. *Vesuvianite*-monticellite-diopside-wollastonite (*grossularite*)
9. *Grossularite*-diopside-wollastonite

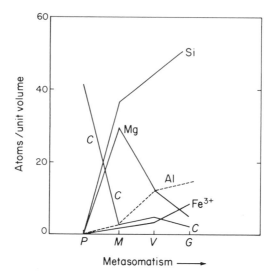

Fig. 6-25. Pyroxene-hornfels facies, Crestmore, California. Variation in rock composition during metasomatism of brucite-calcite marble. *P*, marble; *M*, monticellite zone; *V*, vesuvianite zone; *G*, grossularite zone. (*After C. W. Burnham—simplified.*)

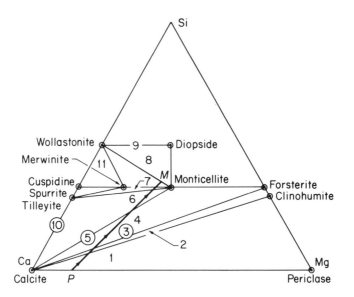

Fig. 6-26. Pyroxene-hornfels facies, Crestmore, California. Silica-deficient assemblages in the triangle Calcite-Dolomite-Silica. *PM* represents the path of metasomatism from brucite-calcite marble into and through the monticellite zone. (*After C. W. Burnham—simplified.*)

236

Assemblage 10, calcite-spurrite, is found in the outer part of the aureole in contact with pure calcite marble. This and assemblages approximating 11, spurrite-merwinite (cuspidine-wollastonite), represent the rare case where silicon is the only metasomatically introduced element. The usual case is that in which early introduction of magnesium as well as silicon diverts the compositional trend into triangle 6 of Fig. 6-26.

Burnham's study has demonstrated that the mineral assemblages— contrary to a view once generally held (Harker, 1932, p. 95; Turner and Verhoogen, 1951, p. 377)—closely approximate divariant equilibrium.[1] The reactions involved, however, have occurred in systems open to many components. So most of Burnham's equations do not represent reversible reactions such as those which have been used throughout this book to illustrate stable or metastable univariant equilibria. Take, for example, the development of monticellite by introduction of silica into forsterite marble under some continuously maintained low partial pressure of CO_2

$$Mg_2SiO_4 + 2CaCO_3 + SiO_2 \rightarrow 2CaMgSiO_4 + 2CO_2$$
$$\text{Forsterite} \qquad \text{Calcite} \qquad \text{(in solution)} \qquad \text{Monticellite}$$

The corresponding univariant equilibrium that would represent stable co-existence of four solid phases under the same P_{CO_2} at some lower temperature would be

$$Mg_2SiO_4 + CaMgSi_2O_6 + 2CaCO_3 \rightleftharpoons 3CaMgSiO_4 + 2CO_2$$
$$\text{Forsterite} \qquad \text{Diopside} \qquad \text{Calcite} \qquad \text{Monticellite}$$

Again it is emphasized that the phase rule can be applied only to the second of these equations; for it alone represents a heterogeneous system in a state of equilibrium. Nor does any modification of the phase rule introducing the concept of mobile components make it possible to predict the nature of the final equilibrium product. Burnham (1959, p. 914) has used textural and chemical data to determine what components and what quantities of them have been introduced to give the mineral assemblages in the three zones. The compositional changes depicted in Fig. 6-25 and 6-26 are based, moreover, on certain assumptions that seem reasonable: the initial composition was that of the brucite-calcite and calcite marbles as they now exist beyond the aureole; and metasomatism proceeded without change in volume. The criteria of equilibrium in the final phase assemblages are three: (1) each assemblage consists of a limited number of phases; (2) there is usually no simple relation (never more than one) between associated phases (including a simple gas phase), such as might be

---

[1] There are expectable departures. For example, two intergrown phases may be seen in process of replacing a third. Again an anhydrous equilibrium assemblage may have been partially converted to hydrous phases during postmetamorphic cooling (e.g., Forsterite → Serpentine + Brucite).

expressed by a conventional chemical equation; (3) the whole paragenesis of Fig. 6-26 is consistent with that postulated by Bowen (1940) for equilibrium at an advanced grade of low-pressure metamorphism—after appearance of merwinite at "step 11" and prior to development of larnite at maximum grade (cf. Chap. 4, p. 133).

The Crestmore paragenesis recalls the skarn assemblages of the hornblende-hornfels facies at dolomite-granite contacts in Skye (Tilley, 1951; cf. also pp. 214–215). But the slightly higher grade of the Crestmore rocks is indicated by the presence of spurrite and melilite—minerals that are completely absent from the calc-magnesian-silicate rocks of Skye.

SANIDINITE FACIES

General Characteristics

The sanidinite facies was erected by Eskola to cover mineral assemblages whose mineralogical composition and geological occurrence show that they have formed at maximum temperatures and minimum pressures of metamorphism (cf. Eskola, 1939, p. 347). They are represented by xenoliths in basic lavas (or near-surface intrusions), by fragments in tuffs, and by the rocks of narrow contact zones bordering shallow basic pipes and necks. In this latter situation, unusually high temperatures have been maintained by continuous flow of magma along the contact.

The geological occurrence of the sanidinite facies is insignificant compared with that of the other facies of contact metamorphism. But it shows some interesting and unusual features of mineral paragenesis. Some of the characteristic phases are analogous with products of crystallization from melts at atmospheric pressure; tridymite, mullite, monticellite, forsterite, larnite, and so on. The characteristic alkaline phase is sanidine, commonly a variety rich in Na. Cordierite, wollastonite (usually containing excess Mg or Fe^{2+}), and anorthite are all typical of siliceous assemblages. Micas, amphiboles and garnets are absent. The only carbonate mineral is calcite. Some of the principal phase assemblages of the sanidinite facies, as recorded by Eskola (1939, pp. 347-349) are shown graphically in Fig. 6-27 and 6-28.

Quartzo-feldspathic and pelitic rocks in the sanidinite facies in most cases have been brought to the point of partial fusion. These are buchites: rocks in which minerals such as cordierite, corundum, mullite or tridymite are enclosed in glass. When the crystalline phases are minerals not normally found in common igneous rocks it is customary to consider the assemblage as metamorphic, in the sanidinite facies. But quartzo-feldspathic rocks at only slightly higher pressures may become converted to what can only be considered igneous products, namely granophyres. Even at near-surface

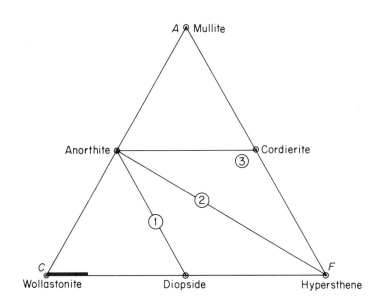

Fig. 6-27. Sanidinite facies. *ACF* diagram for rocks with excess SiO_2 and K_2O. (*After P. Eskola.*)

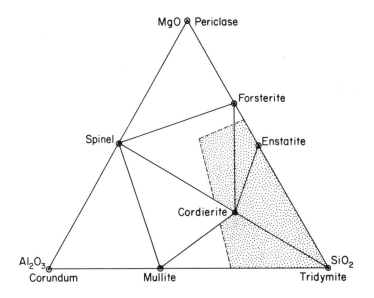

Fig. 6-28. Sanidinite facies. Assemblages in the triangle $MgO–Al_2O_3–SiO_2$. (*After P. Eskola.*) Field of pelitic rocks stippled.

239

pressures there is a merging of metamorphic into igneous rocks via the sanidinite facies.

Pelitic and Quartzo-feldspathic Assemblages

Classic examples of the sanidinite facies paragenesis are the suites of pelitic xenoliths in trachyte tuffs of the Laacher See region, German Eifel (Brauns, 1911), and in minor tholeiitic intrusions on the Scottish island of Mull (Thomas, 1922). The Laacher See rocks have been modified by the pneumatolytic introduction of sodium, and include various combinations of sanidine, cordierite, spinel, hypersthene, and sillimanite. Many of the rocks have not reached equilibrium at low pressure and contain unstable relics—garnet, staurolite—inherited from an earlier facies. In the Mull xenoliths, representative assemblages are corundum-spinel-anorthite, cordierite-spinel-mullite, cordierite-glass, and mullite-glass. In quartzo-feldspathic xenoliths in the Mull suite, tridymite has crystallized around nuclei of unfused quartz enclosed in glass.

Generally similar assemblages have been described and excellently illustrated by Searle (1962) from the Pleistocene basaltic province of Auckland, New Zealand. The agent of metamorphism is alkaline olivine basalt. The metamorphic rocks are xenoliths in lava flows and pyroclastic deposits, and baked silts (porcellanites) intercalated between or underlying surface flows. So this is a clearly demonstrated case of metamorphism at near-atmospheric pressure. As is usually the case in the sanidinite facies, reciprocal diffusion has modified both the metamorphic rock and the immediately adjacent basalt magma. The result is relative enrichment of the metamorphic rock in Ca, Mg, and Fe, with complementary loss of Si and Al. The principal metamorphic assemblages are mullite-glass, cordierite-mullite-glass, cordierite-mullite, cordierite-quartz, cordierite-plagioclase (calcic) sanidine-clinopyroxene, sanidine-clinopyroxene-hematite-glass. The sanidine is the high-temperature polymorph. Quartz in many assemblages (e.g., in the sanidinites) appears to have inverted from tridymite which had crystallized in the first place from glass.

Basic Assemblages

There are many records of basic hornfelses formed by recrystallization of basalt on the walls of conduits or in shallow basalt magma chambers. Xenoliths of such material in the Auckland basalts (Searle, 1962) consist essentially of calcic plagioclase and hypersthene. Ejected blocks from the walls of the Kilauea crater vent in Hawaii (Muir and Tilley, 1958) consist of plagioclase(An_{62})-augite-hypersthene, with minor pseudobrookite and tridymite. Relict phenocrysts of olivine are in process of conversion to hypersthene-magnetite by a reaction involving oxidation of iron.

Agrell and Langley (1958) have recorded a suite of unusual mineral assemblages resulting from low-pressure metamorphism of basalt and its associated weathering products, adjacent to and within a Tertiary plug of olivine diabase in Antrim, Ireland:

1. Olivine-clinopyroxene-plagioclase-magnetite-ilmenite
2. Hypersthene-plagioclase-magnetite-ilmenite-pseudobrookite
3. Cordierite-plagioclase-magnetite-hematite-pseudobrookite-tridymite (or cristobalite)-mullite

The sequence 1 to 3 (numbered as in Fig. 6-27) represents premetamorphic compositional changes from olivine basalt to a montmorillonitic weathering product (bole). A second suite of assemblages, very rich in Al and Fe and deficient in Si, has formed by marginal metamorphism of an engulfed block of porcellanite. This represents an initial lateritic weathering product of basalt

4. (a) Corundum-hematite   ⎫ + pseudo-
   (b) Corundum-mullite-hematite   ⎬ brookite
   (c) Mullite-hematite-cristobalite (or tridymite) ⎭ + magnetite
5. (a) Corundum-hercynite-ilmenite-magnetite
   (b) Corundum-mullite-hercynite-ilmenite-magnetite
   (c) Mullite-hercynite-cristobalite (or tridymite)
   (d) Mullite-hercynite-cordierite-cristobalite (or tridymite)
   (e) Mullite-cordierite-cristobalite (or tridymite)

Assemblages 4 are highly oxidized; both corundum and mullite carry significant Fe^{3+}. Assemblages 5, which occur closer to the contact, have been reduced to a comparatively low oxidation ratio; corundum and mullite are normal. Cordierite appears in assemblages with appreciable MgO (cf. Fig. 6-28).

Calcareous Assemblages

According to Eskola (1939, p. 348) the characteristic silica-saturated assemblages in calcareous rocks are combinations of wollastonite, anorthite and diopside. Grossularite, which is so common in hornfelses of other facies, is a notable absentee. In its place appears the pair anorthite-wollastonite. This assemblage, once thought to be critical of the sanidinite facies, has now been recorded, with associated quartz, in situations which indicate pressures certainly much higher than those of the sanidinite facies. It has been observed in some granite aureoles in the Californian Coast Ranges (e.g., near Inverness, north of San Francisco), and is widely developed adjacent to granite plutons on Nanga Parbat, in the Himalayas (Misch, 1964).[1] Anorthite-wollastonite may also prove to be characteristic

---

[1] Whether or not Misch is correct in interpreting this granitic massif as a product of granitization representing the culmination of deep regional metamorphism of the Barrovian type, pressures must have been much higher than those of the near-surface sanidinite facies.

of the pyroxene-hornfels facies (cf. p. 226).

Silica-deficient marbles and dolomitic marbles in the sanidinite facies display mineral assemblages unique in metamorphic paragenesis. At Scawt Hill in northern Ireland, chalk with enclosed nodules of flint has been metamorphosed at the contact with an intrusion of diabase. The assemblages developed by reaction between flint and calcite have been recorded in detail by Tilley (e.g., 1929; 1942). They correspond to the products of the later steps in Bowen's (1940) sequence of progressive reactions, with rankinite, $Ca_3Si_2O_5$, as an additional phase. Since reaction has involved outward diffusion of Si from the chert nodule, and inward diffusion of Ca and Mg from the chalk, each metamorphosed nodule is now concentrically zoned as to composition and mineral paragenesis. The full inward sequence follows the three-phase triangles 1 to 4 in Fig. 6-29. Magnesian variants include merwinite, melilite or monticellite, as shown in Fig. 6-29. Where aluminum and iron are present they are represented by melilite and/or pleonaste. While melilite, spurrite and monticellite appear rarely in the pyroxene-hornfels facies (presumably where partial pressures of CO_2 are kept at a low level) larnite and rankinite have not yet been recorded outside the sanidinite facies.

A remarkable paragenesis occurs in blocks of limestone engulfed in flows of leucite tephrite near Mayen in the Laacher See region (Jasmund

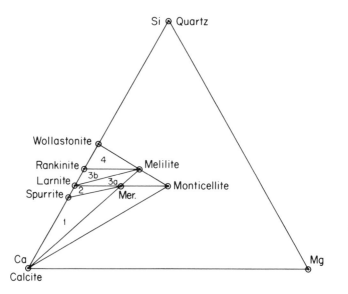

Fig. 6-29. Sanidinite facies. Mineral assemblages formed by reaction between flint nodules and enclosing calcite (chalk), Scawt Hill, Ireland. (*After C. E. Tilley*, 1942).

and Hentschel, 1964). These rocks have a very high ratio Ca/Mg (mostly 20–50), and contain 10 to 20 percent SiO_2 and a few percent each of Fe_2O_3 and Al_2O_3. Neglecting late hydrated phases such as afwillite and portlandite, there are two groups of assemblages.

1. Wollastonite-melilite-magnetite (or spinel)
2. (a) Calcite-brownmillerite ($\pm$ mayenite)
   (b) Calcite-larnite-brownmillerite-mayenite
   (c) Larnite-brownmillerite-mayenite

The minerals brownmillerite, $Ca_2(Al, Fe)_2O_5$, and mayenite, $Ca_{12}Al_{14}O_{33}$, are unique in that they are otherwise recorded only as constituents of cement clinker. Their appearance is attributed to gas pressures even lower than those normally developed in shallow contact zones as exemplified by Scawt Hill (Jasmund and Hentschel, 1964, p. 311).

TEMPERATURE GRADIENTS OF LOW-PRESSURE METAMORPHISM

Criteria of Metamorphic Conditions

We have now reviewed the nature and occurrence of metamorphic facies generally attributed to reaction and crystallization in the low-pressure range: at a guess perhaps 2 kb or less. What is the geologic significance of this information? Whether general, regional or local, the nature of the problem is the same; it has been stated thus (Fyfe and Turner, 1966, p. 363):

> As studies of metamorphic phenomena proceed, emphasis becomes placed more and more heavily on the major controlling geophysical and geochemical parameters, whose varied perturbations are expressed in the various recognizable types of metamorphism. What we wish to know regarding some particular metamorphic terrane is the general temperature-pressure regime over a certain period of time.

To answer such a question we turn to two independent kinds of evidence: that which may be termed broadly geological, and the narrower but more precisely defined data of mineral paragenesis treated in the light of experimental findings. Before examining any particular case, we shall enumerate the criteria to be employed and the basic assumptions that underlie their use.

General geologic criteria. Some limits, though far from precise, may be set upon the possible range of metamorphic pressures and even temperatures, by stratigraphic and structural estimates of depth of cover. This approach applies especially to metamorphism over the low-pressure range discussed in this chapter. Since, however, plutonic intrusion and accompanying metamorphism tend to be associated with or to follow tectonic episodes, field data are seldom adequate to permit more than a rough estimate of cover thickness.

Where a thermal gradient is demonstrably due to intrusion of magma, upper possible limits of temperature at the contact may be inferred from the nature of the intrusive rock. The temperature of the magma itself probably lies between 700 (granitic) and 1100°C (near-surface basaltic magma). Possible gradients of temperature in relation to distance from plutonic contacts have been illustrated in Chap. 1 (Figs. 1-7 to 1-9). These are based on a simple and rather artificial model of a mass of hot magma instantaneously intruded into dry rock or into water-saturated sediment, and thereafter remaining static. Among expectable departures from such a model is elevation of contact temperatures toward that of magma where this flows freely past the contact for a considerable time.

A particularly important control of most metamorphic equilibria is the nature of the participating gas phase, especially the relative values of P_{CO_2} and P_{H_2O}. These depend on a number of factors: initial rock composition (e.g., shale versus limestone), permeability of the system, and the nature of the prevailing gas in the immediate environment. Again it is possible to limit the range of possibilities on the basis of geologic evidence. At pressures of a few kilobars and temperatures of a few hundred degrees, marble is much more ductile (and hence presumably less permeable) than dolomite. Minor calcareous beds in a dominantly pelitic sequence of sediments are likely to be surrounded by a metamorphic environment in which the gas phase is essentially aqueous. Near granite contacts a permeable rock undergoing metamorphism may be continuously flushed with outward-flowing water, so that P_{CO_2} is always low.

Clearly, in assessing the physical gradient in a metamorphic province or aureole, the inferences based on mineralogical evidence must conform to the limits, however vague, set by the particular geologic situation.

Mineralogical criteria. More precise inferences may be drawn from the evidence supplied by the mutually associated mineral assemblages—the data of metamorphic facies and local subfacies. Here the background data are those of laboratory experiment and thermochemical reasoning. These have been discussed in Chap. 4. Some of the potentially useful equilibria have been reproduced in Fig. 6-30.

Curves 1 *and* 2 limit the fields of stability of the three polymorphs of Al_2SiO_5 below 3 kb. The commonly observed passage from an andalusite to a sillimanite zone can be fixed at 600 to 700° below 1 kb, 550 to 600° between 2 and 1 kb. Newton's triple point (cf. p. 115) would extend the andalusite zone a further 100°.

Curves 3 *and* 4 represent the breakdown of muscovite, respectively with and without quartz, to potash feldspar and an aluminous phase.

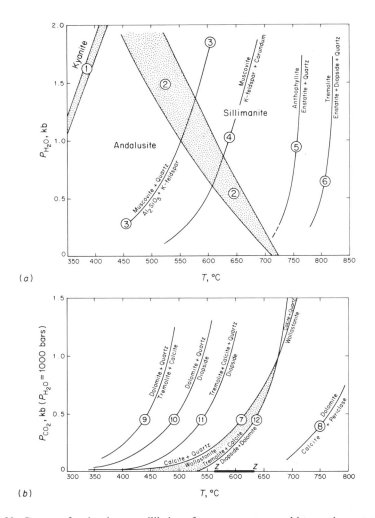

Fig. 6-30. Curves of univariant equilibrium for some metamorphic reactions at total pressure less than 2 kb. (*a*) In noncarbonate assemblages: (1), (2) Kyanite $\rightleftharpoons$ Andalusite $\rightleftharpoons$ Sillimanite. (*After data of W. S. Fyfe.*) Stippled area indicates probable margin of uncertainty. (3) Muscovite + Quartz $\rightleftharpoons$ Sanidine + Sillimanite + Water. (*After B. W. Evans.*) (4) Muscovite $\rightleftharpoons$ Sanidine + Corundum + Water. (*After B. W. Evans.*) (5) Anthophyllite $\rightleftharpoons$ 7 Enstatite + Quartz + Water. (*After H. J. Greenwood.*) (6) Tremolite $\rightleftharpoons$ 2 Diopside + 3 Enstatite + Quartz + Water. (*After F. R. Boyd.*) (*b*) In carbonate assemblages at constant P_{H_2O} = 1 kb.: Curves (7) and (8) based on experimental data of R. I. Harker and O. F. Tuttle. Curves (9) to 12) calculated from thermochemical data (cf. Figs. 4-14, 4-16, 4-18), and adjusted (by raising temperatures) to the same temperature intervals relative to curve (7). (7) Calcite + Quartz $\rightleftharpoons$ Wollastonite + CO_2. (8) Dolomite $\rightleftharpoons$ Calcite + Periclase + CO_2. (9) 5 Dolomite + 8 Quartz + H_2O $\rightleftharpoons$ Tremolite + 3 Calcite + $7CO_2$. (10) Dolomite + 2 Quartz $\rightleftharpoons$ Diopside + $2CO_2$. 11) Tremolite + 3 Calcite + 2 Quartz $\rightleftharpoons$ 5 Diopside + $3CO_2$ + H_2O. (12) Tremolite + Calcite $\rightleftharpoons$ 4 Diopside + Dolomite + CO_2 + H_2O. ZZ upper temperature limit of stability of Clinozoisite + Quartz.

245

Muscovite-quartz is eliminated over the interval 500 to 600°C between 500 bars and 2 kb. Muscovite alone breaks down perhaps 80° beyond these temperatures.

Curves 5 and 6. The critical dehydration of common hornblende to pyroxenes has not been investigated experimentally. Reactions of this kind will depend on the composition of the amphibole and the degree of oxidation or reduction concerned. An extreme upper limit is set by curves 5 and 6 for the equilibria

$$\text{Anthophyllite} \rightleftharpoons 7 \text{ Enstatite} + \text{Quartz} + \text{Water}$$

and $$\text{Tremolite} \rightleftharpoons 2 \text{ Diopside} + 3 \text{ Enstatite} + \text{Quartz} + \text{Water}$$

The natural assemblages must lie within the stability fields of both diopside (containing 20 to 30 percent hedenbergite) and hypersthene. Judging from the melting behavior of such pyroxenes and data relating to dehydration of the annite-phlogopite mica series, iron-bearing pyroxenes might well be stable with respect to ferrous hornblendes at temperatures 150° or so below those of curve 5*b*. In experiments on the crystallization and behavior of basaltic melts at varying water pressures, Yoder and Tilley (1962) found that the hornblende-plagioclase assemblage gives way to pyroxenic assemblages only at extreme temperatures (900 to 1000°C in the 500 to 2000 bar range). Their experimental environment was one of extreme oxidation in which the oxidation ratio in the quenched products reached values of 60. The environment of contact aureoles normally is one of reduction (Chinner, 1960, p. 211). The oxidation ratios in the assemblages of the inner aureole of Lochnagar, as recorded by Chinner (1962) are less than 2. Analyses of metamorphic hornblendes and pyroxenes show that the Hornblende → Pyroxenes reaction involves considerable reduction. Equilibrium temperatures in the reducing environment of an aureole will be far below those of Yoder and Tilley's experiments.

Curves 7 to 12. For likely sequences of decarbonation reactions in calcite-dolomite rocks the reader is referred back to Figs. 4-8 to 4-19. We shall see presently that for some of the common assemblages in marbles and dolomitic rocks to be compatible with associated pelitic assemblages, it will be necessary to assume that the ratio P_{H_2O}/P_{CO_2} has been maintained at a high level in the carbonate rocks. Curves 7 to 12 illustrate the effect of increasing P_{CO_2} from a few bars to 1 kb while maintaining P_{H_2O} at the constant value 1 kb. Curves 7 and 8 are based on direct experiment and so are considered superior to the thermochemically based curves 9 to 12. On the assumption that the relative positions of these latter with respect to the thermochemically based curve for the wollastonite reaction 7 in Fig. 4-19 are accurate, curves 9 to 12 in Fig. 6-30*b* have been adjusted, by general displacement to the right, to maintain the same relation to the experimentally established curve 7.

Finally there are experimentally determined values for temperatures, over a range of P_{H_2O} and P_{CO_2} at which rocks in close contact with magma might undergo complete or partial fusion: At $P_{H_2O} = 2000$ bars, graywackes begin to melt at about 700°C, and by 750°C are more than half melted. The melt fraction approximates granodiorite (Winkler, 1961, p. 361). At the same pressure the melting range of shales is of the same order or possibly somewhat higher (Wyllie and Tuttle, 1961). Again the melt phase is more or less granodioritic. At fluid pressures of between 500 and 2000 bars, if the ratio P_{H_2O}/P_{CO_2} is maintained at a high level, dolomite would begin to melt between 600 and 700°C (Wyllie, 1965, p. 121). The products of solidification should then contain, as well as carbonates, hydrated phases such as brucite.

Definition of a Temperature Gradient

The temperature regime in a metamorphic terrane can be expressed by gradients of increasing temperature drawn with reference to another variable: usually pressure, or alternatively, distance as measured in some specified direction on the map. A pressure-temperature gradient is directly comparable with pressure-temperature phase diagrams. A temperature-distance gradient on the other hand can be plotted from the field distribution of mapped isograds; but here it is necessary to make some assumption regarding the pressure regime in order to calibrate the isograds in terms of experimental data.

The ensuing discussion of low-pressure metamorphic gradients is based on a simple model which cannot be greatly different from the true situation; it is assumed that the present mapped land surface is parallel to the surface at the time of metamorphism. Pressure across the aureole is thus assumed to be constant, and the T-P gradient dT/dP expressed by the mapped isograds will be parallel to the pressure coordinate on a P-T diagram. The maximum temperature-distance gradient dT/dD will be in the direction, not necessarily horizontal, of the heat source. However, where the heat source is a vertical-sided pluton, the maximum temperature-distance gradient is in a direction normal to the outcrop of the pluton; and pressure may be assumed to be constant.

Illustrative Examples

Procedure. We now propose to reconstruct possible or likely temperature-distance gradients based on the field sequence of phase assemblages of contact metamorphism in particular aureoles. P-T ranges are inferred from experimental data. Only those cases are considered where the plutonic contact is known from field data to be vertical or steeply dipping. The reconstructed gradients are shown as full lines in Figs. 6-31, 6-32.

For comparison the broken curves XX, YY are computed gradients based on the data of Jaeger (1959). His model invokes a sheet of magma intruded instantaneously at its crystallization temperature into rocks initially at temperatures no greater than 200°C. The assumptions made in constructing XX and YY are compatible with the nature and dimensions of the stocks of Comrie (p. 6), Ardara (pp. 12–13) and Santa Rosa (pp. 209–210). They are as follows:

Thickness of sheet: 4 km
Initial magmatic temperature = 800°C
Initial country-rock temperature = 100°C
Crystallization range of magma = 800 to 600°C
ΔH of crystallization of magma = 100 cal/gm

Curve XX represents the ideal simple case where heat has been transferred outward from the contact purely by conduction through dry nonreactive rock (Jaeger, 1959, fig. 1). More realistic is a curve which would also take into account endothermic dehydration reactions in the aureole. The effect would be analogous to a second model of Jaeger (1951, pp. 49-51) where heat is dissipated by converting pore water in the country rock to steam. Endothermic reactions of this kind would lower the maximum temperature at the contact, possibly by 100°C, with corresponding reduction in temperatures along the gradient. The width of the aureole would also be reduced. Hydration reactions (exothermic) such as conversion of pyroxene-labradorite of basalt to hornblende-bearing assemblages would have an opposite effect.

From Jaeger's models it also seems likely that maximum temperatures near the contact might be maintained for a period of 50,000 or 100,000 years after intrusion. A time lag of similar magnitude might be expected between the date of intrusion and the time at which maximum temperatures were reached a kilometer or so out from the contact.

Comparison of Comrie, Ardara, and Santa Rosa aureoles. The field and mineralogical data relating to three aureoles developed adjacent to granodioritic or dioritic stocks of similar dimensions are compared in the light of the following indicator reactions (numbered as in Fig. 6-30):

(0) First appearance of biotite: guessed to be about 350°C over the pressure range 500 to 2000 bars.

(2) Development of andalusite versus sillimanite. The fact that andalusite has been observed to become replaced by sillimanite with rising temperature (as in the inner Ardara aureole), while the reverse inversion does not occur during subsequent slow cooling, suggests that significant overstepping of the equilibrium temperature may be necessary for the reaction Andalusite → Sillimanite. To allow for this, the temperature indicated by appearance of sillimanite is taken to be on the outer boundary of the stippled field in Fig. 6-30a.

Table 6-2. Possible values of T and P ($= P_{H_2O}$) for critical reactions (see text) in three contact aureoles at distances D from contacts

Reaction no.	Comrie ($T_1 = 850°$) D, m	P, bars	T, °C	Ardara ($T_1 = 750°$) D, m	P, bars	T, °C	Santa Rosa ($T_1 = 750°$) D, m	P, bars	T, °C
0	500		350–400	1500		350–400	1500		350–400
2				150	750	640	100–200	1200	570
					1000	600			
3	300	500	500	700	750	520	100–200	1200	570
		1000	550		1000	550			
4	<300	500	600						
		1000	630						
7	150	500	<650				200	1200	550²
13¹		1000	<680		750	>640	200	1200	>570
11					1000	>600	1000±	1200	500–550²

¹Inferred from data for reactions (1) to (4). Preferred value underlined.
²Assuming $P_{CO_2} < 200$ bars.

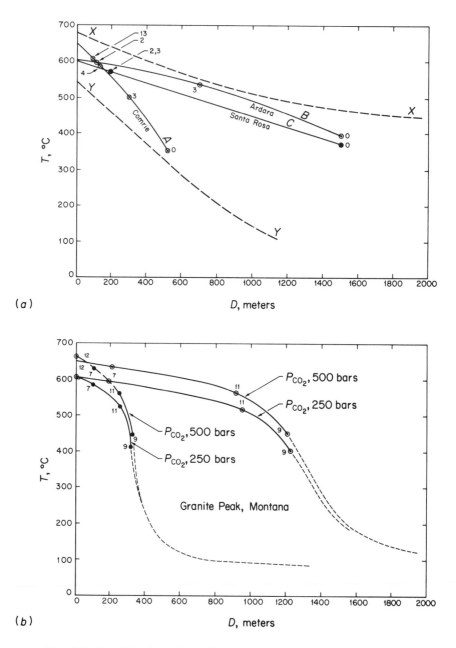

Fig. 6-31. Possible thermal gradients for four contact aureoles round intrusive stocks. D = distance from contact. *XX*, theoretical gradient following the ideal models of *J. Jaeger* (1959). Numbers refer to equilibria of Fig. 6-30 (see also text).

(3) Dehydration of muscovite-quartz

(4) Dehydration of muscovite in the absence of quartz to yield corundum-orthoclase assemblages

(7) Calcite + Quartz → Wollastonite + CO_2

The appearance or nonappearance of wollastonite merely sets a limit to P_{CO_2} at temperatures inferred from other reactions.

(13) Hornblende ⇌ Pyroxenes + Water

Some idea of the P_{H_2O}-T conditions for this equilibrium may be gained from the persistence or the breakdown of hornblende at temperatures and pressures indicated by reactions (2) to (4) in associated rocks. In this case the geological data are used to calibrate the equilibrium curve, not vice versa.

(14) Breakdown of staurolite to Al_2SiO_5 and garnet or cordierite.

Contact temperatures are based on Jaeger's (1959, table 1) values for "granite-shale," and "granite-quartzite," assuming initial magmatic temperatures of 850 (diorite) to 750°C (granodiorite) and relatively cold country rock (T = 100°C, consistent with depths of only two or three kilometers). Values so computed are about 600 to 700°C.

The resulting data are summarized in Table 6-2. Corresponding pressure-temperature gradients are shown as curves A (Comrie), B (Ardara), and C (Santa Rosa) in Fig. 6-31a. Some additional notes are appended.

Only in the inner aureole at Comrie has hornblende been converted to diopside-hypersthene. This, together with absence of sillimanite and presence of corundum-orthoclase assemblages (in silica-deficient hornfelses) strongly indicates intrusion of the Comrie pluton at low pressure. The initial magma, being dioritic, was probably hotter than in the other two plutons. So gradient A has been drawn for a uniform pressure $P_l = P_{H_2O} = 500$ bars, corresponding to a depth of perhaps $1\frac{1}{2}$ to 2 km.

The outward sequence sillimanite-andalusite in the Ardara aureole implies a relatively low slope for gradient B. Pressure cannot have been either much more or much less than 1000 bars. At 500 m from the contact there has been no reaction between calcite and quartz in an extensive massive limestone member (Akad, 1956). At the corresponding temperature on gradient B (550°C) if $P_f = 1000$ bars, wollastonite could form in the limestone only if its permeability were high enough to permit continuous penetrative flow of water vapor, thus maintaining P_{CO_2} at values not exceeding 200 bars.

In the Santa Rosa aureole (gradient C) the virtually simultaneous inversion of andalusite to sillimanite, and breakdown of muscovite-quartz in the innermost zone, fix the range of P_{H_2O} and T as 1000 to 1500 bars[1] and 550 to 590°C. The gradient must be close to that in the Ardara aureole;

[1] This agrees with Compton's (1960, p. 1401) estimate based solely on geologic evidence.

the rocks are mineralogically similar. Here the calcareous beds are relatively thin minor components of essentially pelitic and semipelitic formations (in contrast with the massive limestone formation at Ardara). Probably for this reason, wollastonite has formed freely in the inner aureole, and diopside-grossularite further out. For these reactions P_{CO_2} must have been maintained at very low values consistent with curves 7 and 11 of Fig. 6-30b.

Staurolite, sometimes considered an index of high pressure, is widely distributed in rocks of appropriate composition in the outer and intermediate zones of the Santa Rosa aureole, and at Ardara. Clearly it forms freely at pressures no higher than 1 or 2 kb. It has become completely eliminated in favor of cordierite-andalusite at temperatures of perhaps 500 to 550°C in the inner zone at Santa Rosa (reaction 14). The ubiquitous presence of hornblendic assemblages in two of the aureoles place some limits on the breakdown of hornblende to pyroxenes (Fig. 6-34).

The three aureoles that have just been discussed have developed around plutons of similar size and rather similar composition. The steeply dropping gradient at Comrie (A in Fig. 6-31) corresponds more to Jaeger's model of intrusion into cool water-saturated porous sediments. Gradients B and C approximate Jaeger's simpler model of outward conduction of heat through dry rocks.

Granite Peak aureole, Montana. The paragenesis described by Melson (1966) in the contact aureole developed in siliceous and argillaceous dolomitic limestones in the Granite Peak aureole (Fig. 6-19) illustrates the situation where reactions are controlled by relative values of P_{CO_2} and P_{H_2O}, as well as by T and P. Stratigraphic evidence cited by Melson indicates that load pressures were probably around 1 kb, though possibly somewhat higher. Melson (1966, pp. 412, 419) prescribes a model with consistently high P_{CO_2}, but with local gradients—especially in the outer zone—controlled by composition of individual beds: higher P_{H_2O} in argillaceous, higher P_{CO_2} in carbonate bands. This writer prefers a model in which (as assumed by Melson) $P_f = (P_{CO_2} + P_{H_2O}) = P_l$, but with P_{H_2O} generally exceeding P_{CO_2}. Only thus is it possible to reconcile the survival of clinozoisite and tremolite in the innermost zone where wollastonite forms freely (stippled region of Fig. 6-30b).

Possible temperature gradients based on this model are shown in Fig. 6-31b. The steeper gradients are based on Melson's section showing the granite contact dipping at 30°; the flat gradients are drawn for a vertically dipping contact. In each case, gradients are drawn for $P_{H_2O} = $ 1 kb and $P_{CO_2} = 250$ and 500 bars, respectively. Such spans of temperature and pressure fall completely within the range of conditions here thought to be characteristic of the hornblende-hornfels facies (cf. Fig. 6-35).

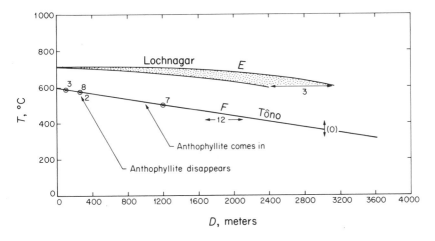

Fig. 6-32. Possible thermal gradients in aureoles round two small batholiths (see text). D = distance from contact.

Aureoles and small batholiths. The Locknagar (Scotland) and Tôno (Japan) aureoles illustrate contact effects induced by plutons large enough to be classified as batholiths. Pressures of the order of at least 2 kb at Lochnagar are indicated by the direct breakdown of muscovite-quartz to sillimanite rather than to andalusite. Since corundum-orthoclase assemblages have also been recorded, temperatures near the contact may have approached 700°C. This is borne out, too, by prevalence of two-pyroxene assemblages in place of those with hornblende in basic rocks. One of the corundum hornfelses is located 1500 m from the exposed contact on Chinner's map (Chinner, 1962, p. 319, point *B*). The pyroxene-hornfels zone extends at least 2000 m from the contact. Clearly the outward gradient has a flat slope (Fig. 6-32, *E*). It represents high temperature combined with a pressure unusually high for the pyroxene-hornfels facies.

The rocks of the Tôno aureole lie entirely in the hornblende-hornfels facies. Within a few hundred meters of the contact the andalusite-sillimanite transition (2) occurs at somewhat lower temperature than the muscovite-quartz breakdown (3) (Fig. 6-32, *F*). This fixes pressures in the vicinity of 1500 bars. Here, as at Lochnagar, the drop in temperature with distance from the contact is gentle. Development of diopside-assemblages (11), rather than those with tremolite, and appearance of wollastonite (7) show that at the corresponding temperatures (520 and 570°C, respectively) partial pressures of CO_2 were maintained at less than about 100 bars. Judging from the distance from the contact at which hornblende-plagioclase is first developed, the transition from the albite-epidote-hornfels to the hornblende-hornfels facies is fixed as about 420 to 450°C.

Roof of Sierra Nevada batholith. Pressures in the roof region of the Sierra Nevada batholith of California have been variously estimated on geologic evidence as between 2 and 5 kb. The possibility of much lower pressures controlled by burial under a relatively thin cover is raised by the small time interval between the emplacement of the latest of the component plutons (about 90 million years ago) and the deposition of later covering sediments on the eroded granitic surface in Eocene times.

Considering the size and composite nature of the batholith, the pattern of mineral paragenesis in the larger enclosed pendants is remarkably constant. Temperatures close to contacts in many places rose beyond the limit of stability of muscovite-quartz. The usual breakdown product is andalusite (with K-feldspar); but occasionally it is sillimanite. Assuming that Al_2SiO_5 normally crystallizes as the stable polymorph we must infer pressures no greater than 1 to $1\frac{1}{2}$ kb and temperatures mainly below 600°C. The prevalence of hornblendic assemblages bears out this conclusion. At such temperatures periclase could form from dolomite (as it does in one or two localities) only at extremely low partial pressures of CO_2. Widespread occurrence of wollastonite in Sierra pendants carries the same implication.

Without reconstructing actual gradients at any one locality, it is concluded that the general level of the roof of the Sierra Nevada batholith reached to within 3 to 5 km of the surface at the time of intrusion ($P_l = 1 - 1\frac{1}{2}$ kb).

Low-pressure regional gradients. The mineral parageneses of the Ryoke belt, Japan, and the broad concentric zones surrounding migmatitic and granitic bodies in the central Pyrenees and in northern Portugal are consistent only with metamorphism at low pressure. This was clearly recognized by those who have worked in these areas: Miyashiro (1961), Zwart (1962), and Brink (1960). In each case a broad zone in which andalusite appears to be the stable polymorph of Al_2SiO_5 passes with increasing metamorphic grade (temperature) into a zone of sillimanite. Muscovite-quartz may be ubiquitous in pelitic assemblages. The breakdown to K-feldspar-sillimanite, where it does occur, coincides approximately with the Andalusite → Sillimanite transition.

Possible pressure-temperature gradients consistent with these data fall between limits such as *LL* and *MM*, Fig. 6-33 (stippled field). There is no conflict between these values of pressure and those deduced by Zwart (1962, p. 63), who computed the probable cover, from stratigraphic and structural data, as about 4 km. His temperatures (0–2 on curve *ZZ*) seem too high; but they are based on Winkler's estimate of the first appearance of biotite, which has been criticized on p. 118. Miyashiro's (1961, p. 285, curve 2) estimate of a pressure range of 5 to 6 kb for the

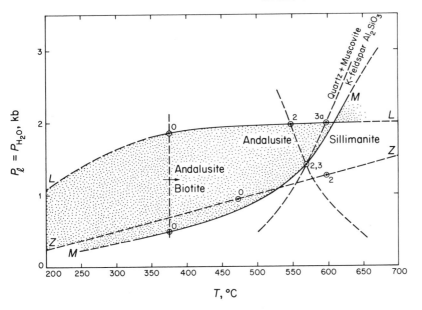

Fig. 6-33. Possible temperature gradients (between *LL, MM* within stippled field) for hornblende-hornfels facies in regional metamorphism. *ZZ* is gradient deduced by *H. J. Zwart* (1962) for the Bosost area, Pyrenees. Numbers refer to equilibria of Fig. 6-30 (see also text). Broken curves refer to experimentally determined equilibria (Fig. 6-30).

Ryoke metamorphism is obviously too high if andalusite is assumed to crystallize within the stability field of Fig. 6-30.

The temperature-pressure regime in the Bosost area is hard to reconcile with Zwart's view that the central granite-migmatite complex is the result of granitization involving partial fusion of rocks at depths of 3 or 4 km. Where is the heat source for metamorphism and granitization at so shallow a depth? Much more likely is the alternative interpretation that the granite-migmatite body represents intrusion of hot magma rising from the depths. In this model the granite would be the heat source, not the expression of heat concentration from shallow sources unknown.

TEMPERATURE-PRESSURE FIELDS OF INDIVIDUAL LOW-PRESSURE FACIES

The lower limit of temperature reflected in low-pressure metamorphism at the fringe of a contact aureole cannot be defined precisely. The initial mineral assemblage was not necessarily in equilibrium at the onset of metamorphism. Reaction kinetics possibly play a significant role.

The most satisfactory and widespread mineralogical data are the appearance of biotite, in many instances accompanied or closely followed by andalusite. The only satisfactory experimentally established datum for calibrating this point in metamorphism is the pyrophyllite dehydration curve. Andalusite can form freely only at temperatures beyond this curve, that is, above 430°C at $P_{H_2O} = 3$ kb, 410° at 2 kb, and 380° at 1 kb (Kerrick, 1966).[1] Temperatures of this order are taken as marking the lower limits of the albite-epidote-hornfels facies.

Even less satisfactory is the boundary between this facies and the hornblende-hornfels facies. The transition is marked by a sharp rise in the anorthite content of plagioclase, elimination of epidote, and the change from actinolite to aluminous hornblende. These reactions presumably do not occur precisely simultaneously; but field evidence strongly points to a narrow temperature interval for the transition (estimated in the Tôno aureole as perhaps between 420 and 450°C at $P_{H_2O} = 1.5$ kb). On these grounds we assign to the albite-epidote-hornfels facies a temperature span no greater than 50° at any give pressure.

A much wider temperature range must be allotted to the hornblende-hornfels facies. It certainly extends to or beyond one of our best-established boundaries, that of the breakdown of muscovite to corundum-orthoclase. The high-temperature limit is pictured, not as a sharp line but as a band enclosing a family of equilibrium curves for the breakdown of metamorphic hornblendes to pyroxene assemblages. Following Chinner (1960, pp. 211-212) it is permissible to attribute the general reducing environment of contact aureoles to the influence of magmatic water diffusing steadily outward from the cooling magma. The low values of P_{O_2} in such water are pictured by Chinner as being controlled by "equilibrium with ferrous silicates and magnetite-spinel phases of the crystallizing melt." The boundary between the hornblende-hornfels and the pyroxene-hornfels facies in Fig. 6-34 is based on the occurrence of hornblendic versus two-pyroxene assemblages in the Comrie and Lochnagar aureoles. Reducing conditions might well permit the hornblende-pyroxene reaction in the inner zone of an aureole at temperatures possibly hundreds of degrees below those recorded by Yoder and Tilley (1962) for an extreme environment of oxidation.

The high-temperature limit of the pyroxene-hornfels facies at pressures above a few hundred kilobars could extend into the field of incipient fusion of common rocks. On Jaeger's model of cooling by conduction and outward migration of water, it should lie significantly below the temperature

[1] H. D. Kerrick: Results of experimental work carried out in the Department of Geology and Geophysics, University of California, Berkeley.

range of largely molten granodioritic and tonalitic magmas, which might well be not much greater than 800°C at P_{H_2O} = 2000 bars. At very low pressures there is a Pyroxene-hornfels → Sanidinite boundary. A convenient datum might be the experimentally established curve for the Diopside-calcite ⇌ Akermanite equilibrium. This has been arbitrarily selected in Fig. 6-35 (curve D in Fig. 4-8). The field of the sanidinite facies certainly overlaps far into that of fusion of pelitic and quartzo-feldspathic sediments. Aramaki (1961) experimentally investigated the beginning of fusion in pelitic and calcareous assemblages of the sanidinite facies occurring as bombs ejected during eruption from the Asama volcano, of a lava whose temperature was directly measured as 1000°C. He placed the P-T range of the metamorphic assemblages between 945 and 1005°C at P_l = 200 to 800 bars.

Boundaries in Fig. 6-35 have been drawn on the basis of collective data just presented. Computed natural gradients taken from the preceding figures are shown as broken lines.

It is emphasized that Fig. 6-35 is valid only insofar as there is no general significant deviation from the assumptions upon which it is based:

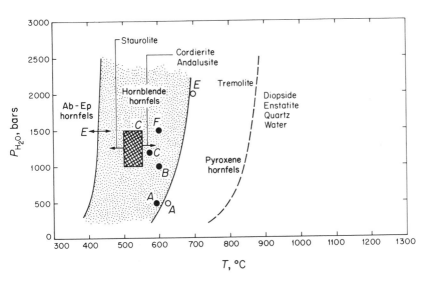

Fig. 6-34. Limits of hornblende-hornfels facies (stippled field) from geologic data of Figs. 6-31, 6-32 (*same letters*). Cross-hatched rectangle shows limits for transition Staurolite ⇌ Cordierite-andalusite inferred from Santa Rosa aureole. Broken curve is experimentally determined for tremolite breakdown (6, Fig. 6-30b). (*After F. R. Boyd.*)

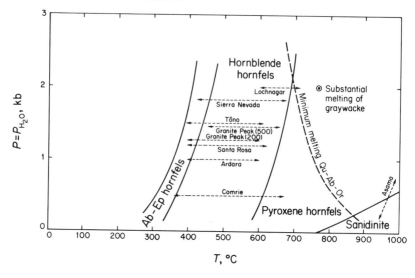

T, °C

Fig. 6-35. Tentative diagram showing P-T fields of the four facies of low-pressure metamorphism. Inferred gradients (assuming uniform pressure) for six examples described in the text are shown as horizontal broken lines. Granite Peak gradients drawn for $P_{CO_2} = 200$ and $P_{CO_2} = 500$ bars, respectively.

(1) $P_{H_2O} = P_l$;* (2) The natural assemblages of phases used to construct natural gradients express divariant equilibria (in terms of the variables T and P); (3) Experimentally determined equilibrium curves used for calibration of natural assemblages are not grossly in error. The gradients of Fig. 6-35 clearly are open to current criticism by others, and to future modification.

If the above model is accepted, two further conclusions emerge. First is the generalization that the ratio P_{CO_2}/P_{H_2O} in the pore fluid of carbonate rocks is normally maintained at a low level during contact metamorphism. This situation could allow fusion of dolomite in the pyroxene-hornfels facies. In the second place there is close agreement

---

*Yoder and Tilley (1962, p. 469) favor the alternative possibility that the pyroxene-hornfels facies develops in an environment where P_{H_2O} is significantly lower than load pressure. This conclusion is based on their experimental evidence regarding the Hornblende $\rightleftharpoons$ Pyroxenes equilibrium under highly oxidizing conditions. This writer's preference for Chinner's model of a system open to magmatic water, such that P_{H_2O} is not significantly lower than P_l, was stated on p. 246. The model of Yoder and Tilley raises the difficulty of invoking "deficiency" of water in the course of a reaction involving dehydration of amphibolite, and dehydration of micas in adjacent pelitic schists. To this writer this difficulty is insuperable.

between gradients based on combined geologic, mineralogical, and experimental data and those predicted by Jaeger. The petrologist is indebted to Lovering and Jaeger whose imagination prompted them to examine the working of a complicated geologic system in terms of a purely physical model permitting the use of experimentally determined physical constants.

REFERENCES

Agrell, S. O., and J. M. Langley: The dolerite plug at Tievebulliagh near Cushendall, Co. Antrim, *Proc. Roy. Irish Acad. Sec. B*, vol. 59, no. 7, pp. 93–127, 1958.

Almond, D. C.: Metamorphism of Tertiary lavas in Strathaird, Skye, *Trans. Roy. Soc. Edinburgh*, vol. 65, no. 16, pp. 413–434, 1964.

Aramaki, S.: Sillimanite and cordierite from volcanic xenoliths, *Am. Mineralogist*, vol. 46, pp. 1154–1165, 1961.

Bateman, P., et al.: The Sierra Nevada batholith, *U.S. Geol. Surv. Prof. Paper* 414-D, 1963.

Best, M. G.: Petrology and structural analysis of metamorphic rocks in the southwestern Sierra Nevada foothills, California, *Univ. Calif. Berkeley Publ. Geol. Sci.*, vol. 42, no. 3, pp. 111–158, 1963.

————, and L. E. Weiss: Mineralogical relations in some pelitic hornfelses from the southern Sierra Nevada, California, *Am. Mineralogist*, vol. 49, pp. 1240–1266, 1964.

Bowen, N. L., and J. F. Schairer: The system $MgO-FeO-SiO_2$, *Am. J. Sci.*, vol. 29, pp. 151–217, 1935.

Brauns, R.: "Die kristallinen Schiefer des Laacher See-Gebietes und ihre Umwandlung zur Sanidinit," Stuttgart, 1911.

Brink, A. H.: Petrology and ore geology of the Villa Real region, northern Portugal, *Comm. Serv. Geol. Portugal*, no. 93, 1960.

Burnham, C. W.: Contact metamorphism of magnesian limestones at Crestmore, California, *Bull. Geol. Soc. Am.*, vol. 70, pp. 879–920, 1959.

Chesterman, C. W.: Contact metamorphism of the Twin Lakes region, Fresno County, California, *Calif. J. Mines Geol.*, vol. 38, pp. 243–281, 1942.

Chinner, G. A.: Pelitic gneisses with varying ferrous/ferric ratios from Glen Clova, Angus, Scotland, *J. Petrol.*, vol. 1, pp. 178–217, 1960.

————: Almandine in thermal aureoles, *J. Petrol.* vol. 3, pp. 316–340, 1962.

————: The distribution of pressure and temperature during Dalradian metamorphism, *Geol. Soc. London Quart. J.*, vol. 122, pp. 159–186, 1966.

Compton, R. R.: Significance of amphibole paragenesis in the Bidwell Bar region, California, *Am. Mineralogist*, vol. 43, pp. 890–907, 1958.

————: Contact metamorphism in Santa Rosa Range, Nevada, *Bull. Geol. Soc. America*, vol. 71, pp. 1383–1416, 1960.

Curtis, G. H., J. Evernden, and J. Lipson: Age determination of some granitic rocks in California, *Calif. State Div. Mines Spec. Rept. 54*, 1958.

DeBooy, T.: Géologie de la région de Francardo (Corse), academic dissertation, University of Amsterdam, 1954.

Deer, W. A., R. A. Howie, and J. Zussman: "Rock-forming minerals," vol. 1, Wiley, New York, 1962.

Durrell, C.: Metamorphism in the southern Sierra Nevada northeast of Visalia, California, *Univ. Calif. Publ., Bull. Dept. Geol. Sci.*, vol. 25, no. 1, pp. 1–118, 1940.

Eskola, P.: On the relation between chemical and mineralogical composition in the metamorphic rocks in the Orijärvi region, *Comm. géol. Finlande Bull.* 44, 1915.

————: Die metamorphen Gesteine, "Die Entstehung der Gesteine" (T. F. W. Barth, C. W. Correns, P. Eskola), pp. 263–407, 1939.

Eugster, H. P., and D. R. Wones, Stability relations of the ferruginous biotite, annite, *J. Petrol.*, vol. 3, pp. 82–125, 1962.

Floyd, P. A.: Metasomatic hornfelses of the Land's End aureole at Tater-du, Cornwall, *J. Petrol.*, vol. 6, pp. 223–245, 1965.

Fyfe, W. S., F. J. Turner, and J. Verhoogen: Metamorphic reactions and metamorphic facies, *Geol. Soc. Am. Mem.* 73, 1958.

Goldschmidt, V. M.: Die Kontaktmetamorphose im Kristianiagebiet, *Kristiania (Oslo) Vidensk. Skr. I, Math.-Naturv. Kl.*, no. 11, 1911.

Harker, A.: The Tertiary igneous rocks of Skye, *Mem. Geol. Surv. United Kingdom*, 1904.

————: "Metamorphism," Methuen, London, 1932.

Jasmund, K., and G. Hentschel: Seltene Mineralparagenesen in den Kalksteineinschlüssen der Lava des Ettringer Bellerberges bei Mayen (Eifel) *Beitr. Mineral. Petrog.*, vol. 10, pp. 296–314, 1964.

Joplin, G. A.: The exogenous contact-zone at Ben Bullen, New South Wales, *Geol. Mag.*, vol. 72, pp. 385–400, 1935.

Kanisawa, S.: Metamorphic rocks of the southwestern part of the Kitakami mountainland, Japan. *Tohoku Univ. Sci. Repts.*, Ser. 3, vol. 9, pp. 155–198, 1964.

Loomis, A. A.: Contact metamorphic reactions and processes in the Mt. Tallac roof remnant, Sierra Nevada, California, *J. Petrol.*, vol. 7, pp. 221–245, 1966.

MacGregor, A. C.: Scottish pyroxene-granulite hornfelses and the Odenwald beerbachites, *Geol. Mag.*, vol. 68, pp. 506–521, 1931.

Melson, G. M.: Equilibria in calc-silicate hornfels, Lewis and Clark County, Montana, *Am. Mineralogist*, vol. 51, pp. 402–421, 1966.

Misch, P.: Stable association wollastonite-anorthite and other calc-silicate assemblages in amphibolite-facies crystalline schists of Nanga Parbat, *Beitr. Mineral. Petrog.*, vol. 10, pp. 315–356, 1964.

Miyashiro, A.: Regional metamorphism of the Gosaisyo-Takanuki district in the central Abukuma plateau, *Tokyo University J. Fac. Sci.*, sec. 2, vol. 11, pp. 219–272, 1958.

————: Evolution of metamorphic belts, *J. Petrol.*, vol. 2, pp. 277–311, 1961.

Muir, I. D., and C. E. Tilley: The compositions of coexisting pyroxenes in metamorphic assemblages, *Geol. Mag.*, vol. 95, pp. 403–408, 1958.

Newton, R. C.: Some calc-silicate equilibrium relations, *Am. J. Sci.*, vol. 264, pp. 204–222, 1966.

Osborne, G. D.: The metamorphosed limestones and associated contaminated igneous rocks of the Carlingford district, Co. Louth, *Geol. Mag.*, vol. 69, pp. 209–233, 1932.

Parker, R. B.: Petrology and structure of the pre-Tertiary rocks in western Alpine County, California, doctoral dissertation, University of California, Berkeley, 1953.

Read, H. H.: Metamorphism and migmatization in the Ythan Valley, Aberdeenshire, *Trans. Geol. Soc. Edinburgh*, vol. 15, pp. 265–279, 1952.

Rose, R. L.: Metamorphic rocks of the May Lake area, Yosemite Park, and a metamorphic facies problem, *Bull. Geol. Soc. Am.*, vol. 69, p. 1703, 1958.

Searle, E. J.: Xenoliths and metamorphosed rocks associated with the Auckland basalts, *New Zealand J. Geol. Geophys.*, vol. 5, pp. 384-403, 1962.

Seki, Y.: Petrological study of hornfelses in the central part of the Median Zone of Kitakami Mountainland, *Saitama Univ. Sci. Repts.*, ser. B, vol. 2, no. 3, pp. 307–361, 1957.

———, and M. Yamasaki: Aluminian ferroanthophyllite from Kitakami Mountainland, northeastern Japan, *Am. Mineralogist*, vol. 42, pp. 506–520, 1957.

Suwa, K.: Petrological and geological studies on the Ryoke metamorphic belt, *Nagaya Univ. J. Earth Sci.*, vol. 9, pp. 224–303, 1961.

Thomas, H. H.: On certain xenolithic Tertiary minor intrusions in the island of Mull, *Geol. Soc. London Quart. J.*, vol. 78, pp. 229–259, 1922.

———: *in* The geology of Ardnamurchan, northwest Mull, and Coll, *Geol. Surv. Scotland Mem.*, 1930.

Tilley, C. E.: Contact metamorphism in the Comrie area of the Perthshire Highlands, *Geol. Soc. London Quart. J.*, vol. 80, pp. 22–71, 1924.

———: On larnite and its associated minerals from the contact zone of Scawt Hill, Co. Antrim, *Mineral. Mag.*, vol. 22, pp. 77–86, 1929.

———: Metasomatism associated with the greenstone hornfelses of Kenidjaik and Botallack, Cornwal, *Mineral. Mag.*, vol. 24, pp. 181–202, 1935.

———: Tricalcium disilicate (rankinite) a new mineral from Scawt Hill, Co. Antrim, *Mineral. Mag.*, vol. 26, pp. 190–196, 1942.

———: Earlier stages in the metamorphism of siliceous dolomites, *Mineral. Mag.*, vol. 28, pp. 272–276, 1948.

———: The zoned contact skarns of the Broadford area, Skye, *Mineral. Mag.*, vol. 29, pp. 621–666, 1951.

Turner, F. J.: Mineralogical and structural evolution of the metamorphic rocks, *Geol. Soc. Am. Mem.* 30, 1948.

Turner, F. J.: Note on the genesis of brucite in contact metamorphism of dolomite, *Beitr. Mineral. Petrog.*, vol. 11, pp. 393–397, 1965.

———: Thermodynamic appraisal of steps in progressive metamorphism of siliceous limestones and dolomites, *Neues Jahrb. Mineral. Monatsh.*, 1967, pp. 1–22, 1967.

———, and J. Verhoogen: "Metamorphic Petrology," 2d ed., McGraw-Hill, New York, 1960.

Watanabe, T.: Geology and mineralization of the Surian district, Tyôsen (Korea), *J. Fac. Sci. Hokkaido Univ.*, ser. 4, vol. 6, pp. 205–303, 1943.

Winkler, H. G. F.: Genesen von Graniten und Migmatiten auf Grund neuer Experimente, *Geol. Rundschau*, vol. 51, pp. 347–364, 1961.

Wyllie, P. J.: Melting relationships in the system CaO–MgO–CO$_2$–H$_2$O, with petrological applications, *J. Petrol.*, vol. 6, pp. 101–123, 1965.

———, and O. F. Tuttle: Hydrothermal melting of shales, *Geol. Mag.*, vol. 98, pp.
56–66, 1961.

Yoder, H. S., and C. E. Tilley,: Origin of basaltic magmas, *J. Geol.*, vol. 3, pp. 342–
532, 1962.

Zwart, H. J.: On the determination of polymetamorphic mineral associations and its
application to the Bosost area (Central Pyrenees), *Geol. Rundschau*, vol. 52,
pp. 38–65, 1962.

———: Geological map of the Paleozoic of the central Pyrenees, Sheet 6, *Leidse
Geol. Mededel.*, vol. 33, pp. 193–254, 1965.

Review of
Metamorphic Facies
II: Facies of Medium
to High Pressure

THE LOW-GRADE FACIES OF REGIONAL METAMORPHISM

Initial Stages of Metamorphism

By burial alone, water-saturated geosynclinal sediments and associated volcanic rocks eventually reach an environment of temperature and
pressure conducive to mutual reaction between associated mineral phases.
It is customary to treat as diagenesis the first incomplete responses to
conditions of increasing load. The initial assemblages may have approximated equilibrium in the sedimentary environment: e.g., montmorillonitic
and illite-bearing shales and many calcareous sediments. Or, as in volcanic
sands consisting of high-temperature phases (glass, pyroxenes, hornblendes, etc.), they may, from the moment of deposition, have been significantly out of equilibrium. Upon such factors as these, and especially upon

the environmental temperature, depends the activation energy necessary to make the early metamorphic reactions effective.

There must be a transition, with increasing depth of burial, between diagenesis and regional metamorphism. Many of the changes involved (e.g., reconstitution of clays, crystallization of quartz and alkali feldspars, destruction of high-temperature minerals, and precipitation of carbonates) are common to both. Where the bulk of the rock, including even coarse particles of sand grade, is substantially affected, the process may properly be called metamorphic. A criterion of incipient metamorphism is schistosity, for this is the result of ruptural deformation which reduces grain size and accelerates reaction even at relatively low temperatures. Exceptionally, however, even without the aid of deformation, chemically unstable rocks may become completely converted to low-temperature assemblages, rich in zeolites and duplicating the products of diagenesis. Whether the resulting mineral facies (in this case the zeolite facies) are termed diagenetic or metamorphic is of no great significance (Fyfe, Turner, and Verhoogen, 1958, p. 215). Our knowledge of their mineralogical characteristics and of the depths at which they may develop to a mature state comes from the researches of metamorphic petrologists (Coombs, 1954; Brothers, 1956) and of workers in the fields of stratigraphy and sedimentary geology (Packham and Crook, 1960; Hay, 1966).

On geologic and mineralogical (including experimental) grounds it is possible, as will be done later, to construct probable fields of temperature and pressure for each of the facies representing the onset of regional metamorphism. Initiation of metamorphism in a given situation may be referred to some point in a rather wide P-T field. The point of first significant metamorphism will depend upon the local P-T gradient in relation to depth, and on the activation energy required to render reaction effective in each sedimentary or volcanic system. Also significant will be the effect of contemporaneous deformation as a source of energy and a stimulus to reaction. The sequence of facies in low-grade metamorphism differs, therefore, in different metamorphic terranes. In Miyashiro's terminology each low-grade sequence marks the beginning of a separate facies series.

Following Coombs (1960, 1961) we recognize four facies of low-grade regional metamorphism: (1) zeolite, (2) prehnite-pumpellyite-metagraywacke, (3) greenschist, (4) glaucophane-lawsonite-schist. The first two are based on the observations of Coombs and his associates in the regional metamorphic terrane of southern New Zealand (Chap. 1, pp. 33; Fig. 1-15). The most comprehensive accounts of the mineralogical characteristics of the first three facies refer to observations in the same region. For this reason, in the following sections relating to these three low-grade facies, special emphasis is placed on the New Zealand parageneses. But they are duplicated elsewhere.

Zeolite Facies

The zeolite facies was defined (Fyfe, Turner, and Verhoogen, 1958, p. 216) on the basis of Coombs' (1954) account of extensive alteration in deeply buried Triassic eugeosynclinal sediments in southern New Zealand. The type locality, in the Taringatura Hills (Fig. 7-1; cf. also Fig. 1-15), is a stratigraphic section nearly 10 km in thickness, located a few kilometers from the southwestern margin of the Otago Schist terrane. The intervening area is occupied by late Paleozoic metasediments, merging ultimately into the schists themselves. The paragenesis of the zeolite facies at the type locality, and that of metamorphic assemblages in various stages of development in comparable rocks elsewhere in New Zealand, has been recorded by Coombs (1954, 1960) and by Coombs, Ellis, Fyfe, and Taylor (1959).

Characteristic mineral assemblages in the New Zealand metagraywackes, whether fully developed as in many beds at the type locality, or represented merely by products of deep diagenesis in otherwise unaltered rocks, are as follows:

1. Heulandite-analcite-quartz; with montmorillonite, celadonite and sphene as possible additional phases
2. Laumontite-albite-quartz (-chlorite)
3. Quartz-albite-adularia (metasomatic)

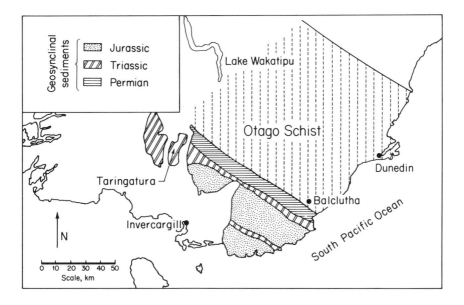

Fig. 7-1. Simplified map of southeastern portion, South Island, New Zealand.

The first assemblage is formed in the upper half of the stratigraphic section, the second and third only in the lower half. Allowing for 3 to 5 km as the maximum possible thickness of post-Triassic overburden at the time of metamorphism (Coombs et al., p. 59), the heulandite-analcite-quartz assemblage of New Zealand is correlated with depths whose upper limits are 1 to 5 km, and lower limits 5 to 10 km. The laumontite-albite-quartz assemblage is formed in a lower zone, the maximum depth of which may have been as great as 15 km, and was not less than 9 km. Throughout the laumontite zone, especially in the deeper levels, pumpellyite and prehnite are beginning to appear in place of laumontite.

Prehnite-pumpellyite-metagraywacke Facies

As early as 1937, Hutton (1937, p. 530) found that pumpellyite is the characteristic calcium-aluminum silicate of half-reconstituted schistose metagraywackes on the borders of the Otago Schist region.[1] In De Roever's account of regional metamorphism in Celebes, there is a discussion of pumpellyite in glaucophanic and in nonglaucophanic parageneses (De Roever, 1947, pp. 150-152, 162). Noting that pumpellyite is by no means always associated with glaucophane, De Roever (1947, p. 162) was "inclined to assume that the pumpellyite in eastern Central Celebes belongs to a separate metamorphic facies, containing among others colorless amphibole, albite, quartz, and carbonate as other typical minerals, and which is a kind of precursor of the lawsonite-glaucophanite subfacies."

De Roever's conclusions were borne out by the work of Brothers (1956) in northern, and of Coombs et al. (1959) in southern New Zealand. In both areas graywackes have been partially converted on a regional scale to pumpellyite- and prehnite-bearing assemblages. On this basis, Coombs (1950, p. 341) defined a prehnite-pumpellyite-metagraywacke facies. Characteristic assemblages (Fig. 7-2) as recorded by Coombs (1960, 1961; Coombs et al. 1959, pp. 65-68) are:

1. Quartz-albite-prehnite-pumpellyite-chlorite-sphene; the usual assemblage of newly crystallized minerals in altered graywackes

2. Quartz-prehnite (-calcite-pumpellyite); in segregation veins in altered graywackes

3. Albite-pumpellyite-chlorite-sphene-epidote-quartz; in spilitic lavas.

4. Prehnite-calcite (-albite-quartz-chlorite); in slightly recrystallized limestone

5. Quartz-albite-muscovite-pumpellyite-epidote-stilpnomelane (-chlorite-actinolite); in largely recrystallized semischists of graywacke parentage in low-grade subzones (Chl. 1, Chl. 2) of the Otago Schist "chlorite zone."

---

[1]Subzones Chl. 1 to Chl. 3 of the "chlorite zone" as recognized at that time.

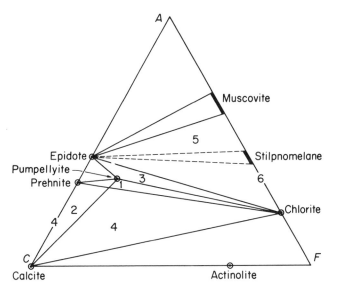

Fig. 7-2. Prehnite-pumpellyite-metagraywacke facies; Permian and Triassic eugeosynclinal sedimentary rocks, New Zealand. *ACF* diagram for rocks with excess SiO_2 and K_2O. Quartz and albite are possible additional phases. Broken ties refer to rocks of relatively high grade, lacking prehnite (actinolite may be present in these).

6. Quartz-albite-muscovite-chlorite; in pelitic schists of subzones Chl. 2, Chl. 3

In the Otago Schist region, passage through subzone Chl. 3 into the fully recrystallized greenschist-facies assemblages of subzone Chl. 4 is marked by disappearance of pumpellyite, in place of which epidote becomes more abundant and more closely approaches clinozoisite.

In New Zealand, and probably elsewhere, the nature of the first recognizably metamorphic assemblages in partially reconstituted gray-wackes and shales is not everywhere the same. It depends partly on variation in rock composition, but probably more on differences between local temperature-pressure gradients and upon the role of deformation in the early stages of metamorphism. In the semischists of the Chl. 1 and Chl. 2 subzones, for example, prehnite is either absent or insignificant; and the first-formed metamorphic products usually include abundant actinolite, chlorite, and stilpnomelane. Except for ubiquitous pumpellyite, the assemblage from the very first is that of the lowest grade in the greenschist facies. On the other hand, in the younger (Triassic) rocks of the Taringatura section, prehnite and pumpellyite are beginning to appear in laumontite-bearing rocks of the zeolite facies at depths where pressures cannot have been much less than 3 kb. Elsewhere, as in the graywackes to the north of the Otago Schist belt (Alpine graywackes), prehnite and pumpellyite appear together without preceding extensive development of laumontite.

Much more restricted than prehnite-pumpellyite metagraywackes in New Zealand, though locally extensive at lower stratigraphic levels, are rather similar simple assemblages containing lawsonite (Fig. 7-3):

    7. Quartz-albite-chlorite-muscovite-lawsonite; in derivatives of shale (possibly bentonitic)

    8. Albite-chlorite-lawsonite (-quartz-calcite); in metamorphosed volcanic sands

    9. Lawsonite-calcite (-quartz-albite); in marble

In lawsonite-bearing rocks such as these, lacking either aragonite or pumpellyite, we see a transition from the zeolite and pumpellyite-prehnite metagraywacke facies on the one hand, to the high-pressure glaucophane-lawsonite-schist facies on the other.

A transition of another type, i.e., presumably along a slightly different *P-T* gradient, is exemplified by the pumpellyite-prehnite-metagraywacke facies as developed in Orcas Island, northwest Washington (Vance, 1966). The recorded mineral assemblages (Fig. 7-4) are much the same as 1 to 4 above (the New Zealand paragenesis), but with a notable exception. The $CaCO_3$ polymorph in recrystallized limestones and in veins is aragonite. Stilpnomelane has not been recorded. The rocks, as in the outer part of the Otago Schist belt of New Zealand, have been fully reconstituted mineralogically on a regional scale.

The mutually exclusive roles of aragonite and lawsonite in the two transitional parageneses do not necessarily imply, as suggested by Vance, that aragonite in metamorphic rocks is not an index of high pressure (see later, p. 358).

Greenschist Facies

Definition and mineralogical characteristics. The greenschist facies includes the common products of low-grade regional metamorphism as represented in all parts of the world by completely recrystallized, usually well-foliated rocks in the zones of chlorite and of biotite (cf. pp. 25–26). From mineral assemblages of even lower grade (usually found only in partially reconstituted rocks), those of the greenschist facies are distinguished by absence of zeolites, prehnite and pumpellyite. Absence of lawsonite, jadeite, omphacite, aragonite, and (except in transitional rocks) the glaucophane amphiboles distinguishes the greenschist from the glaucophane-lawsonite-schist facies.

At higher grades than that of the greenschist facies, beyond the almandine isograd in the Barrovian zonal sequence, regionally metamorphosed rocks enter the amphibolite facies. Here the dominant assem-

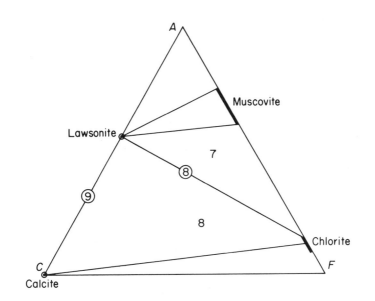

Fig. 7-3. Facies transitional between prehnite-pumpellyite-metagraywacke and glaucophane-lawsonite-schist facies, Nelson, New Zealand. *ACF* diagram for rocks with excess SiO_2 and K_2O. Quartz and albite are possible additional phases.

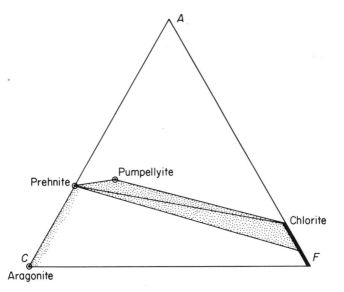

Fig. 7-4. Prehnite-pumpellyite-metagraywacke facies. Orcas Island, Washington, *ACF* diagram for rocks with excess SiO_2 (stippled areas). Quartz and albite are possible additional phases.

blage in basic rocks is hornblende-plagioclase (mostly An_{25} to An_{60}). Plagioclase in the greenschist assemblages, on the other hand, is almost pure albite; and the common amphibole, when present, is nonaluminous actinolite. In the Barrovian facies series, both hornblende and almandine appear well in advance of the point at which plagioclase becomes significantly calcic. So there is a transitional set of mineral assemblages which in the Dalradian series of the southeastern Scottish Highlands covers the outer part of the almandine zone. Its status with respect to facies is debatable (cf. Fyfe, Turner, and Verhoogen, 1958, p. 224; Turner and Verhoogen, 1960, p. 534). We have formerly included it as a subfacies of the greenschist facies. This usage has been criticized (cf. Lambert, 1965, p. 287) and has not found general acceptance among petrologists. To conform to what seemed to be more general practice today, we then reinstated the older term albite-epidote-amphibolite facies. In the present account this facies will be treated simply as a greenschist-amphibolite transition facies (see pp. 303–304).

In the greenschist facies, as restricted above, characteristic minerals are albite, white micas, biotite (restricted to higher grades), prochlorites with a relatively high Fe^{2+}/Mg ratio, epidote minerals, tremolite-actinolite, calcite, dolomite (in silica-deficient rocks), and in magnesian rocks talc and antigorite. The principal white mica is muscovite (the 2M polymorph), characteristically having a phengitic composition. Chloritoid is found in rocks high in ferrous iron and in aluminum; stilpnomelane in assemblages rich in iron and manganese; piedmontite and spessartite in manganiferous rocks such as metacherts. Paragonite occurs only in assemblages having a high $Al/(Na + K)$ ratio, and pyrophyllite in assemblages still richer in aluminum (e.g., metabauxites).

For details of parageneses in the greenschist facies the reader is referred to literature cited by Turner and Verhoogen (1960, pp. 534, 537, 538) and to more recent work: Reed (1958), Zen (1960), Iwasaki (1963), Atherton (1964), Banno (1964), McNamara (1965), Chatterjee (1966), Crawford (1966), and Brown (1967).

Greenschist facies in southern New Zealand. The mineral paragenesis in fully recrystallized rocks (subzone Chl. 4) of the very extensive chlorite zone of the Otago Schist terrane (Fig. 7-1) in southern New Zealand is remarkably uniform (cf. pp. 31–33). It is known especially from Hutton's (1940) account of the northwestern part of this region. Hutton's data are consistent with the latest and more detailed work of Brown (1967) on the southeastern end of the Otago schist belt, twenty or thirty kilometers west of the city of Dunedin. Brown's data were obtained from two closely sampled northeast-southwest traverses each some 60 to 70 km in length (*BB* in inset, Fig. 7-8). The grade rises perceptibly toward the northeast. The southwest end of each traverse is just within the limits of the greenschist facies proper; further southwest lie schists and semischists of subzones Chl. 3 containing abundant pumpellyite and here classified (p. 267) as transitional between the greenschist and the prehnite-pumpellyite-meta-graywacke facies. Biotite and garnet are consistently present, although always in minor amount, in quartz-muscovite-chlorite-albite schists along the northeastern half of Brown's traverses. On this basis, following Robinson (1958), Brown has distinguished a northeastern biotite zone from a southwestern chlorite zone. His biotite isograd and biotite zone, however, are not strictly comparable with the biotite isograd and zone as mapped (Turner, 1938; Mason, 1962) in the Alpine region some 200 km northwest of the area studied by Brown (see later, pp. 275–277).

The mineral assemblages recognized in Brown's chlorite zone represent metamorphosed graywackes, volcanic sands, and much less abundant basaltic tuffs (or lavas), shales and cherts. They are shown on the *ACF* projection in Fig. 7-5; further details are represented on other projections (Figs. 7-6 and 7-7). In the following summary, the identity of the associated opaque phase or phases is given in parentheses:

    A. Quartzo-feldspathic

        1. Quartz-albite-epidote-muscovite-stilpnomelane (graphite); with or without actinolite

        2. Quartz-albite-epidote-muscovite-chlorite (graphite); with or without actinolite and/or stilpnomelane

    B. Manganiferous metacherts

        3. Quartz-spessartite (graphite); minor muscovite, chlorite, epidote

    C. Basic

        4. Chlorite-albite-epidote-muscovite-actinolite-sphene (magnetite or hematite); with or without stilpnomelane and/or calcite

Assemblages in the biotite zone are similar to those of the chlorite zone except in the following respects (cf. Figs. 7-6 and 7-7):

(a) Biotite, which is completely absent in the chlorite zone[1] is present in amounts between 2 and 5 percent in half the quartzo-feldspathic rocks of the biotite zone. The ratio Fe^{2+}/Mg in analysed biotites is high (1.3), as also is $(Fe^{2+} + Mg)/Al$ (about 1.8).

(b) Garnet, also virtually absent in rocks of the chlorite zone, is

---

[1] Reports by McNamara (1965, 1966) of widespread biotite in the chlorite zone of eastern Otago, as here defined, are based on misidentification of a highly pleochroic and birefringent chlorite-vermiculite. This is comparable with the oxidized chlorites of the Italian Alps as described by Chatterjee (1966). In our earlier work of thirty years ago, the same mineral was identified as weathered and oxidized chlorite, and (wrongly) as stilpnomelane growing at the expense of chlorite (e.g., Turner, 1934, p. 165, pl. 23); true stilpnomelane was identified as such, however, in the same rocks.

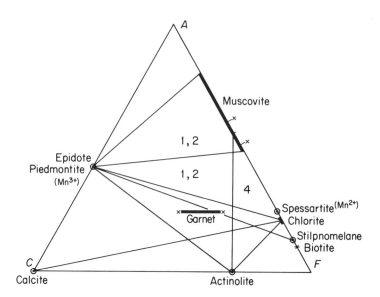

Fig. 7-5. Greenschist facies, chlorite zone (Chl. 4) of east Otago, New Zealand. ACF diagram for rocks with excess SiO_2 [For phases on A edge, total $(Fe^{2+} + Fe^{3+})$ shown as FeO]. Quartz, albite, and graphite are possible additional phases. Compositions of additional phases confined to the biotite zone shown as crosses. (*After data of E. H. Brown.*)

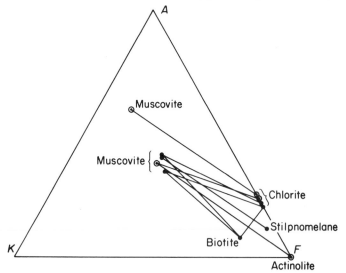

Fig. 7-6. Greenschist facies, east Otago, New Zealand. AKF diagram for rocks with excess SiO_2 [Total $(Fe^{2+} + Fe^{3+})$ shown as FeO]. Quartz, albite, and epidote are possible additional phases. Ties connect coexisting analysed phases. Circled points, chlorite zone; solid points, biotite zone. (*After data of E. H. Brown.*)

272

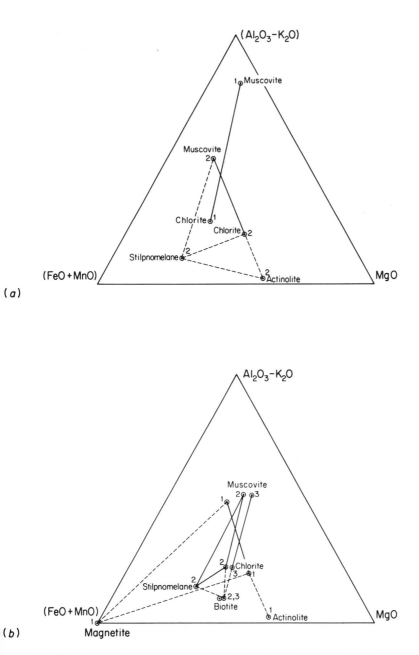

Fig. 7-7. Greenschist facies, east Otago, New Zealand. Plot of (Al$_2$O$_3$– K$_2$O), (FeO + MnO), MgO; total (Fe^{2+} + Fe^{3+}) shown as FeO. Circled points, analysed phases. Ties join coexisting phases—solid lines between analysed phases from same rock specimen. (*a*) Chlorite zone (Chl. 4). (*b*) Biotite zone. (*After data of E. H. Brown.*)

273

present in small quantities (occasionally > 3 percent) in half the rocks of the biotite zone. It is not necessarily associated with biotite. Almandine, grossularite, and spessartite are all important components of the garnet phase; and the core of each grain is relatively enriched in Mn.

(c) Both chlorite and stilpnomelane have diminished in quantity in the biotite as compared with the chlorite zone. But most biotite- and garnet-bearing rocks still are essentially quartz-albite-muscovite-chlorite (-stilpnomelane) schists, with biotite and/or garnet as relatively minor constituents. Coexistence of biotite and stilpnomelane, with no textural indication of disequilibrium, has been observed by Brown in some schists of his biotite zone. The pair biotite-stilpnomelane elsewhere is very rare but not unknown (Niggli, 1956; Miyakawa, 1964).

For other minerals, the compositional range in both zones is much the same. As usual in the greenschist facies the anorthite content of albite is close to zero. Muscovites, as compared with white micas at higher grades of metamorphism elsewhere, are phengitic types with a relatively high Si/Al ratio and containing significant Mg and Fe^{2+}; a typical composition may be represented as

$$K_2Mg_{0.6}Fe^{2+}_{0.2}Fe^{3+}_{0.3}Al_{2.9}(Al_{1.2}Si_{6.8}O_{20})(OH)_4$$

Chlorites are similar to those in other rocks of the greenschist facies elsewhere; not far from

$$Mg_{4.5}Fe^{2+}_5Al_{2.3}Fe^{3+}_{0.2}(Al_{2.5}Si_{5.5}O_{20})(OH)_{16}$$

[Coexisting muscovites and chlorites in the chlorite zone of Scotland have been found by McNamara (1965) to have very similar compositions.] Epidotes, in contrast with iron-rich types in the facies of lower grade in Otago, have a medium content of iron: $Ca_2\ Al_{2.4}\ Fe^{3+}_{0.6}\ Si_3O_{12}(OH)$ is typical. Actinolites have a high ratio $Mg/(Fe^{2+} + Al)$. The stilpnomelanes are highly oxidized ferristilpnomelanes; but there is evidence that they started with a high Fe^{2+} ratio, and that oxidation is essentially a post-metamorphic phenomenon. They are represented thus in the *ACF* and *AFM* diagrams (Figs. 7-5 to 7-7). Sphene and apatite are ubiquitous.

At the northwestern end of the Otago schist belt, 200 km distant from the site of Brown's work, the rocks of the chlorite zone are mineralogically similar to those just described. Additional local assemblages, derived from ironstones and manganiferous cherts are:

5. Chlorite-stilpnomelane-magnetite-actinolite-epidote (-quartz)
6. Quartz-muscovite-piedmontite-spessartite (minor tourmaline, apatite, barite).
7. Quartz-spessartite-stilpnomelane
8. Spessartite-stilpnomelane-calcite

Some of the greenschists in this region contain large amounts of greenish-brown biotite. The typical assemblage is:

9. Albite-biotite-chlorite-epidote-sphene

In northwestern Otago and along the Alpine schist belt of Westland (which is a narrow northeasterly trending continuation of the Otago schists), the chlorite zone is succeeded to the west by a fully developed zone of biotite. Here the width of outcrop of the chlorite zone proper (subzone Chl. 4) is about 5 km. The biotite zone has much the same width. It is limited on the west by an almandine isograd marking the high-grade limit of the greenschist facies. Further west the grade rises through a zone of almandine—also 5 km across—representing the greenschist-amphibolite transition facies. The zonal boundaries along the Haast River and Copland River sections are shown in Fig. 7-8.

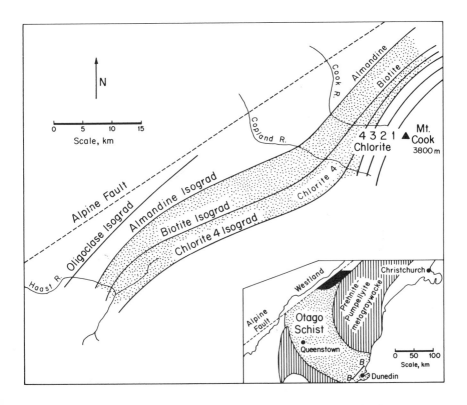

Fig. 7-8. Distribution of metamorphic zones in south Westland, New Zealand—Greenschist facies shown stippled. (*After A. R. Lillie and B. H. Mason, 1955; B. H. Mason, 1962.*) Inset shows location (solid black) in relation to Otago schist belt. (*BB* is *E. H. Brown's* east Otago section.)

The principal mineral assemblages of the biotite zone in the west Otago region are quartzo-feldspathic. Some are high-grade greenschists. They all resemble those of the chlorite zone except that stilpnomelane is completely absent, and biotite is ubiquitous and abundant. The anorthite content of albite is virtually zero (Evans, 1964, p. 175; Crawford, 1966, p. 276). Some rocks contain a little garnet. The general paragenesis is illustrated on an *ACF* diagram in Fig. 7-9, which takes into account also the biotite-zone paragenesis described by Reed (1958) from the northeastern end of the Alpine schist belt, 300 km northeast of the Haast River

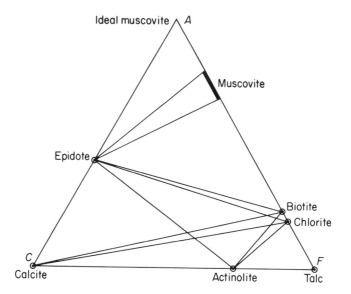

Fig. 7-9. Greenschist facies, biotite zone of northwest Otago and south Westland, New Zealand. *ACF* diagram for rocks with excess SiO_2. Quartz and albite are possible additional phases.

section. Biotite-forming reactions marking mappable biotite isograds are no doubt complex. Muscovite, chlorite, and stilpnomelane all appear to be involved; and it is by no means unlikely that other phases such as epidote may also participate.[1] At the biotite isograd in western Otago and Westland, stilpnomelane is completely eliminated. One element in the complex biotite-forming reaction is probably

$$\text{Muscovite} + \text{Stilpnomelane} \rightleftharpoons \text{Biotite} + \text{Chlorite}$$

[1] McNamara's (1966) suggestion that biotite forms by reaction between chlorite, quartz, and alkaline potassic solutions in carbonate-free rocks is discounted here since his principal evidence rests on misidentification of oxidized chlorite as biotite.

This could be expressed by the crossing muscovite-stilpnomelane and biotite-chlorite ties in Fig. 7-6.

In the biotite zone of Westland, New Zealand, biotite is much more widespread and abundant than in the respective biotite zones of eastern Otago and of the Scottish Dalradian. Atherton (1964) finds that in Barrow's classic biotite zone of the latter region, only 25 percent of the schists contain biotite, and the more characteristic pelitic assemblage is still quartz-muscovite-chlorite. Quartz-muscovite-biotite is more typical of Dalradian quartzo-feldspathic schists.

Greenschist facies of Vermont. Zen's (1960) account of metamorphism in the Castleton area of Vermont presents an unusually complete picture of metamorphic paragenesis in the lower range of metamorphic grade in the greenschist facies. The assemblages are those of a chlorite zone, for biotite is absent except as a minor phase of some pelitic assemblages (quartz-muscovite-biotite-graphite). The recorded assemblages are mainly pelitic; some are derived from impure dolomitic limestones. Thus their compositional range complements that of the Otago-Westland schists described in the previous section. Compositions of individual phases were mostly estimated from refractive-index and X-ray data, supplemented by a few check analyses. It was assumed that the high state of oxidation of iron in stilpnomelane is the result of postmetamorphic oxidation; so total $(Fe^{2+} + Fe^{3+})$ was calculated and plotted as FeO. In the absence of complete analyses, muscovite and paragonite were shown by Zen as ideal types lacking Fe and Mg. Zen's data are shown here in *ACF* and *AKF* projections as Figs. 7-10 and 7-11. In these figures, a composition chemically determined by Crawford (1966, p. 278, no. 19) for a muscovite in a semi-pelitic schist from the biotite zone of western Vermont has been substituted for ideal muscovite. Assemblages including paragonite as well as muscovite have been excluded from Figs. 7-10 and 7-11, since in the standard *ACF* and *AKF* plots, all Na_2O is assigned to albite. Paragonite is present, however, in many of the Vermont rocks. Its relation to associated micas and feldspars is illustrated in Fig. 7-12 (cf. Zen, 1966, p. 151). Assemblages shown in Figs. 7-10 and 7-11 are as follows:

A. Pelitic (in every case with rutile, but not sphene)
   1. Muscovite-chlorite-quartz-albite
   2. Muscovite-chlorite-quartz (-magnetite or hematite)
   3. Muscovite-chlorite-stilpnomelane-albite-microcline-quartz
   4. Muscovite-chlorite-chloritoid-quartz-hematite
   5. Muscovite-chlorite-chloritoid-epidote-quartz-magnetite-hematite
   6. Muscovite-chlorite-albite-microcline-quartz (-graphite)

B. Calcareous

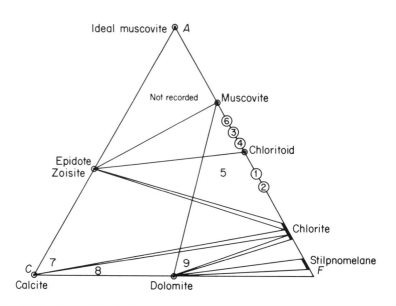

Fig. 7-10. Greenschist facies, Castleton area, Vermont. *ACF* diagram for assemblages with excess SiO₂ and K₂O, lacking paragonite. Quartz, albite, and microcline are possible additional phases. (*Modified after E-an Zen.*)

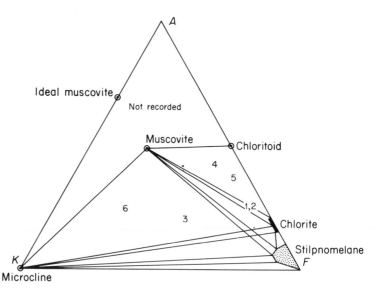

Fig. 7-11. Greenschist facies, Castleton area, Vermont. *AKF* diagram for assemblages with excess SiO₂ and Al₂O₃, lacking paragonite. (*Modified after E-an Zen.*)

278

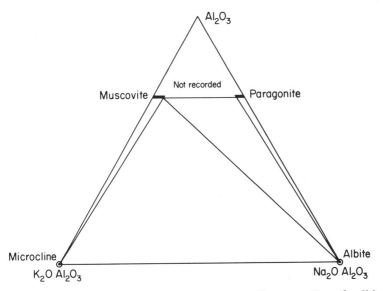

Fig. 7-12. Greenschist facies. Castleton area, Vermont. Plot of pelitic assemblages with excess SiO_2 on Al_2O_3–Na_2O–K_2O projection. (*After E-an Zen.*)

    7. Calcite (with some combination of quartz, albite, microcline, chlorite, muscovite, as minor phases)

    8. Calcite-dolomite (with some minor phases)

    9. Dolomite (with some minor phases)

Calcareous assemblages in the Castleton area, as elsewhere in the chlorite, biotite, and even the garnet zone of most of Vermont, are everywhere characterized by persistence of the dolomite-calcite-quartz trio and absence of tremolite or actinolite. Long ago this peculiarity was noted by White and Billings (1951, p. 691) who stated that "the reason may be very high confining pressure that reduced permeability and prevented the escape of carbon dioxide." Zen, however, notes that in the Rutland marble belt, 20 km east of the Castleton area (cf. Fig. 7-14), common assemblages are calcite-dolomite-quartz, calcite-actinolite-chlorite, and calcite-chlorite-zoisite.

    The more aluminous schists of the Castleton area contain paragonite as well as muscovite, both as nearly pure end members of the solid-solution series. The typical assemblages are

    10. Muscovite-chlorite-paragonite-quartz

    11. Muscovite-chlorite-chloritoid-paragonite-quartz

Pyrophyllite, though carefully searched for, was not found. It might be expected to occur only in rocks with an exceptionally high ratio $Al_2O_3/(K_2O + Na_2O)$ and lacking feldspar.

The mutual relations of ferromagnesian phases in schists of the Castleton area are illustrated in Fig. 7-13. High ratios of Mg/Fe tend to favor chlorite at the expense of chloritoid or stilpnomelane. In rocks with low Mg/Fe, chloritoid appears rather than stilpnomelane in the more aluminous rocks.

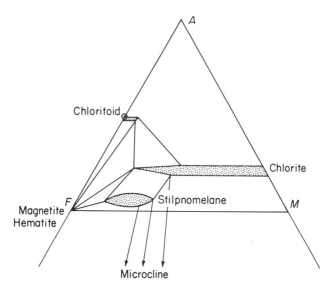

Fig. 7-13. Greenschist facies, Castleton area, Vermont. *AFM* diagram for muscovite-quartz-bearing assemblages (*After E-an Zen.*)

In Vermont-New Hampshire, as is usual elsewhere, the greenschist facies continues into the biotite zone. The paragenesis of the biotite zone as described by Lyons (1955) in the Hanover quadrangle (*H*, Fig. 7-14) is shown on the *ACF* projection in Fig. 7-15.[1] The typical assemblages are:

A. Pelitic and semipelitic

    1. Quartz-albite-muscovite-biotite-chlorite-clinozoisite (or epidote); ankerite and/or calcite are widespread minor constituents; sphene and magnetite common accessories

    2. Chlorite-muscovite-kyanite-quartz-albite. Recorded by Chapman (1939, p. 134) at point *k* in Mascoma quadrangle

B. Calcareous[2]

---

[1] Lyons' data agrees on the whole with those recorded earlier by White and Billings (1951) in the Woodsville quadrangle (*W*, Fig. 7-14) and by Chapman (1939) in the Mascoma quadrangle (*M*). In this earlier literature, however, what in some rocks is probably albite was recorded as oligoclase.

[2] In the Woodsville quadrangle (White and Billings, 1951) carbonates begin to react with quartz to give actinolite and diopside only at the highest metamorphic grades—beyond the actinolite isograd (Fig. 7-14, top right).

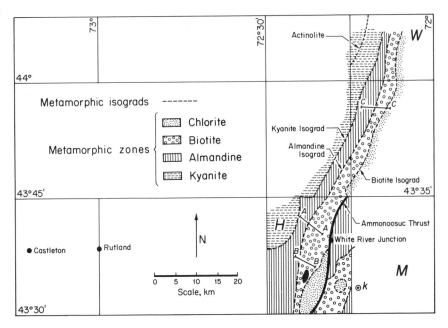

Fig. 7-14. Portion of mid-Vermont and New Hampshire. *H*, Hanover quadrangle; *M*, Mascoma quadrangle; *W*, Woodville quadrangle.

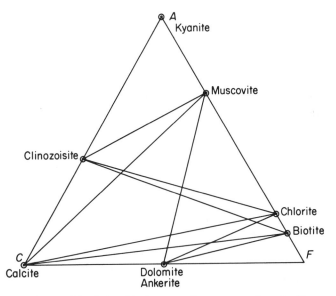

Fig. 7-15. Greenschist facies, biotite zone, Hanover quadrangle, Vermont and New Hampshire. *ACF* diagram for rocks with excess SiO_2, containing carbonates and albite as possible additional phases. K-feldspar rarely present.

    3. Calcite-quartz

    4. Dolomite-calcite-quartz

C. Basic

    5. Quartz-albite-chlorite-biotite-clinozoisite

    6. Quartz-chlorite-muscovite-calcite-clinozoisite

    7. Hornblende-plagioclase (sodic oligoclase)-biotite-quartz; in a metamorphosed basic sill (solid black, Fig. 7-14). Note the absence of carbonate

Lyons (1955, p. 140) records optically determined plagioclase compositions in the biotite zone as An_5–An_{10}. Crawford (1966) made a detailed chemical study of the changes in composition of plagioclase and coexisting minerals with increasing metamorphic grade along three traverses (*AA, BB, CC,* Fig. 7-14) from the chlorite to the kyanite zone. Her data for coexisting phases in biotite-zone assemblages containing albite (An < 2 percent) as the only plagioclase are reproduced in Fig. 7-16. It will be noticed that muscovites are still phengitic types, far from ideal muscovites. The paragenesis shown in Fig. 7-16 is virtually unchanged for distances of 2 km (on *AA*) and 4 km (on *BB*) from the biotite isograd. Then, within about 1 km of the almandine isograd, a second plagioclase (calcic oligoclase) suddenly appears in assemblages that also contain albite. This is the high-grade limit of the greenschist facies as here defined—still well within the zone of biotite.

The role of carbonates in the greenschist facies. Carbonates are essential, though usually minor phases in rocks of the greenschist facies all the world over. They are dominant phases in metamorphosed limestones and dolomites, abundant in magnesian schists and metamorphosed iron formation, and essential minor constituents of many greenschists and some pelitic and semipelitic rocks. Among other instances, carbonate-bearing assemblages have been well documented for the Scottish Dalradian (Harker, 1932, p. 260; Wiseman, 1934, p. 379; McNamara, 1965), the Otago schists of New Zealand (Turner, 1935; Hutton, 1940; Brown, 1967), the lower-grade rocks of Vermont-New Hamsphire (White and Billings, 1951, p. 691; Lyons, 1955; Zen, 1960; Crawford, 1966), the Stuart Fork Formation of northwest California (Davis, Holdaway, Lipman, and Romey, 1965, pp. 938, 939), calcschists of the western Alps (Chatterjee, 1962; Trommsdorff, 1966), and the Huronian iron formation of northern Michigan (James, 1955).

All these parageneses have certain features in common. The noncalcic aluminum-poor phases associated with carbonates are chlorite (Mg–Fe^{2+}–Fe^{3+}), stilpnomelane (Fe^{2+}–Mg), talc (Mg), and (only in iron formation) minnesotaite (Fe^{2+}). Clinozoisite-epidote is almost invariably the only Ca–Al silicate; an exception is the occurrence of vesuvianite in some

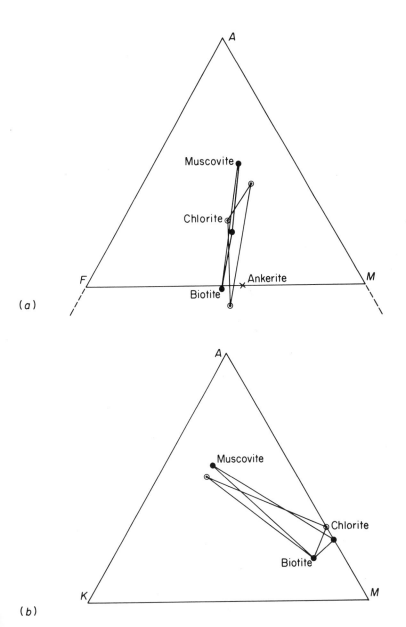

(a)

(b)

Fig. 7-16. Greenschist facies, biotite zone, Hanover quadrangle, Vermont. (*a*) *AFM* and (*b*) *AKF* diagrams for analysed coexisting phases in the assemblage quartz-albite-muscovite-biotite-chlorite-ankerite. (*After data of M. L. Crawford.*) Total ($Fe^{3+} + Fe^{2+}$) plotted as FeO. Solid circles and circled dots represent two rock specimens (same in both diagrams); ankerite in a third specimen.

calcareous assemblages of the European Alps (e.g., Chatterjee, 1962). Universally, even in the biotite zone, relatively pure calcite and dolomite marbles show no indication of reaction between the carbonates and quartz. Reaction between carbonates and clay impurities in such rocks has, however, given rise to muscovite, chlorite and epidote as minor phases (along with quartz) in the marble assemblages.

With all these features in common, there are nevertheless two distinct patterns of paragenesis in rocks, notably greenschists and calcschists, in which a carbonate phase, though essential, is subordinate to silicates.

In the one, exemplified by the ankerite-bearing pelitic schists of the New Hampshire biotite zone, carbonate-quartz persists unchanged without development of amphibole, just as in the massive dolomitic rocks. To this category also belong the iron-formation assemblages of the Huronian in northern Michigan, where characteristic assemblages in both the chlorite and biotite zones (James, 1955, pp. 1462, 1475) are:

Stilpnomelane-minnesotaite-siderite-quartz-magnetite
Chlorite-stilpnomelane-quartz-siderite-magnetite
Hematite-quartz-calcite

The corresponding amphibole, grünerite, appears only in the amphibolite facies beyond the almandine isograd as defined in associated pelites.

The second, and seemingly more common pattern of paragenesis, is characterized by the presence of an amphibole—actinolite-tremolite—in some, but by no means all the calcite-bearing greenschists. Such is the situation, contrary to a statement by McNamara (1965, p. 379) to the opposite effect, in the chlorite (Chl. 4) and biotite zones of New Zealand (cf. Hutton, 1960; Turner, 1935). Pure carbonate beds are lacking in this region, and most rock specimens contain little or no carbonate. But throughout the whole extent of the chlorite and biotite zones of Otago and Westland, calcite is an essential phase in most greenschists, and appears (in amounts up to perhaps 5 percent of the total composition) in many specimens of semipelitic schist. In some greenschists it is accompanied by actinolite. Some typical actinolitic assemblages recorded by Hutton (1940) and by Brown (1967) are:

Albite-epidote-chlorite-actinolite[1]-calcite (-quartz)
Albite-stilpnomelane-actinolite[1]-calcite (-epidote-sphene-pyrite)
Quartz - albite - epidote - muscovite - biotite - stilpnomelane - actinolite (-calcite)

Outnumbering these, but often in close mutual association, are actinolitic greenschists lacking calcite, or calcite-bearing schists without actinolite.

Mineral assemblages of the portion of the chlorite zone studied by

---

[1]These are deep green actinolites whose composition (Hutton, 1940, pp. 12-15) approximates $(Na_{0.4}Ca_{1.6})(Mg_3Fe^{2+}_{1.2}Fe^{3+}_{0.6}Al_{0.2})(Al_{0.4}Si_{7.6}O_{22})(OH)_2$.

Chatterjee (1962) are most unusual in that some contain vesuvianite. They include among others:

Chlorite-muscovite-vesuvianite-almandine-albite-quartz-calcite

Chlorite-epidote-albite-vesuvianite-tremolite

Chlorite-chloritoid-muscovite-paragonite-quartz-epidote-calcite

Chlorite-tremolite-muscovite-calcite-quartz

In the Stuart Fork formation of the Klamath Mountains, northwest California, mineral assemblages containing both actinolite and calcite are again somewhat subordinate to assemblages containing one or other of these phases alone. They include

Actinolite-albite-quartz-calcite

Actinolite-albite-biotite-chlorite-epidote-calcite (-quartz) and in one locality

Epidote-chlorite-glaucophane-albite-calcite

From Harker's (1932, pp. 260, 263) and McNamara's (1965) descriptions, actinolite(tremolite)-calcite is rare compared with muscovite-chlorite-calcite assemblages in calcareous pelitic schists of the zones of chlorite and biotite in the Scottish Dalradian. But Wiseman (1934, pp. 376-377) records calcite as a common minor constituent of actinolite-bearing greenschists derived from associated diabase sills in both zones.

Presence of carbonates in any metamorphic rocks, except perhaps pure marbles, implies a significant partial pressure of carbon dioxide (P_{CO_2}) in the pore fluid during metamorphism. The genesis of the carbonate-bearing assemblage may be viewed in terms of a simple model in which $(P_{CO_2} + P_{H_2O}) = P_f = P_l$. In deep-seated metamorphism, where the permeability of most recrystallized rocks must be minimal, the value of P_{CO_2} relative to P_{H_2O} in any rock is likely to depend largely upon the relative abundance of carbonates and hydrous phases in the rock itself. The very fact of progressive dehydration and decarbonation, so characteristic of metamorphic reactions, shows that fluid pressures generated within any rock rise to the point where fluid can migrate steadily outward. But inward migration of fluid from an external environment into an initially dry rock seems to be much less effective. Witness, for example, the incompletely metamorphosed condition of the interiors of thick diabase sills enclosed in mica schists, which provided an external environment where P_{H_2O} ($= P_f$) must have been maintained at very high levels for tens or hundreds of thousands of years.

With such a model as background, it is easy to explain the absence of talc and tremolite in massive somewhat siliceous marbles of the greenschist facies. At any given pressure and temperature, high values of P_{H_2O} relative to P_{CO_2} facilitate the formation of hydrous silicates from dolomite, and favor the appearance of talc, rather than tremolite, as the hydrous phase (pp. 147–148). The kinetics of fluid diffusion in dolomite under greenschist-facies conditions apparently prevent this situation from being maintained. From experimental and thermochemical data (Figs. 4-9, 4-16, p. 152) at pressures above 2 kb (the minimum possible value for the greenschist facies), talc or tremolite may be expected to appear by reaction between dolomite and quartz only at temperatures above about 450°C, where $P_{H_2O} = P_{CO_2}$. At the same total pressure, increase in P_{CO_2}/P_{H_2O} to a value of 10 would raise this limiting temperature to about 550°C.

The reverse situation, high ratio P_{H_2O}/P_{CO_2} is likely to arise spontaneously in an environment (such as must have prevailed in the Otago and Vermont schists) where metamorphic reactions are mainly those of progressive dehydration. Here tremolite could appear at lower temperatures; perhaps below 400°C at 2 kb, and below 500°C at 4 kb. Under given conditions of pressure, the temperature of the Ankerite-quartz $\rightleftharpoons$ Actinolite-calcite equilibrium presumably is significantly lower than that of Dolomite-quartz $\rightleftharpoons$ Tremolite-calcite. The amphibole-forming reaction in greenschists or calcareous mica schists will, of course, be a complex one involving participation of coexisting phases (epidote-chlorite-magnetite or epidote-biotite-chlorite-magnetite). It will be influenced to a degree unknown by the state of oxidation of the system. But if the final assemblage contains actinolite-quartz, it can be stable only within the field of stability of that pair, i.e., on the high-temperature side of the simple equilibrium curve for Ankerite-quartz-$H_2O \rightleftharpoons$ Actinolite-calcite-CO_2.

The greenschist assemblages of Otago, and similar assemblages in the greenschist facies elsewhere, are here interpreted as products of crystallization over some definite range of temperature and pressure (perhaps 400 to 500°C and 4 to 6 kb), with continuously maintained high P_{H_2O} relative to P_{CO_2}. Minor fluctuations in this latter ratio can account for the local appearance, commonly in close juxtaposition, of alternative assemblages with chlorite-albite-epidote-calcite, chlorite-actinolite-albite-epidote-calcite, epidote-actinolite-chlorite-albite, and so on. The persistence of ankerite-calcite-quartz in the mica schists of the biotite zone in Vermont presents an anomaly. It could be explained on the assumption that total pressure here was higher than in New Zealand, which on other grounds is most unlikely (cf. p. 362), or temperatures were significantly lower.

Finally, reference must be made to McNamara's (1965, pp. 383-384) recent attempt to redefine generally applicable subfacies to cover the assemblages of the chlorite zone in Scotland and New Zealand. This resurrects earlier efforts (Turner, 1935, and others) to define subfacies in terms of relative concentrations of CO_2 and water. It was abandoned long ago (Turner, 1948, pp. 96, 97) because experience has shown that the critical assemblages of all the "subfacies" (such as those now proposed by McNamara) are generally closely associated in the field, along with pelitic assemblages of constant character. This writer still cannot visualize such assemblages as having facies or even subfacies status, but prefers the opinion of Miyashiro (1958, p. 267):

> The actinolite-greenschist facies is the same as the greenschist facies, as the occurrence of actinolite depends largely on the CO_2 and H_2O pressures prevailing.

Facies and subfacies must be defined in terms of observed paragenesis—the assemblages of phases found in close mutual association—not on assumed values of pressure and temperature variables.

Carbonates are essential members, too, of many of the magnesian assemblages formed by metasomatic metamorphism in the chlorite zone of most of the classic terranes. Thus in the Precambrain chlorite zone of regional metamorphism in Anglesey, Wales (Greenly, 1919, pp. 104-106), peridotites have been serpentinized and then converted to the following silica-deficient assemblages:

1. Antigorite
2. Talc-chlorite-magnetite
3. Tremolite (-talc)
4. Dolomite-tremolite-serpentine-magnetite (-chromite)
5. Calcite-tremolite-talc-serpentine-chromite
6. Calcite-talc (-chromite)
7. Dolomite-talc (-chromite)
8. Magnesite-talc (-chromite)
9. Chlorite-chromite-magnetite

Many of the carbonate rocks occur on a large enough scale to be mapped as tremolite-limestone or "ophicalcite." But Greenly demonstrated beyond doubt their origin by carbonation of serpentinite during deformational metamorphism.

The many crossing ties that appear on the corresponding phase diagram (Fig. 7-17) are characteristic of similar magnesian carbonate schists formed by metasomatic metasomatism of serpentinite in other parts of the world. The ultimate product of metasomatism may even be magnesite-quartz, which then replace the pair talc-antigorite of Fig. 7-17 (e.g., Wellman, 1942). It would be misleading to interpret this as evidence of widespread disequilibrium. Each of the principal assemblages consists of two or three mineral phases (excluding accessory constituents involving additional components such as FeO, Cr_2O_3, and so on). Each such assemblage can be considered as a system—possibly of limited volume, but in some instances having the dimensions of a large outcrop—within which the composition of the gas during metamorphism was maintained at constant composition by inward or outward diffusion of CO_2 or water or both. This is the condition analogous to experiments conducted at constant P_{CO_2} and P_{H_2O}. To consider such a system in terms of the phase rule, we must specify three instead of the normal two intensive variables (cf. Turner and Verhoogen, 1960, p. 460). These will be P, T, and either P_{CO_2} or P_{H_2O}. The phase rule thus becomes

$$w = c + 3 - \varphi$$

For none of the two- and three-mineral assemblages of Fig. 7-17 is it possible to write a simple chemical equation relating any pair of phases

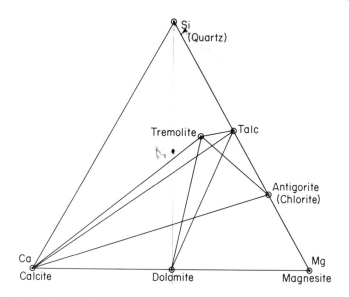

Fig. 7-17. Greenschist facies, magnesian and carbonate assemblages in metamorphosed serpentinite, Anglesey, Wales. (*Data from E. Greenly.*)

even if the system is open to both components of the gas phase. So the number of relations r is 0; and the variance is given by

$$w = (3 - r) = 3$$

Equilibirum for each assemblage considered alone is possible under ranges of T, of P and of gas composition. Where two overlapping assemblages such as calcite-dolomite-talc and dolomite-tremolite-talc are closely associated within a specimen or an outcrop, it is likely that they crystallized under identical conditions of T, P, and gas composition. Here we are dealing with a single system in which four mineral phases and a gas of constant composition are mutually associated. The single possible relation is

$$\text{Calcite} + \text{Talc} \rightleftharpoons \text{Tremolite} + \text{Dolomite} + \text{Gas}$$

Equilibrium in the outcrop is divariant; i.e., if the pressure remains constant, as determined by a given depth, then for any fixed gas composition the temperature of equilibrium between the two assemblages is unique. As for "mobility" of components, field evidence, petrographic data and chemical analyses can show that in replacement of serpentinite by talc-magnesite and magnesite-quartz rocks as described for a New Zealand occurrence by Wellman (1942; cf. also Turner, 1948, pp. 135, 136), water and carbon dioxide have diffused freely into and out of the rock, carrying with them MgO, FeO, and SiO_2. Treating the system according to a phase rule, modified to take into account relative mobility of components, gives no information that cannot be obtained from applying Gibbs' phase rule in its simplest form.

Glaucophane-lawsonite-schist Facies

Definition and mineralogical characteristics. Notwithstanding earlier views to the contrary (e.g., Turner, 1948, p. 100), Eskola's glaucophane-schist facies has long been recognized as having a valid status. In fact, in its typical development, with assemblages containing both glaucophane and lawsonite, it is one of the best defined of metamorphic facies today. As long ago as 1952, Brouwer and Egeler (1952, pp. 56, 57) wrote

> When considering the metamorphism as developed in eastern Corsica it may be mentioned that here no reasons were found to doubt the existence of a separate "glaucophane-schist facies" . . . which can be interpreted as having been principally controlled by special physical conditions.

Today, however, there is more confusion than ever as to how the facies should be defined in terms of mineralogical criteria, and how to deal with the many (frequently overlapping) subfacies that have been proposed during the past decade. For this reason we have recently renamed the facies after the definitive pair glaucophane-lawsonite, as suggested by Winkler (1965, pp. 144-145), and have restricted its diagnostic mineralogical criteria thus (Fyfe and Turner, 1966, p. 361):

> Since the glaucophane minerals are stable over a wide range of tem-perature (Ernst, 1961) and appear in some rocks of the greenschist facies, we propose to rename what has been termed the glaucophane-schist as the *glaucophane-lawsonite-schist* facies (cf. Winkler, 1965, p. 144). The diagnostic assemblages contain lawsonite and commonly aragonite and jadeite-quartz, as well as glaucophane.

Our knowledge of the glaucophane-schist facies and its relations to other facies has been increased and clarified in recent years largely through studies in Japan, California, and the European Alpine zone. Important work in New Caledonia is in progress.[1] It has become increasingly apparent that there are regional transitions between the glaucophane-lawsonite-schist facies as here defined, and the prehnite-pumpellyite-metagraywacke, the greenschist, the amphibolite, and the eclogite facies, respectively. It is on these transition facies, which are by no means everywhere identical in every detail, that locally recognizable subfacies have been erected from time to time. The complex and ambiguous state of subfacies nomenclature arising from this situation has been summarized thus (Fyfe and Turner, 1966, p. 359):

> The glaucophane-schist facies was first subdivided by De Roever (1947, pp. 161–162; 1950, pp. 1457–1461) on the basis of mineralogical variations among glaucophane schists in the Indonesian island of Celebes. He proposed three subfacies, in order of increasing metamorphic grade as follows: lawsonite-glaucophane (with or without jadeite and quartz); almandine-lawsonite-glaucophane; epidote-glaucophane (with lawsonite, jadeite-quartz, or almandine as possible additional phases). This scheme was never widely accepted, largely because it was not backed by adequate knowledge of the mutual relations of the various subfacies in the field. In its place Miyashiro and Seki (1958) proposed an alternative sub-division suited to mineralogical variation within and field distribution of glaucophane schists in Japan. They erected two subfacies respectively based on the assemblages epidote-glaucophane and lawsonite-pumpel-lyite-epidote-glaucophane. The Californian glaucophane schists, how-ever, would more appropriately be subdivided on the alternative appear-ance of albite or jadeite-quartz in lawsonite-glaucophane assemblages (cf. McKee, 1962, p. 381; Ghent, 1965, p. 398); and we would prefer to place assemblages lacking either lawsonite or jadeite or aragonite (e.g., Miyashiro's epidote-glaucophane subfacies) in the greenschist facies, transitional towards the glaucophane-schist facies (Fyfe, Turner, and Verhoogen, 1958, p. 226).

A second series of problems arises from the repeated, though in most instances rather vaguely defined, field association of glaucophanic rocks with bodies of serpentinite and with eclogite. Does this association arise more or less by chance, simply because all three types of rock tend to develop in the eugeosynclinal environment? Or is the connection more direct? For example, may the glaucophanic rocks be formed in the contact aureoles of ultramafic intrusions of the Alpine type? And is it possible that there is a complete passage through transitional facies between the glaucophane-lawsonite-schist and the eclogite facies? Or is the eclogite-glaucophaneschist relation always one of retrogressive metamorphism?

[1] A. R. Lillie and R. N. Brothers, personal communication.

In the treatment presented here, this section is limited to the glauco-phane-lawsonite-schist facies proper, with special reference to occurrences in California. In the immediately following section we shall take up the various transitional facies treated by most writers as subfacies of a more comprehensive "glaucophane-schist facies."

Glaucophane-lawsonite-schist facies in California.[1] The Franciscan formation of the Californian Coast Range is a folded eugeosynclinal mass of Jurassic-Cretaceous sediments and volcanic rocks (of great but unknown thickness) extending along a northwest southeast trend for several hundred kilometers. The predominant rocks are graywackes and basic volcanics (some of them spilitic), with locally prominent ferruginous cherts. Shales, limestones, and conglomerates are greatly subordinate. Throughout the whole extent of the Franciscan terrane, but locally concentrated in areas of up to a few tens of square kilometers, are metamorphic rocks of the glaucophane-lawsonite-schist facies. Otherwise the Franciscan is largely unmetamorphosed or shows incipient metamorphism to assemblages reminiscent of the zeolite or the greenschist facies. There are numerous intrusive ultramafic bodies, for the most part completely or almost completely converted to serpentinite. The general character of the Franciscan formation and the geologic problems related to it have been described in detail by Taliaferro (1943) and by Bailey, Irwin, and Jones (1964).

Widely distributed in California (as in some other glaucophane-schist terranes in Corsica, Japan, and elsewhere) are rocks containing various combinations of the characteristic minerals jadeite (containing significant Fe^{3+} and associated with quartz), lawsonite, and aragonite, together with a mineral of the glaucophane-crossite series. The rare minerals deerite, howieite, and zussmanite, possibly overlooked elsewhere, are confined, so far as is known at present, to a single locality of ferruginous metachert. Pumpellyite, a mineral characteristic otherwise only of assem-blages in the prehnite-pumpellyite-metagraywacke facies, is widespread. It is also a common constituent of incipiently metamorphosed rocks.

Affinities with the greenschist facies (chlorite zone) are indicated by ubiquitous assemblages containing some combination of chlorite, epidote, albite, phengitic muscovite, stilpnomelane, and actinolite. Biotite is conspicuously lacking. Albite, actinolite, and epidote, though not un-common, are far less conspicuous than in chemically equivalent assem-blages of the greenschist facies. Affinities with facies of higher grade are also obvious. Garnet and pyroxenes (in addition to jadeite) are rather widely distributed. In some rocks, generally interpreted as retrogressively metamorphosed eclogites, garnet and omphacite are obviously in the

---

[1] Parts of this section are direct or somewhat modified quotations from Essene, Fyfe, and Turner (1965).

process of replacement by glaucophane-schist minerals. In others either mineral is present, apparently in equilibrium with minerals more typical of the glaucophane-schist facies. Both omphacite and glaucophane may be late vein minerals. Spessartite-rich garnet and aegirine are typical of metacherts. Aegirine-jadeite, aegirine-augite, and chloromelanite are common in greenstones.

In California, as elsewhere, the phase assemblages are too complex to be treated in terms of three or four components. Na enters into a number of the characteristic phases. Fe^{3+} and Al^{3+} cannot be combined as a single component in minerals such as jadeite-aegirine, as compared with stilpnomelane. Presence or absence of manganese influences the chert parageneses. And finally there are three common hydrous Ca-Al silicates: lawsonite, pumpellyite, and epidote. Some typical assemblages (cf. Brothers, 1954; Borg, 1956; Turner and Verhoogen, 1960, p. 542; Coleman and Lee, 1963; Ernst, 1963b, 1965) are as follows, but the list is by no means exhaustive, and some of the assemblages probably represent locally distinct subfacies (cf. Coleman and Lee, 1963).

A. Pelitic
1. Quartz-muscovite[1]-chlorite-glaucophane (garnet)
2. Quartz-muscovite[1]-glaucophane (-lawsonite)

B. Quartzo-feldspathic
3. Quartz-jadeite-muscovite-chlorite-stilpnomelane;   quartz-jadeite metagraywackes with minor glaucophane, lawsonite, aragonite, muscovite, and stilpnomelane, are widespread in California (Bloxam, 1956). The jadeite carries significant Fe^{3+}. These rocks are identical with those first recognized by de Roever (1955) in Celebes.
4. Quartz-jadeite-lawsonite-glaucophane
5. Quartz-lawsonite-glaucophane (-aragonite)
6. Quartz-albite-crossite

C. Basic
7. Pumpellyite-lawsonite-glaucophane-sphene; muscovite and/or chlorite are common additional phases.
8. Glaucophane-lawsonite-almandine
9. Jadeite-lawsonite-glaucophane-aragonite-chlorite-quartz
10. Glaucophane-lawsonite-sphene-aragonite-chlorite-muscovite-quartz
11. Albite-epidote-chlorite-muscovite-glaucophane
12. Epidote-pumpellyite-omphacite[2]-glaucophane

[1]Typically a phengitic variety (Ernst, 1963b).

[2]Omphacite is used here to cover a range of pyroxenes in which Ca, Mg, Na, Al, and Fe^{3+} are all essential components and which have a significant content of jadeite. These are discussed in a recent publication by Essene and Fyfe (1967).

13. Epidote-muscovite-chlorite-omphacite-albite
D. Calcareous
14. Aragonite, in association with one or two additional phases (lawsonite, glaucophane, pumpellyite)
15. Calcite veins, some of which include relict aragonite in process of replacement by calcite
E. Ferruginous metacherts
16. Crossite (or riebeckite)-stilpnomelane-spessartite-quartz
17. Quartz-crossite-aegirine-spessartite-stilpnomelane
18. Stilpnomelane-spessartite-riebeckite and combinations of deerite, howieite, and zussmanite (Agrell, Brown, and McKee, 1965)

There are parts of the Californian Coast Ranges where partly or completely metamorphosed rocks have been mapped over areas 50 to 100 km^2 (e.g., Ernst, 1965; Ghent, 1963). The regional paragenesis then tends to conform to that of the glaucophane-lawsonite-schist facies, except that jadeite-quartz is absent and its chemical equivalent albite is everywhere conspicuous. In such regions there are local areas where the paragenesis grades into that of the prehnite-pumpellyite-metagraywacke facies and lacks either lawsonite or aragonite. Elsewhere within the same terrane, there are mappable subareas where the full glaucophane-lawsonite-paragenesis is developed, including assemblages with jadeite-quartz, aragonite, and lawsonite. Some of the typical albite-bearing and associated assemblages recorded by Ernst (1965) and by Ghent (1963) are
A. Pelitic
1. Muscovite-chlorite-albite-quartz-stilpnomelane (-lawsonite)
B. Metagraywacke
2. Quartz-albite-lawsonite-chlorite-muscovite-stilpnomelane (-aragonite or calcite)
C. Basic
3. Albite-chlorite-lawsonite-glaucophane
4. Glaucophane-lawsonite-chlorite (-sphene-muscovite-aragonite-albite)
5. Glaucophane-muscovite-epidote-albite-quartz
D. Metacherts
6. Quartz-albite-crossite-epidote (-stilpnomelane-pumpellyite)
7. Quartz-riebeckite-hematite-epidote
8. Quartz-riebeckite-stilpnomelane

It is possible to state some general conclusions on the problems concerning the relationship of glaucophanic rocks to bodies of serpentinite and of eclogite in California. These conclusions need not necessarily apply to other regions with which this writer is less familiar. Several kinds of relationship have been demonstrated between Franciscan glaucophane schists and serpentinite bodies of the Alpine type. Many of these are "cold intrusions": they have been emplaced at their present sites as masses of serpentinite squeezed up from an original site of intrusion (or conceivably outpouring) in the depths below.

1. There are large areas (many square kilometers) of jadeite meta-graywackes, in some cases associated with coarsely crystalline glaucophane schists, that are virtually devoid of serpentinite. Here we see products of localized but still "regional" metamorphism, unrelated to ultramafic intrusions.

2. Very commonly (e.g., Brothers, 1954) blocks of glaucophane-lawsonite schists of all kinds, many very coarsely crystalline, appear to have been transported from elsewhere (presumably below) by large intrusions of serpentinite. These blocks are commonly coated with a skin of actinolite-talc, formed by reaction with the enclosing serpentinite. The chrome mica, fuchsite, may be a constituent of the actinolite-talc assemblage.

3. At some serpentinite contacts there are narrow zones of meta-somatism where new mineral assemblages, sometimes including glauco-phane, have formed for distances of a few meters (e.g., Chesterman, 1960; Crawford, 1965). Here almost unaltered graywacke may be transformed into a fine-grained glaucophane-muscovite schist, the structure of which indicates contemporaneous localized intense deformation. Another common change at such contacts is from jadeite-quartz metagraywacke to silica-deficient assemblages containing hydrogrossular and prehnite. Here, perhaps, is retrogressive change from the glaucophane-lawsonite-schist to the prehnite-pumpellyite-metagraywacke facies.

4. Less clearly established is a tendency for blocks of coarse glauco-phane-schist, eclogite, and transitional rocks to be concentrated toward the margins of serpentinite bodies. Do we see in these, fragments of a high-grade contact zone transported by a serpentinite vehicle to their present site?

Two generalizations regarding relation of glaucophane schist to eclogite now seem to be established:

1. There are clear instances (cf. Borg, 1956) where the eclogite assemblage garnet-omphacite-rutile shows every stage of replacement by glaucophane-lawsonite-schist minerals. Garnet is pseudomorphed by chlorite, chlorite-aragonite, chlorite-muscovite, and even by lawsonite. Omphacite is progressively transformed to hornblende and this in turn to glaucophane, lawsonite, chlorite, pumpellyite-epidote, and muscovite. Rutile is replaced by sphene. Here there is evidence beyond doubt that blocks of eclogite transported into the environment of the glaucophane-lawsonite-schist, and perhaps in some instances the greenschist facies, have responded to their new environment by retrogressive metamorphism.

In these reactions hydration was an important factor, and in some instances there was even some carbonation.

2. It is now becoming apparent (cf. Fyfe and Essene, 1967) that, in certain instances, the relation of glaucophane-lawsonite schist to eclogite may be of a precisely opposite character. Field relations between eclogite and glaucophane schist in California are difficult to establish except on the scale of an outcrop, a hand specimen or a thin section. But an omphacitic pyroxene identical with that of Californian eclogite is an integral member of some glaucophane-schist assemblages, and even constitutes mono-mineralic veins and bands in some such rocks (Brothers, 1954, p. 620). Moreover, some glaucophane schists contain garnet with no textural indication of internal disequilibrium in the garnetiferous assemblage. Some of these garnets are pyrope-almandines whose compositions fall within the range of Californian eclogite garnets. We now class these rocks in a facies transitional between the glaucophane-lawsonite-schist and the eclogite facies (Essene, Fyfe, and Turner, 1965, p. 699). As such they will be considered further in a subsequent section.

Glaucophane-lawsonite-schist facies and transitional facies, western Alps. Metamorphism in the western Alps of Europe is concentrated in a central arcuate core, 400 × 70 km, known as the *Pennine zone* (Fig. 7-18). This is a pile of nappes thrust many kilometers northwest over a crystalline basement, the extension of which is now exposed in a series of massifs extending south of Mt. Blanc outside, i.e., west of, the Pennine arc. Each of the larger Pennine nappes consists of an envelope of Mesozoic meta-sediments and basic metavolcanics (ophiolites) enclosing a detached core torn from the crystalline basement. Regional metamorphism accompanied and followed the Tertiary Alpine orogeny; but in the crystalline Paleozoic cores of the nappes, the imprint of an earlier (Hercynian) metamorphism has not been entirely obliterated by the Alpine episode.

Glaucophane schists are conspicuous in the Pennine zone, especially throughout a belt 200 km long extending from Simplon in the north to the southern limit of Fig. 7-18. This region has been mapped and studied petrographically by Bearth (1952, 1958, 1962, 1966) whose views are the main basis of the summary that follows. Important constituents of the whole Mesozoic envelope are basic metavolcanics. The most widely distributed assemblage of this composition is albite-epidote-chlorite-actinolite, familiar in the Alps (as elsewhere) as characteristic of the greenschist facies (Bearth, 1962, pp. 128, 129; 1966, p. 15). But there are also many bodies of metavolcanic rock whose constituent assemblages are typical of the glaucophane-lawsonite-schist, eclogite, and allied transitional facies. Bearth considers these to be survivals from a somewhat earlier

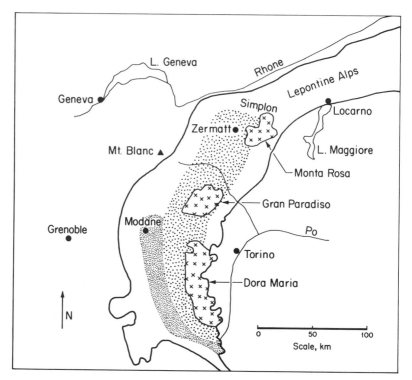

Fig. 7-18. Southern part of Pennine zone (outlined in heavy lines), Western Alps, Europe. Metamorphic zones of *P. Bearth* (1962): lawsonite-pumpellyite, light, dense stipple; garnet-chloritoid, heavy stipple.

phase of the Alpine metamorphism, subsequently partially overprinted by recrystallisation under conditions of the greenschist facies. Both phases are thought to be syn- and post-tectonic with respect to the principal episode of folding.

Without mapping isograds, Bearth (1962, 1966) has delineated two longitudinal zones whose trend parallels that of the major structure.

1. An external *lawsonite-pumpellyite zone*, 100 km long, whose northern limit is in the vicinity of Modane.

2. An internal *garnet-chloritoid zone*, of higher metamorphic grade, about 200 km in length extending from the southern end of the map (Fig. 7-18) to the border of the Lepontine Alps beyond Zermatt and Monte Rosa. Both zones contain glaucophane schists. But the two are totally different in character and represent two distinct metamorphic facies.

Only the rocks of the lawsonite-pumpellyite zone belong to the glaucophane-lawsonite-schist facies proper. Typical assemblages in weakly metamorphosed basic volcanics include various combinations of albite, epidote (or clinozoisite), lawsonite, glaucophane, and pumpellyite. Stilpnomelane is uncommon. Quartz-jadeite metagraywackes have been recognized in the outermost part of the lawsonite-pumpellyite zone. Bearth (1966) correlates the assemblages of the lawsonite-pumpellyite zone with low-grade metamorphism under high pressure at the base of the Pennine nappe pile. But, like most other Swiss geologists, he rejects the possibility that pressure is due to burial under a sedimentary column 20 to 30 km thick, as generally supposed for the glaucophane-lawsonite-schist facies in California and elsewhere (Bearth, 1966, pp. 16, 17). The greenschist assemblage albite-epidote-chlorite-actinolite is attributed to later re-crystallization under increasing temperature within the still deeply buried mass. Bearth (1966, p. 17) concludes that in the western Alps the glaucophane-lawsonite-schist facies passes inward (i.e., to the east) into the greenschist facies, but not into the completely independent glauco-phane-garnet schists of the garnet-chloritoid zone still further east.

The typical glaucophane schists of the garnet-chloritoid zone consist of glaucophane, garnet, an epidote mineral, paragonite, muscovite, chloritoid, and rutile. The unusual association glaucophane-chloritoid is considered critical. Everywhere in this zone the glaucophane schists can be shown to be products of retrogressive metamorphism (hydration) of eclogite.[1] Moreover, the glaucophane schists themselves are usually in the process of replacement by assemblages of the greenschist facies: combinations of albite, actinolite, epidote, chlorite, biotite, and sphene. So in the whole zone three parageneses are seen to be mutually associated, as well as showing various stages in the transition series eclogite → glauco-phane-garnet schist → greenschist. This situation poses questions on which opinions are bound to differ. Do all three parageneses represent distinct facies? Are the first two to be regarded as metastable with respect to the third? Do the eclogite and the greenschist facies of the Pennine zone reflect greatly different conditions of metamorphism? To these questions we shall return in the next chapter. In the meantime, we note that the existence of a widespread glaucophanic paragenesis different from and independent of that of the glaucophane-lawsonite-schist facies as defined here. Some inkling of the conditions of its origin is supplied by a para-genesis of completely different composition that developed contem-poraneously in immediately adjacent massifs of Paleozoic crystalline rocks:

The dominantly "ophiolitic" Mesozoic rocks of Bearth's chloritoid-garnet zone are pierced by several extensive inlying massifs representing the cores of older crystalline rocks torn from the basement. Such are the

---

[1] The eclogites of this zone are Bearth's "type I", in which the garnet is less magnesian than in eclogites of "type II" further north in the Lepontine Alps.

massifs of Monte Rosa and Gran Paradiso. The Monte Rosa massif, 40 × 15 km, consists of granitic gneisses and high-grade pelitic schists (products of the Hercynian metamorphism), that, along a border zone some 20 km long, have been completely remetamorphosed during the Alpine orogeny (stippled area in Fig. 7-19). The typical assemblages (Bearth, 1952, p. 85), presumably isofacial with the enveloping glaucophane schists of the garnet-chloritoid zone in the adjacent Zermatt region, are

A. Pelitic and quartzo-feldspathic (Fig. 7-20)
  1. Quartz-albite-muscovite-kyanite-chlorite
  2. Quartz-albite-muscovite-chloritoid-kyanite (-garnet)
  3. Quartz-muscovite-chlorite-garnet-biotite (garnets partly relict, but with rims of later origin attributed to the Alpine metamorphism)
  4. Quartz-muscovite-chloritoid-garnet-chlorite
  5. Quartz-muscovite-biotite-albite

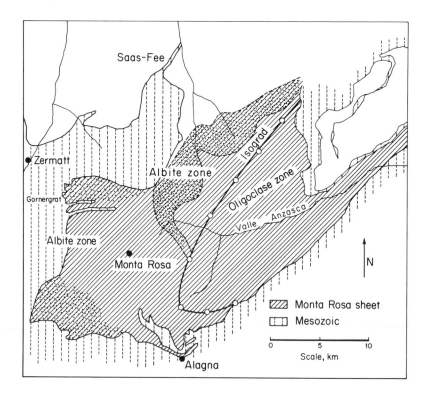

Fig. 7-19. Monte Rosa region, Swiss Alps. Stippled areas of Monte Rosa sheet are strongly affected (densely stippled, completely reconstituted) by Alpine metamorphism. (*After P. Bearth,* 1952.)

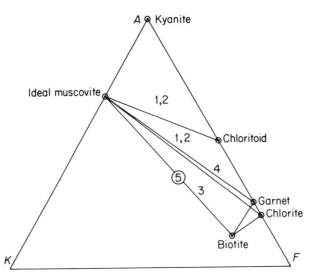

Fig. 7-20. Glaucophane-schist-amphibolite transitional facies, Monte Rosa region, Swiss Alps. *AKF* diagram for pelitic and quartzo-feldspathic assemblages. (*After data of P. Bearth*, 1952.) Quartz and albite are possible additional phases.

Particularly noteworthy is the widespread occurrence of simultaneously crystallized kyanite and chloritoid in many pelitic and micaceous rocks.

  B. Carbonate-bearing
    6. Quartz-albite-muscovite-biotite-ankerite
    7. Calcite-grossularite-clinozoisite
  C. Basic
    8. Albite-hornblende-clinozoisite-chlorite-biotite-quartz-sphene
    9. Hornblende-garnet-muscovite

Low-grade Facies Transitional to the Glaucophane-lawsonite-schist Facies

Partial transitions. If, as we think likely, the glaucophane-lawsonite-schist facies is a product of regional metamorphism at low temperature and very high pressure (Fyfe, Turner, and Verhoogen, 1958, p. 226), transitional facies toward all other medium- and high-pressure facies, in the low- and medium-temperature range are to be expected. Such, indeed, do occur. We have long recognized a transition to the greenschist facies, marked by profuse development of glaucophane in greenschists, apart from which the paragenesis is precisely that of the greenschist facies as developed in the chlorite zone (Fyfe, Turner, and Verhoogen, 1958, pp. 227-228). Glaucophanic greenschists of this kind may be localized within greenschist facies terranes. For example, Yen (1966) records this paragenesis as occurring sporadically over a small area (20 km²) in a broad region of low-grade rocks belonging to the greenschist facies in eastern Taiwan. The Precambrian glaucophane greenschists of Anglesey in Wales are more extensive; but they are associated with preponderating normal pelitic and basic mineral assemblages of the chlorite zone (Greenly, 1919, pp. 115-118).

When we considered the prehnite-pumpellyite-metagraywacke facies, it was noted that a transition toward the glaucophane-lawsonite-schist facies in New Zealand is marked by a localized paragenesis in which lawsonite is an essential phase. The same facies, but containing aragonite (though never lawsonite) in parts of Washington, has a similar but not identical significance.

Development of transitional facies on a regional scale is characteristic of some metamorphic provinces. This is the case in the Sanbagawa belt of Japan, to which we now turn.

The Sanbagawa belt of Japan. Southeast of and immediately adjoining the Ryoke metamorphic belt of Japan is a parallel zone of completely different metamorphic facies. This is known as the *Sanbagawa belt* (Fig. 7-21). It has no obvious connection with granitic intrusions, and it is separated longitudinally from the adjoining Ryoke belt by a great dislocation known as the *Median Line.* The age of Sanbagawa metamorphism has been disputed among Japanese geologists. On the basis of radiometric evidence it is now generally thought to be synchronous with metamorphism in the Ryoke belt, i.e., Cretaceous. The rocks affected are Paleozoic sediments and associated basic volcanics. For details of the geology, structure, and age of the Sanbagawa belt, and exceptionally full data on mineral paragenesis, the reader is referred to Banno (1958, 1959, 1964), Iwasaki (1963), Miyashiro and Banno (1958), Miyashiro and Seki (1958), Seki (1961). The account of Suzuki (1930) is classic in the older literature.

Throughout the Sanbagawa belt the trend of the isograds is roughly parallel to that of the belt itself and to the strike of formations within it. The grade of metamorphism increases to the northeast, i.e., toward the Median Line. The heat source is unknown. Since the regional structure in some portions of the belt (e.g., in Sikoku) is an anticlinorium whose axis runs more or less along the middle of the belt itself, the grade of metamorphism is not directly controlled by stratigraphic depth.

The generalized sequence of metamorphic zones in order of increasing grade (cf. Iwasaki, 1963, pp. 15-17; Banno, 1964, pp. 297-300) is as follows. The accompanying correlation with metamorphic facies, though not in conflict with that of Japanese workers, is in accordance with the nomenclature adopted in this book.

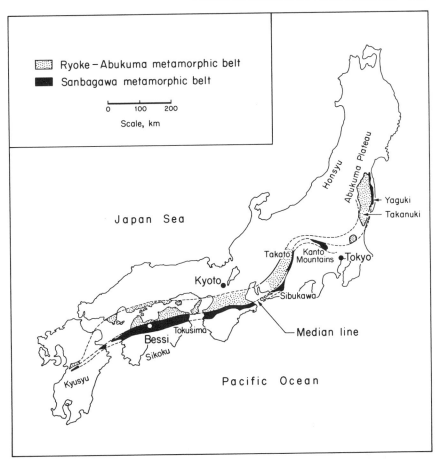

Fig. 7-21. Sanbagawa (black) and Ryoke (stippled) metamorphic belts, Japan. (*After A. Miyashiro.*)

1. Lawsonite schist: Glaucophane-lawsonite-schist facies
2. Pumpellyite schist:
3. Epidote-glaucophane-schist: } Transitional facies
4. Subcalcic hornblende: Greenschist facies
5. Epidote amphibolite: Greenschist-amphibolite transition facies

The paragenesis of the lawsonite-schist zone duplicates almost exactly that of the typical glaucophane-lawsonite-schist facies in the Californian Franciscan, except that albite is common and jadeite[1]-quartz is rare, and the calcium-carbonate phase is recorded as calcite.

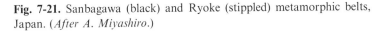

[1] Jadeite typically has a significant content of aegirine.

The transitional facies as represented in the pumpellyite zone is a greenschist (chlorite zone) paragenesis, but with conspicuous pumpellyite and/or a glaucophane mineral in basic mineral assemblages. Typical of these are

Albite-epidote-chlorite-glaucophane
Albite-epidote-chlorite-actinolite-glaucophane
Albite-epidote-chlorite-pumpellyite-actinolite

An assemblage, previously unknown to this writer, but combining in itself characteristics of both facies is

Quartz-glaucophane-piedmontite-spessartite-muscovite-hematite
(-spessartite-calcite-albite)

The glaucophane may be nearly colorless, or some deeply colored variety.

With further transition toward the greenschist facies proper, as illustrated by the paragenesis of the epidote-glaucophane schist zone, pumpellyite is eliminated. Only the common occurrence of glaucophane in greenschists and its continued presence in the quartz-piedmontite schists is distinctive. Banno (1964, p. 298) compares this paragenesis with that which characterizes much of the lower-grade zones of the Pennine schists in the Alps of Europe.

The zone of subcalcic hornblende as defined by Banno, with minor but interesting exceptions, shows the typical greenschist-facies paragenesis of the chlorite zone, as developed, for example, in the Otago schist belt of New Zealand. The exceptions concern the nature and incidence of actinolitic amphiboles and almandine garnets. Some of the amphiboles classed as glaucophanic actinolite or as subcalcic hornblende contain distinctly more Al_2O_3 (though no more Na_2O) than analysed actinolites in greenschists from Otago or Scotland. A manganiferous almandine is an essential constituent of many pelitic assemblages. Typical compositions are $Al_{50}Sp_{25}Gr_{20}Py_5$ and $Al_{48}Sp_{29}Py_{23}Gr_0$ (Banno, 1964, p. 253). Yet biotite still has not appeared.

Finally, with passage into the epidote-amphibolite zone, the mineral assemblages are similar to those described from other parts of the world for the greenschist-amphibolite transitional facies. (These are discussed in a later section.)

THE HIGHER-GRADE FACIES OF REGIONAL METAMORPHISM

To distinguish higher from lower grades of metamorphism at some particular line cutting across facies series is a purely arbitrary device used by an author to clarify his presentation of the picture of mineralogical metamorphic phenomena. Again, it is emphasized that in the deeper levels of the crust, magmatic and metamorphic phenomena are intimately associated. It is no longer possible to speak of some kinds of metamorphism as contact, others as regional. But it is recognized that in some terranes (e.g., the high-grade zones of Vermont and New Hampshire) the configuration of the isograds may well have been strongly influenced by local upward penetration of granitic plutons.

Many of us have now attempted to locate the well-recognized facies of metamorphism upon some kind of pressure-temperature diagram. In the first part of this chapter, we surveyed the regionally developed facies, generally relegated to the low-temperature side of such diagrams. In the high-temperature realm lies the amphibolite-granulite facies sequence in the field of moderate pressure. At high pressures, and in the model of Fyfe and Turner (1966) spanning a broad temperature range, is the eclogite facies. For descriptive purposes it is now proposed to consider a facies series (not necessarily a natural one) extending from the greenschist transition through the amphibolite to the granulite facies. Then we shall turn to the eclogite facies and its possible lower-temperature transition into the glaucophane-lawsonite-schist facies.

The Greenschist-amphibolite Transition Facies

Variable nature of transition. A number of critical mineralogical criteria sharply distinguish the parageneses of the greenschist facies (chlorite and biotite zones) from those of the amphibolite facies. In the latter, kyanite or sillimanite, staurolite, almandine, hornblende, plagioclase (An > 25 percent), diopside, grossularite, and others are common phases in rocks of appropriate composition. These are unknown or (as in the case of almandine) rare in the greenschist facies. On the other hand stilpnomelane, albite-clinozoisite, muscovite-chlorite, calcite-actinolite, dolomite-quartz, and piedmontite, are absent or rare in the amphibolite facies.

The mineralogical changes that accompany the transition from one facies to the other could be represented, then, by a family of closely spaced equilibrium curves, each corresponding to some simple dehydration or decarbonation reaction. Some reactions, in any given situation, doubtless are coupled. Many that have been invoked on geologic evidence lead to one or more end products in common. Among the amphibolite-facies minerals that may originate, not only in the imagination but in nature, by more than one reaction are almandine, plagioclase, hornblende, sillimanite, and biotite. Were it possible to compute accurately the equilibrium curves corresponding to all these reactions, most would be found to have the same general configuration (with a rather steep positive slope). But they would not be precisely parallel; some of the closely spaced curves would cross. So there must be some equilibria that are stable at high but metastable at low pressures, and vice versa.

Geologic evidence suggests that the transition from the greenschist to the amphibolite facies represents a *P-T* field in which a number of the critical equilibrium curves are indeed closely spaced and do intersect each other. This is the explanation here suggested for the observed differences in the field sequence in which certain critical minerals, notably almandine, plagioclase and hornblende, appear in the transitional facies in different individual terranes. This characteristic feature of the transitional facies will now be illustrated by a few well-documented examples.

Transition in the biotite zone of Vermont. In Vermont, a plagioclase significantly more calcic than pure albite first appears in quartz-muscovite-biotite-chlorite-plagioclase schists containing ankerite (but not epidote) in the biotite zone, still within 1 or 2 km of the almandine isograd. It is calcic oligoclase, An_{20} to An_{26}, and is accompanied by nearly pure albite, An_3 to An_7. The typical assemblage is

    1. Quartz - oligoclase - albite - muscovite - biotite - chlorite - ankerite (or calcite)

Closer to the almandine isograd there are two alternative assemblages. The two plagioclases coexist only in rocks containing no carbonate.

    2. Quartz-oligoclase-albite-muscovite-biotite-chlorite

    3. Quartz-oligoclase-muscovite-biotite-chlorite-ankerite (or calcite)

But assemblage 3 is far the commoner of the two, and the anorthite content of the plagioclase coexisting with carbonate is mostly close to An_{25}.

Within the garnet zone itself, lenticles of hornblende-schist (Lyons, 1955, p. 110, table 1, no. 5) have the composition quartz-plagioclase (An_{27}) hornblende-biotite-chlorite (-ankerite-calcite). The transition to the amphibolite facies is now complete.

Transition in the almandine zone of the Dalradian, southeastern Highlands, Scotland. At the almandine isograd in the Scottish Dalradian, biotite, according to Atherton (1964), becomes abundant for the first time in pelitic schists. (In the biotite zone he finds biotite to be virtually confined to the less aluminous quartzo-feldspathic schists.) The paragenesis of the almandine zone is shown graphically in Fig. 7-22. According to Wiseman (1934, p. 379) the composition of amphibolites (metadiabases) immediately beyond the almandine isograd is hornblende-albite-clino-zoisite-biotite (-almandine) or hornblende-albite-epidote-chlorite-biotite. These hornblendes, however, are somewhat low in Al_2O_3 (about 8 percent by weight). The garnet is an almandine notably high in grossularite. The amphibolite facies proper, in which the metadiabase assemblage is horn-blende-andesine (-epidote-garnet-biotite), is attained only at maximum grades in the almandine zone.

Transition in the almandine zone of south Westland, New Zealand. The almandine isograd in the Alpine schists of Westland, New Zealand (cf. Fig. 7-8) is difficult to map, because the dominant rocks in both the biotite and the almandine zone are quartzo-feldspathic schists without garnet.

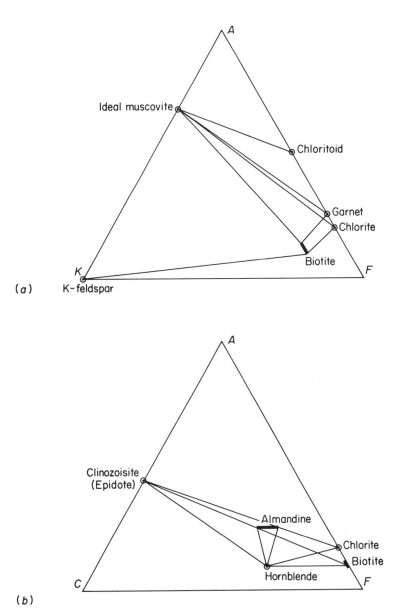

Fig. 7-22. Greenschist-amphibolite transitional facies, almandine zone, Dalradian, southeast Highlands, Scotland (somewhat schematic for want of mineral analyses). (*a*) *AKF* diagram for rocks with excess SiO$_2$ and Al$_2$O$_3$. Quartz, albite, and epidote are possible additional phases. (*b*) *ACF* diagram for albite-epidote-amphibolites. (*Data after J. D. H. Wiseman.*)

305

The essential phases of the typical assemblage are quartz-plagioclase-biotite-muscovite-epidote. These may be accompanied by chlorite in the biotite zone or by garnet, chlorite and microcline in the almandine zone. There is no obvious difference between the compositions of coexisting chlorites and biotites in the two zones (Crawford, 1966, p. 279). Hornblende, rather than the pair actinolite-chlorite, appears for the first time in basic rocks at the almandine isograd (Mason, 1956, p. 6). Evans (1964) and Crawford (1966) have discussed in some detail the transition from albitic to oligoclase-andesine assemblages which occurs in the almandine zone of Westland. At the almandine isograd, and across the full width (about 5 km) of the almandine zone, there are two plagioclase phases in quartzo-feldspathic schists containing micas and epidote. One is nearly pure albite, the anorthite content of which (4 to 5 percent) is significantly greater than in albites of the preceding biotite zone (An_1 to An_2). The other is oligoclase in the range An_{21} to An_{26}. This may prove to be a characteristic feature of rocks of similar composition and metamorphic grade elsewhere. Amphibolites proper, with a single plagioclase phase (oligoclase-andesine or more calcic) are found only at the next isograd, which in New Zealand marks the beginning of an oligoclase zone (cf. Fig. 7-8).

Transition in the epidote-amphibolite zone of the Sanbagawa belt, Japan. In the Sanbagawa belt as described by Banno (1964, pp. 297-299), the lowest grades of metamorphism are represented by the glaucophane-lawsonite-schist facies. Transition between this and the greenschist facies, with increasing grade, has been described earlier in this chapter. The maximum grade recorded is that of Banno's epidote-amphibolite zone. Here again is a transition toward the amphibolite facies proper, but marked by a unique order of appearance of the index minerals, almandine, oligoclase, and biotite. Two grades of metamorphism can be distinguished within the epidote-amphibolite zone. The respective parageneses are as follows:
- A. Basic: Hornblende-epidote-albite-chlorite-almandine
  Pelitic: Quartz-muscovite-chlorite-almandine
- B. Basic: Hornblende-epidote-oligoclase-almandine
    Hornblende-epidote-oligoclase-diopside
  Pelitic: Quartz-muscovite-biotite-almandine
  Calcareous: Quartz-calcite-diopside-grossularite

In paragenesis *B*, we see the full development of the amphibolite facies (cf. Fig. 7-23) except that the oligoclase is not more calcic than An_{15}. Moreover, in parts of this zone there are kyanite- and omphacite-bearing assemblages of a most interesting nature, marking a transition from the amphibolite to the eclogite facies (Banno, 1964, pp. 287-288).

Relative order of appearance of index minerals. The characteristic of amphibolite facies assemblages, as contrasted with the greenschist facies, is the ubiquitous presence of one or more of the phases biotite, almandine, hornblende and plagioclase (An_{20}). Japanese geologists (e.g., Banno, 1964, pp. 251, 301) have drawn attention to the difference in the order of appearance of these minerals in different metamorphic terranes. They correlate the early appearance of almandine (exclusive of highly manganiferous types) and of hornblendes with high metamorphic pressures. In the transitional facies which has just been discussed, the distinctive sequence of index phases in quartzo-feldspathic schists and basic assemblages conforms to one or other of the patterns listed below, in presumed order of decreasing pressure (1 to 5), grade increasing toward the right:

1. Sanbagawa, Japan	Hornblende Almandine	Biotite		Plagioclase	
2. East Otago, New Zealand		Biotite Almandine		Plagioclase Hornblende	
3. Dalradian, (Barrovian) Scotland		Biotite	Almandine Hornblende	Plagioclase	
4. Westland, New Zealand		Biotite		Plagioclase Almandine Hornblende	
5. Vermont, U.S.A.		Biotite		Plagioclase Hornblende	Almandine

The Amphibolite Facies

Definition and mineralogical characteristics. Eskola (e.g., 1939, pp. 351-355) defined the amphibolite facies to include metamorphic parageneses in which basic rocks are represented by hornblende-plagioclase assemblages, the plagioclase being oligoclase-andesine or some more calcic variety. This was later divided by Fyfe, Turner, and Verhoogen (1958, pp. 201, 202) into two facies. One is the hornblende-hornfels facies as defined in Chap. 6. The other, typical of medium- to high-grade metamorphism in the deeper levels of the crust, was named the almandine-amphibolite facies. In so doing, we emphasized a sharp criterion of distinction from the hornblende-hornfels facies. This nomenclature has now been abandoned (Fyfe and Turner, 1966, p. 362) and the time-honored, but not precise, term amphibolite facies reinstated:

Strictly speaking the diagnostic basic assemblage of the facies corresponding to the zones of staurolite to sillimanite in the Scottish Highlands, New England, and elsewhere, is hornblende-plagioclase-almandine. But amphibolites without almandine are much more widely developed. In consequence, many writers prefer the classic term "amphibolite facies," to the "almandine-amphibolite facies" as previously used by ourselves. We revert, therefore, to the more popular usage—*amphibolite* facies. But it must be noted that the plagioclase of the diagnostic basic assemblage is more calcic than An_{20} (commonly about An_{30}) and it is commonly accompanied by epidote, less so by almandine.

Basic assemblages in which hornblende and plagioclase ($An > 20$) are essential phases constitute an important criterion of the two facies to which they are confined—amphibolite and hornblende-hornfels. Epidote amphibolites are very widely developed and almandine amphibolites are not uncommon in the amphibolite facies. Both are virtually absent from the hornblende-hornfels facies. Characteristic of the amphibolite facies, too, are pelitic assemblages in which micas are associated with almandine, staurolite, kyanite, or sillimanite, but never with andalusite or cordierite.

The amphibolite facies covers the complete span of the medium- to high-grade zones in many of the classic areas of progressive regional metamorphism. Therefore a convenient starting point for a survey of facies variants in relation to pressure, temperature (grade), and geologic environment will be to examine the amphibolite facies in the almandine, staurolite, kyanite, and sillimanite zones of the Barrovian sequence. This corresponds to the higher-grade portion of what Miyashiro (1961, p. 285) has termed the kyanite-sillimanite facies series. Complete data are available for this series as developed in Scotland (with emphasis on Barrow's type region in the Dalradian of the southeast Highlands), and in the New Hampshire-Vermont section of the Appalachian fold region of western United States. Both illustrate the parageneses in deeply eroded roots of Paleozoic fold systems. Although not everywhere identical, the two areas complement each other in exhibiting a single pattern of variation within the facies as a whole.

Other, though by no means wholly different, patterns of variation are seen in intensely deformed rocks of some of the younger fold systems. Illustrations will be drawn from the western Alps of Europe and the northwestern Himalaya, with special reference to calcareous assemblages.

Yet another pattern is typical of regional metamorphism and migmatite development in the Precambrian continental shields. Here the amphibolite facies may pass with increasing metamorphic grade, via transitional parageneses, into the granulite facies. The transition is well exemplified in parts of the Canadian shield, the Adirondacks of New York, the Broken Hill region of New South Wales, Australia, and Ceylon. Reference to these regions will be made in this and the immediately following section of the chapter.

Almandine zone of Scottish Highlands. In the original region mapped by Barrow (1893) and Tilley (1925), the zone of almandine is very extensive; and that of staurolite, for lack of pelitic rocks of appropriate composition, is scarcely separable from the zone of kyanite. In the higher-grade portion of the almandine zone, the paragenesis is already within the amphibolite facies. Its principal features are illustrated in Figs. 7-23 and 7-24. These are based mainly on the descriptive data of Harker (1932, pp. 222-224, 253-254, 257), Wiseman (1934; pp. 386-392), and Williamson (1953). Some of the typical assemblages are

A. Pelitic
    1. Quartz-muscovite-biotite-almandine-plagioclase
    2. Quartz-muscovite-chloritoid-almandine-chlorite
B. Quartzo-feldspathic
    3. Quartz-microcline-biotite-muscovite (-plagioclase)
C. Basic
    4. Hornblende-plagioclase-almandine-epidote (-biotite)
    5. Hornblende-plagioclase-almandine-biotite
    6. Hornblende-plagioclase-epidote (-biotite)
    7. Hornblende-plagioclase
D. Calcareous

Note that in siliceous dolomitic rocks diopside now appears instead of tremolite-calcite (-quartz).

    8. Calcite-diopside-grossularite
    9. Diopside-grossularite-vesuvianite
    10. Diopside-clinozoisite (zoisite)-grossularite-quartz
    11. Quartz-calcite
    12. Calcite-diopside (-quartz)
    13. Calcite-hornblende (edenite)
    14. Calcite-diopside-forsterite (rare; Harker, 1932, p. 257)

Staurolite-kyanite zone, New Hampshire-Vermont. The only obvious change in paragenesis with passage from the almandine zone to that of staurolite and kyanite is in the more aluminous pelitic assemblages. Chloritoid and chlorite are no longer present; staurolite and/or kyanite may appear in rocks deficient in K_2O (that is, in assemblages lacking K-feldspar). Some of the recorded assemblages are as follows (Lyons, 1955, pp. 110, 115, 118, 140-142):

A. Pelitic (cf. Fig. 7-25)

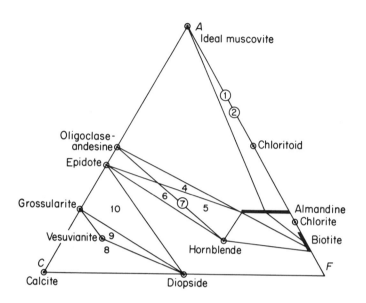

Fig. 7-23. Amphibolite facies, almandine zone, Dalradian, Scotland. *ACF* diagram for rocks with excess SiO$_2$ and deficient in K$_2$O. Quartz is a common additional phase.

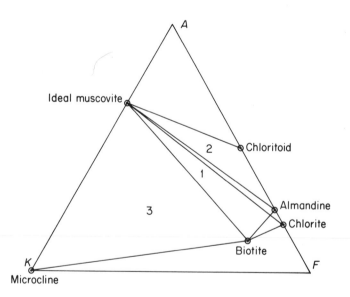

Fig. 7-24. Amphibolite facies, almandine zone, Dalradian, Scotland. *AKF* diagram for rocks with excess SiO$_2$ and Al$_2$O$_3$. Quartz is an additional phase.

310

    1. Quartz-andesine-muscovite-biotite-almandine-kyanite (-staurolite)[1]

    2. Quartz-oligoclase-muscovite-biotite-almandine-staurolite

B. Basic

    3. Quartz-andesine-hornblende-biotite- (-clinozoisite-almandine)

C. Calcareous

    4. Quartz-clinozoisite (-hornblende-garnet)

    5. Calcite-actinolite (-hornblende)

    6. Calcite-quartz

D. Magnesian

    7. Chlorite-anthophyllite-talc (-magnetite-ankerite)

Sillimanite-muscovite zone, New Hampshire. Over much of western New Hampshire, some 50 km east and southeast of the Hanover quadrangle described by Lyons, the pelitic paragenesis is characterized by sillimanite in association with muscovite. Otherwise it resembles that depicted in Fig. 7-25. These are the rocks of the sillimanite-muscovite zone,

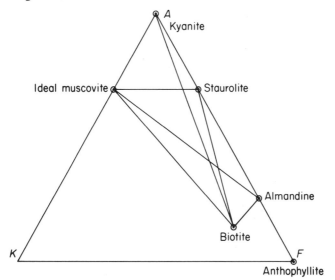

Fig. 7-25. Amphibolite facies, staurolite-kyanite zone, Hanover quadrangle New Hampshire-Vermont. *AKF* diagram for pelitic rocks with excess SiO_2 and Al_2O_3. Quartz and plagioclase are additional phases.

as distinguished from assemblages of even higher grade in which sillimanite is associated with K-feldspar while muscovite and staurolite are lacking.

[1] This assemblage (with magnetite plus graphite) marks the kyanite isograd in the Barrovian sequence in Scotland (Chinner, 1966, p. 163).

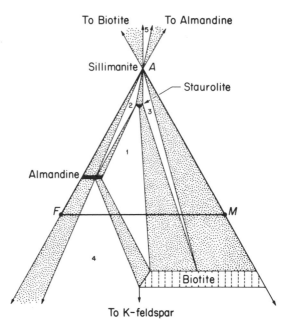

Fig. 7-26. Amphibolite facies, sillimanite-muscovite zone, west-central New Hampshire. *AFM* diagram for pelitic assemblages with quartz and muscovite as additional phases. (*After J. B. Thompson.*) Fields of two-phase assemblages stippled; three-phase fields blank.

Thompson (1957) has illustrated the pelitic paragenesis in detail by means of his *AFM* projection, here reproduced as Fig. 7-26:

1. Quartz-muscovite-biotite-almandine-staurolite
2. Quartz-muscovite-almandine-staurolite-sillimanite
3. Quartz-muscovite-biotite-staurolite-sillimanite
4. Quartz-muscovite-biotite-almandine-orthoclase
5. Quartz-muscovite-biotite-almandine-sillimanite

In the same zone of New Hampshire, Heald (1950, pp. 48-50) recorded the paragenesis of pelitic schists similar to the above, but containing oligoclase (An_{28}) and no staurolite:

6. Quartz-oligoclase-biotite-muscovite-almandine
7. Quartz-oligoclase-biotite-muscovite-sillimanite-almandine
8. Quartz-oligoclase-biotite-microcline

With these are associated thinly bedded alternating calc-magnesian and calc-pelitic schists with the assemblages

9. Microcline-anorthite-diopside (-quartz)
10. Diopside-actinolite-microcline-bytownite (-quartz)
11. Actinolite-anorthite-microcline (-garnet-quartz)
12. Anorthite-biotite-microcline (-quartz-biotite)

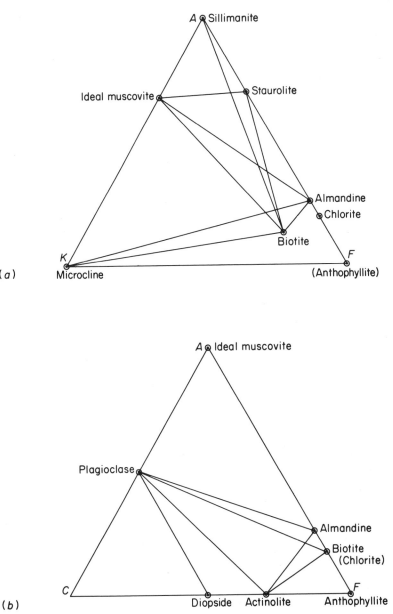

Fig. 7-27. Amphibolite facies, sillimanite-muscovite zone, New Hampshire. (*a*) *AKF* diagram for pelitic and quartzo-feldspathic assemblages containing quartz and muscovite. Plagioclase (typically oligoclase-andesine) is a possible additional phase. (*b*) *ACF* diagram for rocks with excess SiO_2 and K_2O. Microcline and quartz are possible (almost ubiquitous) additional phases.

The complete paragenesis of the New Hampshire sillimanite-muscovite zone is shown in Fig. 7-27.

Sillimanite zones of Scottish Highlands and New Hampshire. The respective parageneses representing the highest grade of metamorphism attained in these two regions have much in common. Pelitic assemblages contain sillimanite, not kyanite. In New Hampshire it is associated with orthoclase and biotite, but not with muscovite. In Scotland all four phases are commonly present, and textures suggest that in many rocks the pair muscovite-quartz is in process of breaking down to sillimanite orthoclase. Ideal muscovite-free assemblages (Harker, 1932, pp. 227-229, 255, 263, 283; Wiseman, 1934, pp. 394, 395; Heald, 1950, pp. 50-55) are

A. Pelitic and quartzo-feldspathic
   1. Quartz-plagioclase (An_{30})-biotite-almandine-sillimanite-orthoclase (-muscovite)
   2. Quartz-plagioclase (An_{30})-biotite-almandine-sillimanite
   3. Quartz-plagioclase (An_{30})-biotite-sillimanite
B. Basic
   4. Hornblende-andesine-almandine (-quartz); epidote and biotite, common at lower grades, are absent.
C. Calcareous (cf. Kennedy, 1949, p. 49)
   5. Zoisite-biotite-quartz
   6. Grossularite-anorthite-diopside-hornblende)

Recent geochemical studies on pelitic assemblages in the higher grades of regional metamorphism in Scotland and eastern United States have brought out several interesting details:

(a) In the Scottish Dalradian, the boundary (sillimanite isograd) between the zones of kyanite and sillimanite is by no means sharply defined. The two aluminum silicates commonly coexist. Chinner (1960) records the influence of different degrees of oxidation, reflected by occurrence of ilmenite-magnetite, ilmenite-magnetite-hematite and magnetite-hematite in pelitic gneisses in which the principal silicate phases are quartz-oligoclase-muscovite-biotite-almandine-kyanite-sillimanite. These rocks occur on the outer fringe of the sillimanite zone in Glen Clova in the classic region of Barrow's zones. Chinner finds that in each sedimentary unit, the degree of oxidation, reflecting the partial pressure of oxygen during metamorphism, remained constant. The range of oxidation ratio is from 6 (in ilmenite-magnetite assemblages) to 75 (in magnetite-hematite assemblages). With increasing oxidation ratio, the amounts of biotite and garnet decrease, and there is a complementary increment in the amounts of muscovite and iron oxides. At the same time there is a marked rise in MgO/FeO in biotite and in MnO/FeO in associated garnet (Fig. 7-28).

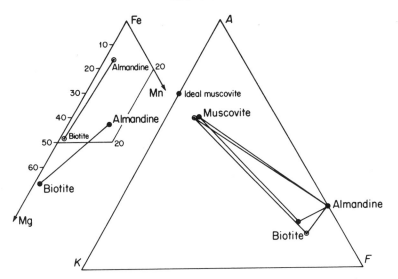

Fig. 7-28. Amphibolite facies, sillimanite isograd, Glen Clova, Scottish Highlands. Compositions of coexisting muscovites, biotites, and garnets in pelitic gneisses plotted on AKF and $MgFe^{2+}Mn$ diagrams. Circled points low-oxidation assemblages with magnetite-ilmenite; solid circles high-oxidation assemblages with magnetite-hematite. (*Data from G. A. Chinner.*)

(*b*) The breakdown of muscovite-quartz to sillimanite-orthoclase has been examined in detail by Evans and Guidotti (1966) on a traverse across the orthoclase isograd between the zones of sillimanite-muscovite and sillimanite-orthoclase in Maine, eastern United States. The "isograd" is not a line, but a zone 10 km wide throughout which sillimanite, muscovite, K-feldspar and quartz coexist, while muscovite is gradually eliminated with rising grade. At the same time, ilmenite diminishes in quantity and there is a corresponding rise in the titanium content of biotite. The composition of muscovites throughout the whole region is very uniform. Analyses plotted in terms of AKF fall very close to those of the Glen Clova sillimanite isograd (Fig. 7-28). The paragonite content is about 8 percent except in muscovites in assemblages lacking K-feldspar below the isograd. Here the composition approximates $Ms_{85}Pa_{15}$. All the assemblages are pelitic. Below the sillimanite-orthoclase isograd

    1. Quartz-biotite-muscovite-oligoclase (-garnet-orthoclase)
    2. Quartz-biotite-muscovite-oligoclase-sillimanite (-garnet)
Above the isograd
    3. The same as 2
    4. Quartz-biotite-oligoclase-muscovite-sillimanite-orthoclase (-garnet)

(*c*) Albee (1965)[1] finds that as metamorphic grade increases from the staurolite through the kyanite to the sillimanite zone, there is a very marked rise in the distribution coefficient (Mg/Fe in garnet)/(Mg/Fe in biotite). At any given metamorphic grade, the coefficient is reduced below its average value if the garnet carries significant manganese.

These and similar studies have clarified the nature of inter-phase reactions, usually complex ones, marking the various classic isograds. They also tend to support, in considerable detail, our tentative hyothesis that the common phase assemblages in metamorphic rocks closely approximate equilibrium.

Amphibolite facies, Lepontine Alps, Switzerland. East of Simplon, the Pennine zone of the Alps curves eastward in the Lepontine region north of Lake Maggiore (Figs. 7-18 and 7-29). Here the pattern of regional metamorphism is different from that in the area around and south of Zermatt and Monte Rosa (pp. 294–299). The rocks show the imprint of a posttectonic Alpine metamorphic episode connected with the uprise of Tertiary granitic plutons; this has completely obliterated the effects of the earlier phase of Alpine metamorphism whose imprint is reflected in Bearth's zones further south. In the Lepontine region the zonal pattern is simple and completely unrelated to the structure of the nappes (Wenk, 1962).

Niggli (1960) mapped isograds based on the successive index minerals stilpnomelane, chloritoid, kyanite, and sillimanite, in pelitic assemblages. Elimination of chloritoid and nearly simultaneous appearance of staurolite and kyanite at the kyanite isograd mark the full development of the amphibolite facies. In the very extensive kyanite zone, pelitic assemblages are combinations of quartz, muscovite, biotite, kyanite, staurolite, and almandine. Associated basic rocks are mainly andesine amphibolites, some of which contain epidote, almandine, and even kyanite (Wenk, 1958).

Interbedded with the dominantly pelitic schists of the Lepontine Alps are numerous bands, from 1 to 50 m thick, of calcsilicate schist and marble. Many contain plagioclase in association with calcite. Wenk (1962) found that the plagioclase of such rocks in the chloritoid zone of Niggli is nearly pure albite ($An_{<5}$). At the kyanite isograd, or just beyond it, the anorthite content rises sharply to values between 18 and 30 percent. With further increase in metamorphic grade across the kyanite zone toward the sillimanite isograd, the anorthite content rises steadily to between An_{80} and An_{100} in the sillimanite zone itself. These plagioclases are much more calcic than those of associated amphibolites. Wenk (1962) mapped a series of isograds (for plagioclase-calcite assemblages) at An_{18}, An_{30}, An_{50}, and An_{70} (Fig. 7-29). These are concentrically disposed around what is interpreted as a thermal high coinciding with the center of Tertiary granitic

---

[1]A. L. Albee, J. Petrol., vol. 6, pp. 246–301, 1965.

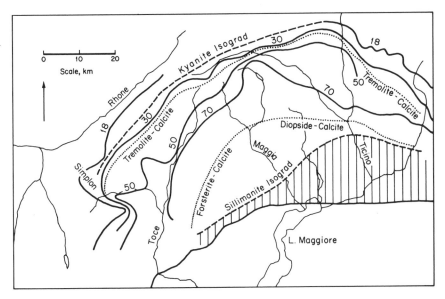

Fig. 7-29. Metamorphic zones in part of Lepontine Alps, Switzerland. (*After E. Jäger, E. Niggli, and E. Wenk.*) *E. Niggli's* (1960) sillimanite zone vertically ruled. *E. Wenk's* (1962) isograds An_{18}, An_{30}, An_{50}, An_{70}, for calcite-plagioclase assemblages are numbered accordingly. *V. Trommsdorff's* (1966) isograds for (1) first appearance of tremolite-calcite and (2) first appearance of diopside or forsterite in dolomitic marbles, are shown dotted.

intrusions in the Ticino area. This, too, is the site of Niggli's sillimanite zone, in which quartz-biotite-muscovite schists contain sillimanite (fibrolite) as an additional phase.

Of great interest is the sequence of reactions observed by Tromms-dorff (1966) in siliceous dolomitic marbles in the same region. The pair dolomite-quartz remains stable up to the kyanite isograd. At this point or just beyond it dolomite and quartz react to give talc, which is followed almost immediately by tremolite. The earliest paragenesis is an association of

      Talc-calcite-dolomite
      Talc-calcite-tremolite
      Tremolite-calcite-dolomite

The last-named marks elimination of talc from dolomitic marbles. Thereafter the paragenesis beyond Trommsdorff's tremolite-calcite isograd (Fig. 7-29) is

      Tremolite-calcite-quartz
      Tremolite-calcite-dolomite

This is the ideal paragenesis of Fig. 4-17*a*; and its first appearance coincides approximately with the first development of the amphibolite facies (Wenk's An_{30} isograd).

The tremolite-calcite zone is some 20 km wide. Its high-grade limit is marked by nearly simultaneous appearance of assemblages with diopside, forsterite, or both, well beyond the An_{70} isograd of Wenk. Observed assemblages beyond the diopside-forsterite isograd include

  Diopside-tremolite-calcite
  Diopside-calcite
  Forsterite (-chondrodite)-calcite.

Scapolite is widely distributed in marbles of the tremolite and diopside zones.

Calcareous assemblages, Nanga Parbat, northwest Himalayas. The Himalayan peak Nanga Parbat lies in a massif of "granitic" garnetiferous quartzo-feldspathic gneiss. This is enveloped in, and perhaps passes gradually into, a sheath of pelitic metasediments, possibly Precambrian in age. Metamorphism is correlated with the early Tertiary Himalayan orogeny; and the metamorphic grade decreases outward from the central zone of gneiss. An area of about 3000 km² in the Nanga Parbat region has been investigated by Misch (1949), who finds that the isogradic surfaces, in a terrane where the topographic relief is around 6 km, have a nearly vertical attitude. Their trend seems unrelated to that of the regional structure or to stratigraphic boundaries.

As regards metamorphic facies, it is immaterial whether the central core of the massif has been subject to alkali metasomatism ("granitization") as contended by Misch, or whether it is merely a culminating product of high-grade metamorphism. It could indeed be partially anatectic. But it certainly appears to represent a thermal high from which the temperature of metamorphism declined radially outward.

Much of the undoubtedly metamorphic envelope is composed principally of pelitic schists in which kyanite and almandine are essential constituents. There is even an area in which sillimanite takes the place of kyanite in pelitic rocks containing, among other phases, K-feldspar. Intercalated basic rocks are amphibolites. So the whole of the higher-grade portion of the envelope lies in the amphibolite facies.

Within the essentially pelitic metasedimentary mass, many thin beds, originally limestone (in places dolomitic), display an unusually complete calcareous paragenesis which has been recorded in detail by Misch (1964). The paragenesis varies significantly with increasing grade, and on this basis Misch has recognized three zones (local subfacies). Among the characteristic and most interesting of the calcareous assemblages are the following, listed in order of increasing grade:

  Zone A. Border of kyanite zone of associated pelitic schists
    1. Calcite-quartz-andesine

    2. Calcite-quartz-andesine-scapolite.

Combinations of biotite, muscovite, garnet, epidote minerals, and orthoclase may occur in both. Impure marbles are represented by assemblages of calcite, quartz, andesine, tremolite (or hornblende), phologopite, scapolite, zoisite.

Zone B. Marginal belt of the gneiss massif
    1. Calcite-wollastonite-diopside-grossularite
    2. Diopside-wollastonite-quartz
    3. Diopside-anorthite-grossularite-quartz
    4. Diopside-anorthite
    5. Calcite-phlogopite-tremolite
    6. Quartz-diopside-hornblende-bytownite

Zone C. Within the gneiss massif
    1. Quartz-anorthite (bytownite)—wollastonite-diopside
    2. Quartz-anorthite-wollastonite-grossularite
    3. Calcite-dolomite
    4. Calcite-forsterite-spinel-phlogopite
    5. Calcite-diopside-tremolite-spinel-phlogopite
    6. Calcite-diopside-tremolite

The calcareous assemblages of Nanga Parbat in many ways duplicate those of the hornblende-hornfels and the pyroxene-hornfels facies. Misch concludes that P_{H_2O} was maintained at a high level (with P_{CO_2} values correspondingly low) in the hydrous metamorphic environment controlled by the enclosing mass of pelitic schists. This conclusion seems well justified; otherwise it would be difficult to account for the development of "low-pressure" calcsilicate assemblages in the high-pressure environment inferred from the widespread occurrence of kyanite in pelites.

The occurrence of the anorthite (bytownite)-wollastonite and anorthite-calcite assemblages in the highest-grade area conflicts with some of our previous ideas (e.g., Fyfe, Turner, and Verhoogen, 1958). Hitherto it was generally thought that the chemically equivalent assemblages characteristic of high-grade regional metamorphism were grossularite-plagioclase or grossularite-calcite. Wollastonite-anorthite, on the other hand, was recorded as typical of metamorphism at maximum temperatures and minimum pressures (sanidinite facies). The anorthite-calcite pair, found by Misch in the Himalayas and by Wenk in the Lepontine Alps in the amphibolite facies, has hitherto been considered characteristic of the granulite facies. It would seem that the stability field of grossularite in carbonate assemblages, even at pressures high enough to permit crystallization of kyanite in pelitic rocks, is more restricted than was formerly thought.

Both Wenk and, to a lesser degree, Misch seem to have established a correlation between increase in grade of metamorphism and anorthite content of plagioclase in the calcite-plagioclase assemblages. To explain this, it must be assumed that either aluminum has diffused into, or sodium outward, from the calcareous bands. For there is no other phase than plagioclase to accommodate sodium, and no additional aluminous phase to supply aluminum in the calcareous assemblage.

Amphibolite-granulite Transitional Facies

General nature of the transition. The granulite facies as defined by Eskola (1939, pp. 360-363) is based on ideal assemblages of phases that may form by dehydration of micas and amphiboles at the culmination of metamorphism in the deep-seated zones, today represented in Archaean crystalline complexes of the continental shields. The principal anhydrous end-products are various combinations of feldspars, sillimanite (or kyanite), almandine-rich garnets, cordierite, and clino- and ortho-pyroxenes. Eskola's *ACF* diagram (reproduced here as Fig. 7-33) represents an ideal combination of phase assemblages, seldom if ever achieved in nature. The breakdown of muscovite-quartz to K-feldspar-sillimanite, though by no means a simple reaction (cf. Evans and Guidotti, 1966), is simpler than most other dehydration reactions leading to the granulite facies. And it is already in progress or complete within the amphibolite facies itself. When biotite and hornblende, together or alone, begin to dehydrate in the presence or absence of phases such as quartz and plagioclase, the resulting transformation is a gradual one, probably spread over a significant interval of temperature at any given pressure. It will be affected, too, by the prevailing oxidation state (fugacity of O_2).

Somewhere along the natural gradient of phase transformations, a line must be drawn arbitrarily dividing the amphibolite facies, *sensu stricto*, from the granulite facies. This writer has here accepted the division as it has been drawn by a lifelong student of this pattern of metamorphism, A. F. Buddington (e.g., 1963, pp. 1163-1168). The diagnostic mineral assemblage of the granulite facies, according to this definition, would be that of metagabbro or metabasalt of appropriate composition:

Plagioclase-clinopyroxene-hypersthene-hornblende

At a slightly higher grade appears the even more typical assemblage, that includes the above phases plus almandine.

The transitional facies in "Archaean-type" terranes. The metamorphic component of the "basement complex" over vast areas of the continental shields exhibits the paragenesis of the amphibolite facies. Prominent among the metamorphic rocks in most such areas are the amphibolites themselves. Their associates may include undoubted metasediments—quartzites, marbles and sillimanite- or kyanite-bearing mica schists—other bodies of rock that all geologists would agree to term "granite," and yet other quartzo-feldspathic gneisses of doubtful parentage commonly termed "granitic" or "dioritic" gneiss. The granitic and the metamorphic components are usually intimately associated on a scale that varies from a map sheet to a hand specimen. Some regions, such as the Grenville Lowlands of upper New York State (Engel and Engel, 1953, p. 1053) are predominantly metasedimentary, with enclosed discrete phacolithic granitic bodies perhaps 10 to 20 km in length. Elsewhere (as in the Archaean complex of West Australia, east and southeast of Perth), islands of metasediment of all sizes swim in a sea of granitic gneiss.

The metamorphic pattern is complicated by two obscuring factors. The first concerns the relation of "granite" to metasediment and associated amphibolite. Do the granitic elements represent intrusive magma, products of local anatexis, or simply the expression of metasomatism (addition of alkali) and high-temperature recrystallization ("granitization") of pre-existing sediments? The second factor relates to the long and complicated thermal and deformational history of rock masses whose age is measured in billions of years. How many metamorphic events are still expressed to some degree in the mineral paragenesis? Can one be sure that what appears in the field to be progressive metamorphism with increasing dehydration, is not an expression of an early metamorphic episode involving complete dehydration (ideal granulite facies) followed by a later and completely independent episode of progressive hydration (cf. Buddington, 1963, p. 1180)?

These questions, though of the utmost importance with regard to unravelling the geologic history of such a region, need not complicate our recognition and description of the various facies of metamorphism; for the facies is defined only in terms of mineralogical criteria. What must be borne in mind, however, is that two different facies, each imprinted during a separate metamorphic episode, may be represented in a single outcrop. Moreover, it is possible for two facies to develop simultaneously in a single body of initially anhydrous impermeable crystalline rock. Here, under uniform load pressure and temperature, the metamorphic reactions, involving progressive hydration, will be controlled by, and will create, a steady-state steep P_{H_2O} gradient falling from the outside inward.

In many Archaean regions, and in others much younger, such as the amphibolite-granite complex of Fiordland in southwest New Zealand, it is possible to trace in the field a gradual transition from the amphibolite toward or into the granulite facies. The path of transition, in terms of temperature and pressure factors, is by no means the same in all such regions. The transitional facies, which in many cases cover very large areas, are also subject to variation. This is expressed in the varying roles of hornblende, pyroxenes, garnet, cordierite, and Al_2SiO_5 polymorphs in the different transitional parageneses. We formerly placed all of them in a hornblende-granulite subfacies of a comprehensive granulite facies. On the basis of parageneses observed in zones of progressive high-grade metamorphism in the Adirondack mountains of New York, DeWaard (1965a, b) has gone further and proposed fourfold and sixfold subdivisions of the granulite facies which also take into account the presence or absence of garnet and of cordierite in critical assemblages. This scheme has been the subject of later discussion and some criticism by Buddington (1966).

As might be expected this particular pattern of granulite paragenesis is not, so far as this writer is aware, duplicated in every detail elsewhere. But there are many other regions where rocks transitional between amphibolites and hornblende-pyroxene granulites cover large areas and have many features in common with those of the Adirondacks.

We now propose to discard previous formal schemes of subdivision of the granulite facies, except insofar as such subdivisions may have local significance. Instead we shall trace the details of transition in two well-documented, widely separate regions: the Adirondacks of northern New York State and the Broken Hill mining area of south-central Australia. In both a point in progressive metamorphism is ultimately reached where the paragenesis is that of the granulite facies as defined above. In both this is preceded by transitional zones; and there are consistent mineralogical differences between the two: notably the occurrence of cordierite in pelitic assemblages of Broken Hill but not in the Adirondacks.

Amphibolite-granulite transition, northwest Adirondacks, New York. In the northern part of New York State, the Adirondack massif and the adjacent Grenville lowlands to the west (Fig. 7-30) comprise a southern prolongation of the Canadian continental shield. The lowland area is a metasedimentary (Precambrian) terrane in which marble, semipelitic gneiss, and amphibolites are copiously injected and permeated with granitic rocks, some of which form discrete phacoliths 10 to 30 km long. The massif itself is made up largely of igneous plutons: granite, syenite, anorthosite, and gabbro, with subordinate, but still extensive, enclosed and intervening masses of sedimentary and possibly volcanic rocks. All components of the massif, plutonic, volcanic, as well as sedimentary, have been affected profoundly by high-grade regional metamorphism. Recent fully documented accounts of the metamorphic phenomena, with emphasis on facies relationships and mineral chemistry, include publications by Buddington (1963), Buddington, Fahey, and Vlisidis (1963), Engel and Engel (1960, 1962a, b) and DeWaard (1964, 1965a). The classic older account is that of Buddington (1939).

The nature of the amphibolite-granulite transition is illustrated in unusual detail in the works of Engel and Engel (cited above) relating to progressive metamorphism across the Grenville lowlands to the border of the Adirondack massif. They summarize the evidence of progressive increase in grade of metamorphism along a 60-km section (from Emeryville to

Colton[1]) inclined obliquely to the margin of the massif, as follows (Engel and Engel, 1962a, p. 39):

> The principal geologic features indicating a progressive increase in the grade of metamorphism in the direction of the massif are: (1) systematic and characteristic changes in the metamorphic assemblages of minerals in the paragneiss, amphibolite and associated marble; (2) an increase in the amount of "igneous-looking" granite and in the ratio of igneous to metasomatic granite; (3) an appreciable increase in grain size of minerals; (4) increasing dehydration, reduction, and basification of the paragneiss and amphibolite and progressive decarbonation of the marble; (5) a decrease in the thickness of paragneiss and marble; (6) a zonation in the distribution of mineral deposits formed during specific stages of the regional metamorphism; and (7) systematic changes in solid solutions, ratios of O^{18}/O^{16} in oxides and silicates, and in other temperature-dependent mineral properties.

The same writers estimate the depth of overburden at the time of metamorphism as at least 10 km and possibly as great as 20 km. Individual bodies of gneiss and marble were thick enough (2 to 3 km) to justify a metamorphic model in which P_{CO_2} in marble and P_{H_2O} in paragneiss may be assumed to have approximated the load pressure (3 to 5 kb).

Progressive changes in mineral paragenesis from (a) the amphibolite facies near Emeryville and Edwards to (b) the granulite facies at Colton (Fig. 7-30) are as follows:

In amphibolites (Engel and Engel, 1962a, p. 43); figures in parenthesis are mean modal percentages

(a) Hornblende (68)-andesine (19)-quartz (10)-ilmenite (2)-diopside (0.5)-sphene (0.5)

(b) Hornblende (22)-labradorite (39)-diopside (21)-hypersthene (14)-ilmenite (3.5)

In metasedimentary semipelitic gneiss (Engel and Engel, 1960, p. 1; Buddington, 1963, p. 1163)

(a) Quartz-biotite-oligoclase (minor muscovite, microcline, magnetite)

(b) Quartz-oligoclase (calcic)-almandine (minor K-feldspar)

In marble (Engel and Engel, 1960, p. 53)

(a) and (b) 1. Calcite-quartz
2. Calcite-plagioclase (andesine to anorthite)-phlogopite
3. Calcite-quartz-diopside (with residual undestroyed dolomite). The amount of diopside increases at the expense of dolomite with progressive metamorphism.

---

[1] Emeryville, 15 km west of Edwards, is 20 km distant from the nearest point on the margin of the massif. Colton is just within the massif.

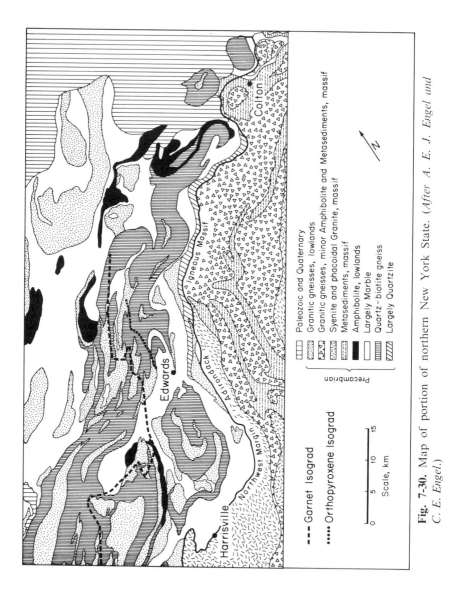

Fig. 7-30. Map of portion of northern New York State. (*After A. E. J. Engel and C. E. Engel.*)

Paleozoic and Quaternary

Granitic gneisses, lowlands

Granitic gneisses, minor Amphibolite and Metasediments, massif

Syenite and phacoidal Granite, massif

Metasediments, massif

Amphibolite, lowlands

Largely Marble

Quartz-biotite gneiss

Largely Quartzite

Precambrian

- - - Garnet Isograd

· · · · Orthopyroxene Isograd

Harrisville

Edwards

Colton

Igneous Massif

Adirondack

Northwest Margin

0   5   10   15

Scale, km

324

On the basis of mineralogical changes it is possible to draw three isograds. These, in order of increasing grade, are marked by

1. Disappearance of sphene in amphibolites
2. Appearance of abundant diopside in amphibolites; elimination of muscovite by the reaction

Quartz + Biotite + Muscovite + Magnetite → Almandine + K-feldspar

3. Appearance of hypersthene giving the granulite assemblage
Plagioclase-hornblende-diopside-hypersthene

At this third isograd, the mineral paragenesis may be classed within the granulite facies.

In the northwest Adirondacks and the adjoining Grenville lowland strip to the north, Buddington has mapped five zones of progressive metamorphism A to E. The area studied by Engel and Engel falls in zones A to C. Sphene is eliminated from amphibolites (isograd 1) within zone A; and the second isograd of Engel and Engel marks the boundary between zones A and B. Incoming hypersthene at isograd 3 defines the outer boundary of zone C and ushers in the granulite facies which continues through zones C to E (cf. p. 330).

For Zones B and C, Buddington and Lindsley (1964, p. 337) have estimated possible limits of metamorphic temperature, based on compositions of coexisting iron-titanium oxide phases, as 550 to 625°C.

Amphibolite-granulite transition, Broken Hill, south-central Australia. The Broken Hill lead-mining region of New South Wales lies in an area of about 10,000 km^2 of high-grade Archaean metamorphic rocks—an inlier enclosed by comparatively unmetamorphosed Proterozoic and Paleozoic sediments. This is an area of repeated metamorphism. Binns (1964, 1965) has described in detail the mineral paragenesis (especially that of basic assemblages) imprinted by the first episode of metamorphism which he has dated radiometrically at about $1\frac{1}{2}$ billion years. The effects of this early episode, the *Willyama metamorphism*, can be deciphered, scarcely affected by later events, over an area of about 1500 km^2 (shown in Fig. 7-31).

The dominant rocks are amphibolites of basaltic composition and quartzo-feldspathic "granitic" gneisses which Binns interprets as metasediments. In any case, the "granitic" gneisses share the mineralogical and structural imprint of the Willyama metamorphism. Pelitic rocks are few, and calcareous rocks rare. Three metamorphic zones have been established (Fig. 7-31).

Zone A: The paragenesis is that of the amphibolite facies. Some characteristic assemblages are as follows:

       1. Basic: Hornblende-plagioclase (labradorite-bytownite)-quartz-ilmenite. Some amphibolites contain combinations of clinozoisite, almandine and biotite.

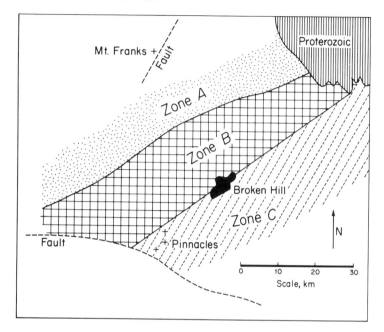

Fig. 7-31. Distribution of isograds in the Archaean Willyama complex, Broken Hill, New South Wales, Australia. (*After R. A. Binns, 1964.*)

2. Pelitic: Sillimanite-muscovite-biotite-quartz-ilmenite. Minor almandine and plagioclase may also be present.
3. Quartzo-feldspathic ("granite"): Quartz-plagioclase-K-feldspar-biotite
4. Minor calcsilicate combinations of plagioclase, diopside, tremolite, hornblende, epidote minerals, wollastonite, vesuvianite.

Zone B: The paragenesis represents the maximum grade still in the amphibolite facies.

1. Amphibolites are mostly similar to those of Zone A, but the hornblende is now brown or greenish brown instead of blue-green as in Zone A amphibolites. There also are amphibolites that carry diopside or cummingtonite as additional phases.
2. Muscovite has been eliminated from pelitic rocks, which now are represented by Sillimanite-biotite-almandine-K-feldspar-quartz(-cordierite-plagioclase)
3. Almandine becomes abundant in the quartzo-feldspathic assemblages.

Zone C: The paragenesis is now that of the granulite facies, and it continues as such for 25 km, in a direction normal to the trend of the isograds, up to the edge of the area investigated by Binns. A generalized *ACF* diagram to illustrate the paragenesis is given as Fig. 7-32. Similar

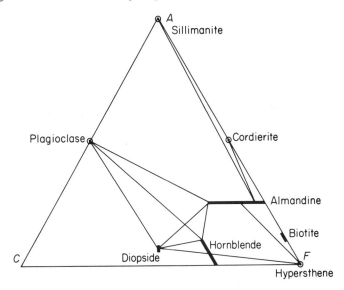

Fig. 7-32. Granulite facies, Zone C, Broken Hill, Australia. *ACF* diagram for rocks with excess SiO_2 and K_2O. Quartz and K-feldspar are possible additional phases. (*After data of R. A. Binns*, 1964, 1965.)

assemblages are found elsewhere in many granulite terranes and are the basis of one of DeWaard's (1966) principal subfacies.

1. The typical basic assemblage is
Hornblende-pyroxenes-plagioclase (with only minor quartz)
In these rocks the pyroxene may be diopside, hypersthene, or both. Hornblende has diminished in quantity and quartz has decreased even to the point of elimination. Some assemblages even lack hornblende completely.
2. The pelitic gneisses consist of
Sillimanite-almandine-cordierite-biotite-orthoclase-quartz.
Biotite has diminished in quantity as compared with pelitic assemblages in Zone B.
Binns (1965) has traced the chemistry of the transition from the paragenesis of Zone A to that of Zone C. In hornblende the titanium content rises markedly at the brown-hornblende isograd. At the same time there is change in the mechanism by which the charge balance is maintained

to accommodate substitution of Al for Si in the Z site of the structure. Binns (1965, p. 324) describes this in terms of changing proportions in the hypothetical end members of the hornblende series: tschermakitic hornblende, $Ca_2(Mg_4Al)(AlSi_7O_{22})(OH)_2$, is gradually eliminated; and there is a complementary increase in the edenite component $(NaCa_2)Mg_5$-$(AlSi_7O_{22})(OH_2)$. Where the orthopyroxene isograd marks the beginning of Zone C, there is now a complete breakdown, expressed in its simplest form by

$$Ca_2(Mg_4Al)(AlSi_7O_{22})(OH_2) \rightarrow CaAl_2Si_2O_8$$

Tschermakitic hornblende   Anorthite

$$+ CaMgSi_2O_6 + 3\ MgSiO_3 + H_2O$$

Diopside   Enstatite

Almandine, throughout the whole terrane, maintains a high FeO/MgO ratio; but there seems to be a significant increase in the pyrope content with rising grade. In basic assemblages of all grades the grossularite content of garnets is consistently high. A typical composition is $Al_{63}Sp_8Py_8Gr_{19}An_2$ (Zone C). Pelitic garnets are essentially almandines with virtually no grossularite component.

The compositions of coexisting magnetite-ilmenite pairs in Zone C, evaluated against experimental data (Buddington and Lindsley, 1964), are compatible with crystallization at temperatures between 600 and 670°C under oxidizing conditions comparable with those controlled by a fayalite-magnetite-quartz buffer. These values overlap the temperature range inferred on the same basis for the beginning of the granulite facies in the Adirondacks (Buddington and Lindsley, 1964, p. 337)—550 to 625°C.

The Granulite Facies

General mineralogical characteristics. Figure 7-33 is an idealized representation of the ultimate phase assemblages resulting from complete dehydration under conditions of the granulite facies. Each of these assemblages, listed below, is indeed found, and many are widely developed, in granulite-facies terranes. But the natural paragenesis is almost invariably complicated by appearance of hornblende in the more basic assemblages. The quantity of hornblende in these, and of biotite in pelitic rocks decreases, however, with rising grade; and this leads to local development of completely anhydrous assemblages conforming to those of Fig. 7-33. These are as follows:

1. Quartz-perthite-garnet (-plagioclase-kyanite or sillimanite). Here belong the khondalites of India and Ceylon: metamorphosed aluminous sediments consisting mainly of sillimanite, garnet, perthite, and quartz.

2. Quartz-perthite-hypersthene (-garnet-plagioclase). This is the

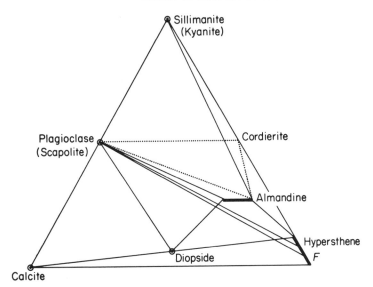

Fig. 7-33. Granulite facies. Generalized *ACF* diagram for anhydrous assemblages with excess SiO_2 and K_2O. (*After P. Eskola; slightly modified.*) Quartz and potash feldspar are possible additional phases.

normal assemblage of charnockites: hypersthene-bearing granitic gneisses, some of which are of metamorphic, others of direct magmatic origin.

3. Plagioclase-hypersthene-garnet (-quartz-perthite).

4. Plagioclase-hypersthene-diopside (-quartz-orthoclase).

These last two assemblages constitute the pyroxene granulites ("Trapp-granulite") and their mineralogical equivalents the noritic members of the charnockite series of igneous rocks.

4a. Plagioclase-hypersthene-diopside-garnet—a silica-deficient basic assemblage.

5. Diopside-plagioclase-calcite-quartz, diopside-scapolite-calcite-quartz.

6. Calcite-diopside-forsterite

7. Dolomite-calcite-forsterite

Among the individual mineral phases, hypersthene is strongly pleochroic and may contain significant amounts of Al_2O_3. Garnets are pyrope-almandines which, in more calcic assemblages (e.g., metadiabase), may contain as much as 20 percent of the grossularite end member. Hornblende is typically brownish in color and high in titanium. K-feldspars are strongly perthitic; and antiperthitic plagioclases whose initial K-feldspar content may have been as high as 7 percent are typical (Sen, 1959). Cordierite is widely developed in some granulite areas. Scapolite may accompany, or substitute for, plagioclase. Rutile and ilmenite are the characteristic titanium phases—never sphene. Olivine, corundum, and green spinel may be essential phases of silica-deficient rocks, and spinel may even appear in quartz-bearing assemblages. While sillimanite is the usual Al_2SiO_5 polymorph, some granulites contain kyanite. A rare but seemingly characteristic phase in silica-deficient assemblages, rich in both Mg and Al, is sapphirine (Ramberg, 1948; Segnit, 1957; Muthuswami and Gnanasekaran, 1962).

Adirondack massif, New York State. The granulite facies as defined by Buddington (1963) extends through the three zones (C, D, E) of maximum metamorphic grade in the rocks of the northwest Adirondack massif, where they cover an area of more than 10,000 km^2. Parageneses in (1) quartz-oligoclase-biotite gneiss, (2) metasyenite, (3) metadiorite, and (4) metagabbro are as follows (cf. also DeWaard, 1965a).

Zone C
1. Quartz-biotite-oligoclase-almandine-magnetite
2. Microcline-oligoclase-quartz-hornblende
4. Labradorite-hornblende-clinopyroxene-hypersthene-ilmenite

Zone D
2a. Oligoclase-microcline-hornblende-quartz
 b. K-feldspar-oligoclase-quartz-clinopyroxene-hypersthene-hornblende
3. Andesine-clinopyroxene-hornblende-quartz, with or without almadine and/or hypersthene
4. Labradorite-clinopyroxene-hypersthene-almandine-biotite (-hornblende)

Zone E
2a. Microline-oligoclase-quartz-hornblende (-minor biotite)
 b. Microcline-oligoclase-quartz-hornblende-hypersthene-clinopyroxene-almandine
4a. Plagioclase (An_{30} to An_{50})-orthopyroxene-clinopyroxene-almandine, with or without hornblende (up to 33 percent) or minor biotite
 b. Plagioclase (An_{30} to An_{55})-orthopyroxene-clinopyroxene-olivine-hornblende-almandine ($\pm$ biotite)

Metamorphic temperature limits deduced from compositions of iron-oxide pairs are Zone D, 600 to 640°C; Zone E, 635 to 665°C.

Central Highlands, Ceylon. Precambrian crystalline rocks occupy the greater portion (30,000 km^2) of the island of Ceylon. A central belt of metasediments with intercalated charnockites, 350 × 100 km, known as the *Highland series* (Fig. 7-34), is flanked on either side by areas composed

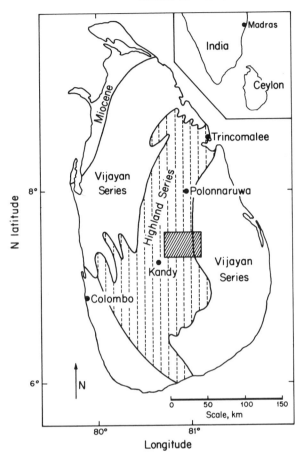

Fig. 7-34. Outline map of Ceylon, showing location of Rangala area (see text). (*After P. G. Cooray.*)

of migmatites, granitic gneisses, and minor metasedimentary bands known as the *Vijayan series.* The petrology and structure and the mutual relations of these two units have been described by Cooray (1961) on the basis of work in the Rangala area on the eastern side of the Highland complex.

Cooray has demonstrated a field transition between the two lithologic units through a zone some 10 to 15 km wide that cuts obliquely across the strike of the metasedimentary beds of the Highland series. In the transition zone, charnockitic members of the Highland series "become increasingly modified into streaky biotite gneisses," and remnants of more resistant quartzite and marble beds persist in a terrane of migmatitic and granitic gneiss. He postulates two major Archaean episodes of metamorphism. The imprint of the earlier one (granulite facies) is preserved almost intact in the Highland series. But the bordering zones of Vijayan migmatitic gneiss are interpreted as products of regional granitization, mobilization and even plutonic intrusion of granite in the second episode. The metamorphic components of these great migmatite zones now have the paragenesis of the amphibolite facies.

The principal assemblages of the granulite facies paragenesis in the Highland series are as follows:

A. Pelitic
    1. Quartz-orthoclase-plagioclase (An_{30} to An_{40})-almandine-biotite (ilmenite, magnetite)
    2. Almandine-sillimanite-orthoclase-quartz (khondalites)
    3. Quartz-orthoclase-plagioclase-biotite-sillimanite-graphite

B. Calcareous
    4. Calcite-dolomite-forsterite (-diopside-phlogopite-graphite)
    5. Diopside-scapolite (minor calcite)

C. Charnockitic (The name applied to all rocks whose compositions range more or less from granitic to gabbroic, and which contain hypersthene and/or almandine)
    6. Quartz-orthoclase-plagioclase-biotite-hornblende-almandine
    7. Plagioclase-hypersthene-almandine-hornblende
    8. Plagioclase-hypersthene-diopside-hornblende

A notable feature is the absence of cordierite. Note also the universal presence of garnet in charnockitic rocks, in contrast with the general absence of this phase in charnockites of Madras (see below).

In a later summary of the geology of Ceylon, Cooray (1962) emphasizes two features characteristic of the Highlands belt as a whole. First, the rocks are for the most part undoubtedly sedimentary. Massive beds can be traced for many kilometers; a thick marble belt, for example, runs continuously along the eastern boundary of the Highland series for 60 km or more. Secondly, charnockites, with all the characteristics of such rocks as developed elsewhere in Ceylon and southern India, are everywhere interbedded with the Highland metasediments. Interbanding of charnockite and metasediment can be seen on all scales from less than 1 to 100 m. Individual bands of quartzite and of charnockite can be traced continuously for 50 to 70 km.

West of the Highlands belt as described by Cooray is an extensive southwestern coastal belt (at least 130 × 30 km), in which the regional granulite paragenesis is different from that just described. Hornblende and biotite are much more prominent in the basic and quartzo-feldspathic assemblages, and pelitic rocks contain cordierite rather than garnet. The whole paragenesis, including diopside-wollastonite-scapolite calcgranulites, has been recorded clearly by D. J. A. C. Hapuarachchi.[1] He attributes the hornblende-granulite and cordierite-granulite parageneses to the second of the two episodes of Archaean metamorphism. The parent rocks are shown to have been anhydrous granulites and charnockites of the Highland-series type, formed in the first metamorphic episode. Here, then, is the beginning of a transition from the granulite facies proper towards the amphibolite facies—a transition involving progressive hydration of granulites and decarbonation of marble. It recalls Buddington's (1963, p. 1180) suggested alternative origin for what has here been termed the amphibolite granulite transition in the northern Adirondacks (the hornblende-granulite and cordierite-granulite facies of other writers).

The charnockite series of Madras. The term *charnockite* is generally applied in India to rocks whose chemical compositions fall within the range of plutonic rocks (acid, basic and ultrabasic), whose textures recall those of corresponding plutonic rocks, but in which the characteristic mafic phase is hypersthene (with or without some combination of clino-pyroxene, hornblende or almandine). Their mineral assemblages correspond closely with those of the granulite facies. There has been a good deal of controversy about the origin of charnockites: igneous versus metamorphic. Doubtless both primary igneous and clearly metamorphic assemblages have been classed by various writers in India, Australia, and elsewhere as charnockitic. From a comprehensive study of charnockites of all types in Madras, southern India, Howie (1955, p. 762) concluded

> There can be little doubt that the rocks of the Madras charnockite series were originally igneous . . . The chemistry of the Madras series affords strong confirmation of the view that these rocks were originally a series of calc-alkali plutonic rocks.

He was unable, however, to find decisive criteria on which to distinguish products of granulite-facies metamorphism from primary igneous rocks crystallizing in a similar deep-seated environment.

The essential charnockite assemblages as developed in Madras are:

A. Acid division
   Microcline (perthitic)-plagioclase (An_{33})-quartz-hypersthene
B. Intermediate division
   Plagioclase (An_{33})-microcline-quartz-hypersthene-(diopside). Rare hornblende
C. Basic division
   Labradorite-hypersthene-diopside-hornblende (-magnetite-ilmenite)

[1] Manuscripts on hornblende-granulite and cordierite-granulite subfacies in southwest Ceylon, in press, *Geol. Mag.* I am greatly indebted to the author for permission to read these two important papers in manuscript form prior to publication.

D. Ultrabasic division

Hypersthene-diopside-hornblende-(magnetite-ilmenite-pyrite)
Noteworthy is the absence of garnet from all assemblages.

Concluding remarks. It is clear that the granulite facies is marked everywhere by common mineralogical features: prevalence of almandine in quartzo-feldspathic assemblages; the plagioclase-hypersthene-diopside assemblage, generally with almandine and/or hornblende in basic rocks; simple calcareous assemblages in which diopside or quartz may be associated with calcite, while diopside and forsterite may occur with dolomite; absence of calc-aluminum silicates other than anorthite.

The zonal sequences show that decrease in hornblende and biotite in the paragenesis as a whole, and complementary increase in pyroxenes and garnet (or cordierite) is to be correlated with increasing metamorphic grade—rise certainly in temperature and perhaps in pressure as well.

Cordierite, over great areas of granulite-facies terrane, characteristically appears in association with almandine. Such is the case in the Broken Hill region of Australia and in Finnish Lappland (Eskola, 1952). Elsewhere, as in the Highland series of Ceylon and in the northwest part of the Adirondack massif, almandine is the sole Fe–Mg–Al silicate. Wynne-Edwards and Hay (1963) have studied the mutual relations of cordierite and almandine in some assemblages, rich in Mg and Al, in the facies of the amphibolite-granulite transition in southern Ontario. They find three associated pelitic assemblages of this type (all containing quartz-K-feldspar).

1. Almandine-sillimanite-cordierite-biotite-plagioclase
2. Almandine-sillimanite-biotite-plagioclase
3. Cordierite-sillimanite-biotite

The phase relations and range of composition of garnets are shown on the $A'F'M'$ projection in Fig. 7-35. From a comparison of the compositions of associated garnet and cordierite in the several Ontario assemblages with each other, and with garnet-cordierite assemblages of other metamorphic facies, Wynne-Edwards and Hay conclude

1. Cordierite in pelitic assemblages of regional metamorphism is restricted to rocks low in CaO.

2. The incidence of cordierite in any paragenesis is favored by a high ratio MgO/FeO in the total rock composition.

3. The field of stability of cordierite on a rock-composition diagram expressed in terms of CaO, MgO, and FeO (Fig. 7-36) diminishes, and that of almandine increases, with increasing pressure.

From these conclusions it may be inferred that pressure is a main factor controlling the incidence of cordierite in the granulite parageneses. In the transitional facies at Westport, Ontario, it can occur without garnet, but only in rocks so low in CaO that plagioclase is absent. In the Australian

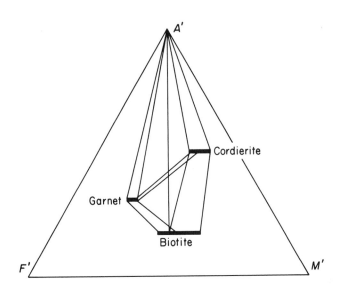

Fig. 7-35. Amphibolite-granulite transitional facies, Westport, Ontario. *A′F′M′* diagram showing coexisting phases in pelitic assemblages, with quartz, K-feldspar and biotite as possible additional phases. (*After H. R. Wynne-Edwards and P. W. Hay.*)

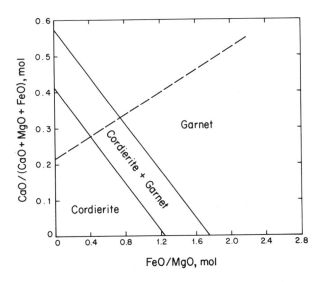

Fig. 7-36. Amphibolite-granulite transitional facies, Westport, Ontario. Rock-composition fields (below broken line) for assemblages with cordierite, cordierite-garnet, and garnet, in pelitic gneisses with excess SiO_2 and K_2O. (*After H. R. Wynne-Edwards and P. W. Hay.*)

335

cordierite granulities it is restricted to assemblages in which almandine also is present. In the Ceylon (Highlands belt) the stability field of cordierite in pelitic rocks has been eliminated.

The above conclusion is in harmony with the widespread occurrence of kyanite in granulites of the Danube area (lower Austria) as described by Scharbert (1964). In this region, the paragenesis closely approaches the ideal one of Eskola's diagram (Fig. 7-33). Cordierite is completely lacking. Hornblende is only a minor phase of the pyroxene granulites; but there are still small quantities of biotite (usually < 3 percent) in most assemblages.

The Eclogite Facies and Associated Transitional Facies

Definition. The eclogite facies in its simplest expression—eclogites of basaltic composition—is easy to define. But its recognition is attended by two difficulties. One concerns the range of composition of the principal associated phases (garnet and omphacite) and the degree of precision with which this can be determined by ordinary laboratory methods. The other arises from a general lack of information about other mineral assemblages that may safely be considered cofacial. For these reasons, and because it has become increasingly recognized that various types of eclogite, each with distinctive mineralogical traits, may form over a wide range of temperature, it has even been proposed "to discontinue the concept of an eclogite metamorphic facies" (Coleman, Lee, Beatty, and Brannock, 1965). Such difficulties are bound to be encountered when dealing with a facies of very deep-seated origin. But there is no need to abandon the facies. It remains as a reliable index of very high pressures. And the mineralogical variation within the facies permits recognition of a temperature gradient that throws light on some problems of great interest while raising others that will stimulate the imagination of a coming generation of petrologists.

Critical of the eclogite facies, according to Eskola's (1921, p. 5) definition, are basic assemblages of jadeite-diopside plus almandine-pyrope, with enstatite or kyanite as possible restricted additional phases. An essential emphasis is placed on the composition of the clinopyroxene: what is now called omphacite, a member of the jadeite-acmite-diopside series with a significant content of jadeite. On this basis we here exclude diopside-garnet assemblages of skarns and granulites as well as the so-called eclogites of some volcanic tuffs and breccas [e.g. those of Salt Lake Crater, Hawaii, and of Kakanui, New Zealand, in which pyrope-rich garnet is associated with a tschermakitic augite containing about 10 percent of acmite (Yoder and Tilley, 1962, p. 483; Mason, 1966)].

The pyrope-almandine of eclogites is a garnet of unusually wide compositional range. The content of pyrope may be as much as 60 percent; grossularite may reach 30 percent; almandine + spessartite rarely exceeds 70 percent; the content of chromium is always appreciable. Rutile is an almost ubiquitous accessory phase in eclogites. The presence of other phases in rocks of more or less basaltic composition in the eclogite facies may result from retrogressive metamorphism in another facies (e.g., that of the glaucophane-lawsonite schists). On the other hand, minerals such as epidote or hornblende may be essential phases of an equilibrium assemblage in a transitional facies.

Problems relating to the modes and environments of origin of eclogite are obscured by the limited volume of individual masses of eclogite, and uncertainty as to possible relationships with immediately associated rocks. Very often eclogites appear in their present surroundings—blocks in serpentinite intrusions, fragments enclosed in kimberlite—as bodies that have clearly been transported upward from unknown depths. Elsewhere, eclogite takes the form of localized lenses and streaks in larger masses of ultramafic rocks: dunite, harzburgite and so on. Here the genetic relation with immediately associated rocks (those of the ultramafic mass) is more certain. But the composite bodies themselves are intrusive and have been variously interpreted as products of magmatic crystallization, or as fragments of deep-seated material tectonically transported to their present sites. Yet other e:logites, among them those of the Alpine type, associated with glaucophane-lawsonite schists, are almost certainly of metamorphic origin. They would generally be considered to have formed at their present sites, except for the anomaly of close association with rocks of a different metamorphic facies.

Eskola (1920, 1939, p. 366) recognized four distinct environments in which eclogite bodies repeatedly tend to occur: (1) in kimberlite; (2) in streaked ultramafic bodies; (3) as lenses in migmatites of the amphibolite facies; (4) in close association with glaucophane schists (and in many instances with serpentinites) in relatively young orogenic zones typified by the Alps. Coleman et al. (1966) have found a correlated characteristic variation in pyrope content of eclogite garnet, and on this basis they recognize three groups of eclogites:

Group A (Eskola's classes 1 and 2): Pyrope >55 percent.
Group B (Eskola's class 3): Pyrope 30 to 55 percent.
Group C (Eskola's class 4): Pyrope < 30 percent.

We shall now consider the eclogite facies as it appears in some of these different environmental situations.

Eclogite facies in kimberlite environment. Eskola (1920, pp. 56, 57) summarized what was known in his day about the eclogite paragenesis as shown by fragments enclosed in kimberlite in South Africa. This is now supplemented by information about eclogite and its associates in the same geologic environment elsewhere, e.g., Congo (Verhoogen, 1940, pp. 37-43), Siberia (Smirnov, 1960; Bobrievitch, Smirnov, and Sobolev, 1960); and

Basutoland (Dawson, 1962; Nixon, von Knorring, and Rooke, 1963).

In all these areas the kimberlite itself is a brecciated, serpentinized, and partly carbonated ultramafic intrusive rock containing unaltered or little altered fragments of extraneous material. Excluding xenoliths obviously derived from the surrounding country rock, these fragments include crystals of individual minerals—ilmenite, garnet (very rich in pyrope), pyroxene, diamond, and so on—and crystalline rocks of deep-seated origin, among them metamorphic granulites and eclogite. These all suggest origin of the kimberlite at great depth; and in this connection the universal presence of diamond is suggestive, for it could form as a stable phase only at very great depths, well within the mantle. There is, however, the rather remote possibility that at shallower but still deep levels, it might form as a metastable phase, the nucleation of which might be favored by presence of olivine (Fyfe, Turner, and Verhoogen, 1958, p. 158).

Granted that the eclogite fragments have been transported upward from some very deep level, quite probably from the mantle itself, we now ask: What are the chemical and mineralogical characteristics of kimberlite eclogites, and what, if any, of its associated rock fragments represent the eclogite mineral facies (whether this be metamorphic or igneous)?

The eclogite assemblage in kimberlites is essentially omphacite-garnet (-rutile). The garnet is a pyrope-almandine, typically with high pyrope content, and the omphacite contains significant $NaAlSi_2O_6$ and very litte $NaFeSi_2O_6$. Two Basutoland eclogites whose minerals have been analysed (Nixon et al. 1963, E4, E16) give the following compositions for pyroxene-garnet pairs which, in more or less equal proportions, are the only essential phases in the rocks:

E4: Garnet, $Py_{45}Al_{37}Gr_{14}An_4$
Omphacite, $Na/Ca = 0.6$; $Fe^{3+}/Al = 0.1$

E16: Garnet, $Py_{57}Al_{29}Gr_9An_4$ (significant Cr and Mn)
Omphacite, $Na/Ca = 0.6$; $Fe^{3+}/Al = 0.13$

Habitually associated with eclogite in kimberlite are two other unusual kinds of rock, either of which may well belong to the eclogite facies: garnet-peridotites and granulites carrying a sodic pyroxene.

1. The garnet peridotites recorded by Nixon et al. (1963) in the Basutoland kimberlites are much more numerous than fragments of eclogite in the same rock matrix. The common assemblage is olivine (50 to 70 percent), enstatite (35 to 40 percent), chrome-diopside (1 to 10 percent), chrome-pyrope (3 percent), and alteration products. The typical pyrope is about $Py_{72}Al_{15}Gr_5Uv_5An_3$—a much more magnesian composition than that of associated eclogite garnets. The chrome diopsides contain up to 10 percent jadeite. Olivine is highly magnesian.

2. Among unusual phase assemblages of granulites found as fragments associated with eclogite in kimberlite pipes, two in particular can be

mentioned as probably related to, or even cofacial with, eclogites

      (a) Katanga, Congo (Verhoogen, 1940, pp. 38, 39): Garnet-sodapyroxene-feldspar

The optic properties of the pyroxene indicate an acmitic omphacite. Other associated granulites contain combinations of plagioclase, hypersthene, diopside, magnesian garnet, and scapolite, and would appear to be assemblages of the granulite facies. Verhoogen (1940, p. 42) suggests that this whole group of rocks spans a transition between the granulite and the eclogite facies.

      (b) Yakutia, Siberia (Bobrievitch, Smirnov, and Sobolev, 1960): Garnet-omphacite-kyanite

The garnet is a unique grossularite unusually high in pyrope-almandine, $Gr_{63}Py_{18}Al_{17}An_2$. The pyroxene is a true omphacite (Na/Ca = 0.5; Fe^{3+}/Al = 0.12). The kyanite has 0.2 percent CaO. Bobrievitch and his associates have incorporated the petrographic data of the Siberian kimberlite inclusions into a generalized ACF diagram for the whole eclogite facies as represented in this particular—presumably very deep-seated—environment of origin. This diagram is reproduced here as Fig. 7-37.

      The significance of the Al content of enstatite in deep-seated rocks as an indicator of pressure has been discussed by Banno (1964). He finds that enstatites in garnet peridotite from Kimberly, and in garnet enstatitite from Siberia (Yakutia), contain significant Al_2O_3; but the Al content is

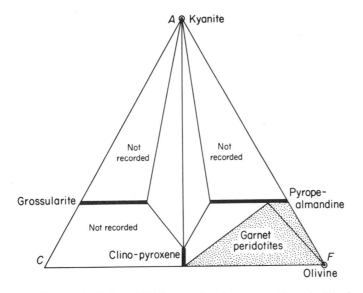

Fig. 7-37. Eclogite facies. ACF diagram for phase-assemblages in Siberian kimberlites. (*After A. P. Bobrievitch, G. I. Smirnov, and V. S. Sobolev.*)

lower than in enstatite associated with almandines in the granulite facies. This observation is consistent with the hypothesis that the kimberlite eclogites and their associated garnetiferous peridotites may have formed at very high pressures, beyond those of the granulite facies environment. This conclusion has been elaborated by Boyd and England (1964) who place the depth of origin of the kimberlite peridotite paragenesis, on the basis of experiments on the enstatite-pyrope system at high pressures, between 125 and 250 km. $(p > 37 \; kb)$

Eclogite facies in garnetiferous peridotites. The association of eclogite with bodies of garnetiferous peridotite in some orogenic zones is illustrated by certain Norwegian eclogites as described by Eskola (1920, pp. 51-57), who concludes that both rocks are products of magmatic crystallization at high pressure. Whether metamorphic or truly igneous, the peridotite and eclogite assemblages in some Norwegian occurrences seem to be isofacial. Eskola (1920, p. 54) figures interbanding of eclogite and olivine rock on a scale of 10 cm. Moreover, he records intimate association within small outcrops of assemblages, such as

Omphacite-garnet (-rutile)
Olivine-garnet-enstatite-diopside
Olivine-enstatite-diopside

Some of the "omphacite" has a low Na_2O content (jadeite less than 8 percent). In other Norwegian eclogites the pyroxene is a chloromelanite approximating $Di_{50}Ja_{35}Ac_{15}$. Garnets of the eclogitic assemblages are high in pyrope; typical compositions are $Py_{60}Al_{27}(Gr\text{-}And)_{13}$, $Py_{43}Al_{42}$ $(Gr\text{-}And)_{15}$. These contain less than 2 percent spessartite.

Eclogite facies associated with glaucophane schists. In many glaucophane-schist terranes, there are subordinate but widely distributed bodies of eclogite. These have been studied especially in the western Alps of Europe (e.g. Bearth, 1959, 1965, 1966; Callegari and Viterbo, 1966), the Sanbagawa belt of Japan (Banno, 1964, pp. 300, 302-306), and the Franciscan formation of California (e.g., Borg, 1956; Coleman et al., 1965; W. A. Crawford, 1965; Essene, 1967). These have been designated eclogites of the ophiolitic (Smulikowski, 1964) or Alpine type (Bearth, 1965), and fall in group C of Coleman et al. (1966).

Eclogites of the Alpine type have two distinctive mineralogical characteristics. The garnets are lower in pyrope (usually < 30 percent) and somewhat higher in grossularite than are garnets of eclogites from other environments. The "omphacite" is much more variable in composition than that of other eclogites; though invariably significantly sodic, its acmite/jadeite ratio is commonly high enough to warrant classification as chloromelanite.

While it is not unlikely that eclogite fragments in kimberlite may represent primary material of the earth's mantle, this is certainly not true for some (and hence probably most) eclogites of the Alpine type. Bearth (1959, 1965) has shown conclusively that eclogites of his garnet-chloritoid zone formed directly from basic rocks: saussurite-uralite gabbros and basaltic pillow lavas; and a similar origin has been demonstrated for some ophiolitic eclogites from the Italian piedmont region (Bianchi and Dal Piaz, 1963).

Both in the Pennine Alps and in California, there is clear textural and field evidence that the eclogite paragenesis is in process of replacement by that of the associated glaucophane schists. In California, the ultimate products of replacement are assemblages of the glaucophane-lawsonite-schist facies: combinations of lawsonite, glaucophane, aragonite, chlorite, sphene, and other phases.[1] In the western Alps (Bearth's inner zone), eclogites are replaced by such combinations as glaucophane-garnet-epidote-chloritoid, which in turn become transformed into the greenschist assemblage albite-epidote-chlorite-actinolite. It seems clear that in the closing stages of metamorphism in both regions, the eclogite-facies assemblages were unstable with respect to glaucophane-bearing assemblages: in California, those characteristic of the glaucophane-lawsonite-schist facies.

A completely different interpretation is here placed upon other assemblages in which eclogitic minerals are associated with minerals of the glaucophane-lawsonite-schist or greenschist facies without evidence of disequilibrium. These may be treated as equilibrium assemblages in transitional facies.

(a) Eclogite to glaucophane-lawsonite-schist transition: glaucophane-epidote-pumpellyite-omphacite, omphacite-garnet-epidote-rutile. This is exemplified in California and in the Italian Alps.

(b) Eclogite to amphibolite transition. In the amphibolite zone of the Sanbagawa zone in the Bessi-Ino district of Japan, Banno (1964, pp. 287, 288) has recorded assemblages transitional to the eclogite facies. These include

 Zoisite-kyanite-paragonite-hornblende-quartz
 Zoisite-paragonite-oligoclase-hornblende
 Garnet-oligoclase-hornblende-quartz
 Garnet-paragonite-oligoclase-epidote-quartz
 Omphacite-garnet-hornblende-quartz

---

[1] Replacement may occur directly or via an intermediate hornblende-garnet assemblage termed "amphibolite" by Essene (1967), but without implying that it represents the amphibolite facies.

The last assemblage is significant, for it shows no textural evidence of disequilibrium. The garnet is typical of eclogites of the Alpine type: $Py_{28}An_{50}Gr_{22}$. The pyroxene is a chloromelanitic omphacite.

Both transitional facies, though imperfectly known, demonstrate that the eclogite facies extends into regions of high crustal pressure, but relatively low temperature: approaching the environment of the glaucophane-lawsonite-schist facies. Bearth (1966) suggests that eclogites of the Alpine type may even develop under conditions close to those of the greenschist facies.

Unity of the eclogite facies. A survey of the eclogite facies in its several environments brings out two significant but seemingly paradoxical characteristics. First is the unique nature of the essential bimineralic basic assemblage that defines the facies. The second is the wide range of compositional variation in both phases throughout the facies as a whole, and the close correlation that exists between this variation in phase compositions and the four field environments in which eclogites are found in nature. Coleman et al. (1966) emphasize this second characteristic of eclogites. In this treatment, emphasis is placed on the first. The eclogite phase assemblages, viewed collectively, fulfill all the criteria of a metamorphic facies. The compositional variation reflects what is probably an unusually wide span of temperature and pressure in the environment of origin of this particular facies. With increasing information as to the details of mineralogical variation in eclogites, it may become desirable to divide the eclogite facies into at least two units each of full facies status. In the meantime the eclogite groups recognized by Coleman and his coauthors are viewed as subfacies that are beginning to assume more than local significance.

REFERENCES

Agrell, S. O., M. G. Brown, and D. McKee: Deerite, howieite and zussmanite, from the Franciscan of the Laytonville district, California. *Am. Mineralogist*, vol. 50, pp. 278–279, 1965.

Atherton, M. P.: The garnet isograd in pelitic rocks and its relation to metamorphic facies, *Am. Mineralogist*, vol. 49, pp. 1331–1348, 1964.

Bailey, E. H., W. P. Irwin, and D. L. Jones: Franciscan and related rocks, *Calif. Dep. Mines Geol. Bull. 183*, 1964.

Banno, S.: Glaucophane schists and associated rocks in the Omi district, Japan, *Jap. J. Geol. Geog.*, vol. 29, pp. 29–44, 1958.

———: Notes on rock-forming minerals (10), glaucophanes and garnets from the Kôtu district, Shikoku, *Geol. Soc. Japan J.*, vol. 65, pp. 658–663, 1959.

———: Petrologic studies on Sanbagawa crystalline schists in the Bessi-Ino district, Central Sikoku, Japan, *Univ. Tokyo, J. Fac. Sci.*, vol. 15, pp. 203–319, 1964.

———: Alumina content of orthopyroxene as a geologic barometer, *Jap. J. Geol. Geog.*, vol. 35, pp. 115–121, 1964a.

Barrow, G.: On an intrusion of muscovite-biotite gneiss in the southeast Highlands of Scotland, *Geol. Soc. London Quart. J.*, vol. 49, pp. 330–358, 1893.

Bearth, P.: Geologie und Petrographie des Monte Rosa, *Beitr. Geol. Karte Schweiz*, vol. 96, 1952.

———: Üeber einen Wechsel der Mineralfacies in der Wurtzelzone des Penninikums, *Schweiz. Mineral. Petrog. Mitt.*, vol. 38, pp. 363–373, 1958.

———: Über Eclogite, Glaucophanschiefer, und metamorphen Pillowlaven, *Schweiz. Mineral. Petrog. Mitt.*, vol. 39, pp. 267–286, 1959.

———: Versuch einer Gliederung alpinmetamorpher Serien der Westalpen, *Schweiz. Mineral. Petrog. Mitt.*, vol. 42, pp. 127–137, 1962.

———: Zur Entstehung alpinotyper Eclogite, *Schweiz. Mineral. Petrog. Mitt.*, vol. 45, pp. 179–188, 1965.

———: Zur mineralfaziellen Stellung der Glaucophangesteine der Westalpen, *Schweiz. Mineral. Petrog. Mitt.*, vol. 46, pp. 13–24, 1966.

Bianchi, A., and G. Dal Piaz: Gli inclusi "micascisti eclogitici" della zona Sesia, *Giorn. Geol. Ann. Museo. Geol. Bologna*, ser. 2a, vol. 31, pp. 39–76, 1963.

Binns, R. A.: Zones of progressive regional metamorphism in the Willyama complex, Broken Hill district, New South Wales, *Geol. Soc. Australia J.*, vol. 11, pp. 283–330, 1964.

———: The mineralogy of metamorphosed basic rocks from the Willyama complex Broken Hill district, New South Wales, *Mineral. Mag.*, vol. 35, pp. 306–326, 561–587, 1965.

Bloxam, T. W.: Jadeite-bearing metagraywackes in California, *Am. Mineralogist*, vol. 41, pp. 488–496, 1956.

Bobrievitch, A. P., G. I. Smirnov, and V. S. Sobolev, On the mineralogy of xenoliths of grossularite-pyroxene-disthene rock in kimberlite of Yakutia, *Geol. i Geofiz.*, *Akad. Nauk SSSR, Sibirsk. Otd.*, no. 3, pp. 17–24, 1960.

Boettcher, A. L., and P. J. Wyllie: Revision of the calcite-aragonite transition, *Nature*, vol. 213, pp. 792–793, 1967.

Borg, I. Y.: Glaucophane-schists and eclogites near Healdsburg, California, *Bull. Geol. Soc. Am.*, vol. 67, pp. 1563–1584, 1956.

Boyd, F. R., and J. L. England: System enstatite-pyrope and its bearing on the genesis of kimberlite, *Geol. Soc. Am. Abstr. Ann. Meeting 1964*, pp. 17, 18, 1964.

Brothers, R. N.: Glaucophane schists from the North Berkeley Hills, California, *Am. J. Sci.*, vol. 252, pp. 614–626, 1954.

———: The structure and petrography of graywackes near Auckland, New Zealand, *Trans. Roy. Soc. New Zealand*, vol. 83, pp. 465–482, 1956.

Brouwer, H. A., and C. G. Egeler: The glaucophane facies metamorphism in the schistes lustrés nappe of Corsica, *Koninkl. Ned. Akad. Wetenschap. Verslag Gewone Vergader. Afdel. Nat.*, vol. 48, pp. 1–71, 1952.

Brown, E. H.: The greenschist facies in part of eastern Otago, New Zealand, *Contrib. Mineral. Petrol.*, vol. 14, pp. 259–292, 1967.

Buddington, A. F.: Adirondack igneous rocks and their metamorphism, *Geol. Soc. Am. Mem.* 7, 1939.

———: Isograds and the role of H_2O in metamorphic facies of orthogneisses of the northwest Adirondack area, New York, *Bull. Geol. Soc. Am.*, vol. 74, pp. 1155–1182, 1963.

———: The occurrence of garnet in the granulite-facies terrane of the Adirondack Highlands, *J. Petrol.*, vol. 7, pp. 331–335, 1966.

———, J. Fahey, and A. Vlisidis: Degree of oxidation of Adirondack iron oxide and iron-titanium oxide minerals in relation to petrogeny, *J. Petrol.*, vol. 4, pp. 138–169, 1963.

———, and D. H. Lindsley: Iron-titanium oxide minerals and synthetic equivalents, *J. Petrol.*, vol. 5, pp. 310–357, 1964.

Callegari, E., and C. Viterbo, I graniti delle eclogiti compresse nella "formazione dei micascisti eclogitici" della zona Sesia-Lanzo, *Soc. Mineral. Ital. Rend.*, vol. 22, pp. 3–23, 1966.

Chapman, C. A.: Geology of the Mascoma quadrangle, New Hampshire, *Bull. Geol. Soc. Am.*, vol. 50, pp. 127–180, 1939.

Chatterjee, N. D.: Vesuvianite-epidote paragenesis as a product of green-schist facies of regional metamorphism in the western Alps, *Beitr. Mineral. Petrog.*, vol. 8, pp. 432–439, 1962.

———: On the widespread occurrence of oxidized chlorites in the Pennine zone of the western Italian Alps, *Contrib. Mineral. Petrol.*, vol. 12, pp. 325–353, 1966.

Chesterman, C. W.: Intrusive ultrabasic rocks at Leach Lake Mountain, California, *Rept. Intern. Geol. Congr. 21st Session, Norden, 1960*, vol. 18, pp. 208–215, 1960.

Chinner, G. A.: Pelitic gneisses with varying ferrous/ferric ratios from Glen Clova, Angus, Scotland, *J. Petrol.*, vol. 1, pp. 178–217, 1960.

———: The distribution of pressure and temperature during Dalradian metamorphism, *Geol. Soc. London Quart. J.*, vol. 122, pp. 159–186, 1966.

Coleman, R. G., and D. E. Lee: Glaucophane-bearing metamorphic types of the Cazadero area, California, *J. Petrol.*, vol. 4, pp. 260–301, 1963.

———, ———, L. B. Beatty, and W. W. Brannock, Eclogites and eclogites: their differences and similarities, *Bull. Geol. Soc. Am.*, vol. 76, pp. 483–508, 1965.

Coombs, D. S.: The nature and alteration of some Triassic sediments from Southland, New Zealand, *Trans. Roy. Soc. New Zealand*, vol. 82, pt. 1, pp. 65–109, 1954.

———: Lower grade mineral facies in New Zealand, *Rept. Intern. Geol. Congr. 21st Session, Norden, 1960*, vol. 13, pp. 339–351, 1960.

———: Some recent work on the lower grades of metamorphism, *Australian J. Sci.*, vol. 24, pp. 203–215, 1961.

———, A. J. Ellis, W. S. Fyfe, and A. M. Taylor: The zeolite facies with comments on the interpretation of hydrothermal syntheses, *Geochim. Cosmochim. Acta*, vol. 17, pp. 53–107, 1959.

Cooray, P. G.: Geology of the country around Rangala, *Dept. Mineral., Geol. Surv. Ceylon, Mem. No. 2*, 1961.

———: Charnockites and their associated gneisses in the Pre-Cambrian of Ceylon, *Geol. Soc. London Quart. J.*, vol. 118, pp. 239–273, 1962.

Crawford, M. L.: Composition of plagioclase and associated minerals in some schists from Vermont, U.S.A. and South Westland, New Zealand, *Contrib. Mineral. Petrol.*, vol. 13, pp. 269–294, 1966.

Crawford, W. A.: Studies in Franciscan metamorphism near Jenner, California, doctoral thesis, University of California, Berkeley, 1965.

———, and W. S. Fyfe: Lawsonite equilibria, *Am. J. Sci.*, vol. 263, pp. 262–270, 1965.

Davis, G. A., M. J. Holdaway, P. W. Lipman, and W. D. Romey: Structure, meta-morphism, and plutonism in the south-central Klamath Mountains, California, *Bull. Geol. Soc. Am.*, vol. 76, pp. 933–966, 1965.

Dawson, J. B.: Basutoland kimberlites, *Bull. Geol. Soc. Am.*, vol. 73, pp. 545–560, 1962.

De Roever, W. P.: Igneous and metamorphic rocks in eastern Central Celebes, in H. A. Brouwer (ed.) "Geological Explorations in the Island of Celebes," pp. 65–173, North-Holland Publishing Co., Amsterdam, 1947.

――――: Preliminary notes on glaucophane-bearing and other rocks from southeast Celebes, *Koninkl. Ned. Akad. Wetenschap., Proc., Ser. B*, vol. 53, no. 9, pp. 1–12, 1950.

――――: Genesis of jadeite in low-grade metamorphism, *Am. J. Sci.*, vol. 253, pp. 283–289, 1955.

De Waard, D.: Mineral assemblages and metamorphic subfacies in the granulite-facies terrane of Little Moose Mountain syncline, South-central Adirondack Highlands, *Koninkl. Ned. Akad. Wetenschap. Proc., Ser. B*, vol. 67, pp. 344–362, 1964.

――――: The occurrence of garnet in the granulite-facies terrane of Adirondack Highlands, *J. Petrol.*, vol. 6, pp. 165–191, 1965a.

――――: A proposed subdivision of the granulite facies, *Am J. Sci.*, vol. 263, pp. 455–461, 1965b.

――――: The biotite-cordierite-almandite subfacies of the hornblende-granulite facies, *Can. Mineralogist*, vol. 8, pt. 4, pp. 481–492, 1966.

Engel, A. E. J., and C. E. Engel: Progressive metamorphism and granitization of the major paragneiss, northwest Adirondack mountains, Part 2, New York, *Bull. Geol. Soc. Am.*, vol. 71, pp. 1–58, 1960.

――――, and ――――: Progressive metamorphism of amphibolite, northwest Adiron-dack mountains, New York, *Bull. Geol. Soc. Am.*, A. F. Buddington vol., pp. 37–82, 1962a.

――――, and ――――: Hornblendes formed during progressive metamorphism of amphibolites, northwest Adirondack mountains, New York, *Bull. Geol. Soc. Am.*, vol. 73, pp. 1499–1514, 1962b.

Ernst, W. G.: Petrogenesis of glaucophane schists, *J. Petrol.*, vol. 4, pp. 1–30, 1963a.

――――: Significance of phengitic micas from low-grade schists, *Am. Mineralogist*, vol. 48, pp. 1357–1373, 1963b.

――――: Mineral parageneses in Franciscan metamorphic rocks, Panoche Pass, California, *Bull. Geol. Soc. Am.*, vol. 76, pp. 879–914, 1965.

Essene, E. J.: Petrogenesis of Franciscan metamorphic rocks, doctoral thesis, Univer-sity of California, Berkeley, 1967.

――――, and W. S. Fyfe: Omphacite in Californian metamorphic rocks, *Contrib. Mineral. Petrol.*, vol. 15, pp. 1–23, 1967.

――――, ――――, and F. J. Turner: Petrogenesis of Franciscan glaucophane schists and associated metamorphic rocks, California, *Beitr. Mineral. Petrog.*, vol. 11, pp. 695–704, 1965.

Eskola, P.: On the eclogites of Norway, *Vidensk. Skr. Kristania (Oslo), I, Mat.-Naturv. Kl.*, no. 8, 1921.

――――: Die metamorphen Gesteine, in "Die Entstehung der Gesteine" (T. F. W. Barth, C. W. Correns, P. Eskola), Springer, Berlin, 1939.

————: On the granulites of Lappland, *Am. J. Sci.*, Bowen vol., pp. 133–171, 1952.

Evans, B. W.: Coexisting albite and oligoclase in some schists from New Zealand, *Am. Mineralogist*, vol. 49, pp. 173–179, 1964.

————, and C. V. Guidotti: The sillimanite-potash feldspar isograd in western Maine, U.S.A., *Contrib. Mineral. Petrol.*, vol. 12, pp. 25–62, 1966.

Fyfe, W. S., and F. J. Turner, Reappraisal of the metamorphic facies concept, *Contrib. Mineral. Petrol.*, vol. 12, pp. 354–364, 1966.

————, ————, and J. Verhoogen, Metamorphic reactions and metamorphic facies, *Geol. Soc. Am. Mem.* 73, 1958.

Ghent, E. H.: Glaucophane-schist facies metamorphism in the Black Butte area, northern Coast Ranges, California, *Am. J. Sci.*, vol. 263, pp. 385–400, 1965.

Greenly, E.: The geology of Anglesey, vol. 1, *Mem. Geol. Surv. Gt. Brit.*, 1919.

Harker, A.: "Metamorphism," Methuen, London, 1932.

Hay, R. L.: Zeolites and zeolitic reactions in sedimentary rocks, *Geol. Soc. Am. Spec. Paper* no. 85, 1966.

Heald, M. T.: Structure and petrology of the Lovell Mountain quadrangle, New Hampshire, *Bull. Geol. Soc. Am.*, vol. 61, pp. 43–89, 1950.

Howie, R. A.: The geochemistry of the charnockite series of Madras, India, *Trans. Roy. Soc. Edinburgh*, vol. 62, pt. 3, pp. 725–768, 1955.

Hutton, C. O.: An occurrence of the mineral pumpellyite in the Lake Wakatipu region, western Otago, New Zealand, *Mineral. Mag.*, vol. 24, pp. 529–533, 1937.

————: Metamorphism in the Lake Wakatipu region, western Otago, *New Zealand Dept. Sci. Ind. Res. Geol. Mem.* 5, 1940.

Iwasaki, M.: Metamorphic rocks of the Kôtu-Bizan area, eastern Sikoku, *Univ. Tokyo J. Fac. Sci.*, sec. 2, vol. 15, pp. 1–90, 1963.

Jäger, E., E. Niggli, and E. Wenk: Rb-Sr Alterbestimmungen an Glimmern der Zentralalpen, *Beitr. Geol. Karte Schweiz*, no. 134, 1967.

James, H. L.: Zones of regional metamorphism in the Pre-Cambrian of northern Michigan, *Bull. Geol. Soc. Am.*, vol. 66, pp. 1455–1488, 1955.

Kennedy, W. Q.: On the significance of thermal structure in the Scottish Highlands, *Geol. Mag.*, vol. 85, pp. 229–234, 1949.

Lambert, R. St. J.: The metamorphic facies concept, *Mineral. Mag.*, vol. 34, pp. 283–291, 1965.

Lillie, A. R., and B. H. Mason: Geological reconnaissance of district between Franz Josef Glacier and Copland Valley, *Trans. Roy. Soc. New Zealand*, vol. 82, pt. 5, pp. 1123–1128, 1955.

Lyons, J. B.: Geology of the Hanover quadrangle, New Hampshire-Vermont, *Bull. Geol. Soc. Am.*, vol. 66, pp. 105–146, 1955.

McKee, B.: Widespread occurrence of jadeite, lawsonite, and glaucophane in central California, *Am. J. Sci.*, vol. 260, pp. 596–610, 1962.

McNamara, M. J.: The lower greenschist facies in the Scottish Highlands, *Geol. Foren. Stockholm Forh.*, vol. 87, pp. 347–389, 1965.

————: Chlorite-biotite equilibrium reactions in a carbonate-free system, *J. Petrol.*, vol. 7, pp. 404–413, 1966.

Martini, J., and M. Vuagnat: Présence du faciès à zéolites dans la formation "grès" de Taveyanne (Alpes franco-suisses) *Schweiz. Mineral. Petrog. Mitt.*, vol. 45, pp. 281–293, 1966.

Mason, B. H.: Metamorphic zones in the Southern Alps of New Zealand, *Am. Museum Novitiates (Am. Mus. Nat. Hist.)*, no. 1815, pp. 1–8, 1956.

————: Metamorphism in the Southern Alps of New Zealand, *Am. Mus. Nat. Hist. Bull. 123*, pp. 211–248, 1962.

————: Pyrope, augite, and hornblende from Kakanui, New Zealand, *New Zealand J. Geol. Geophys.*, vol. 9, pp. 474–480, 1966.

Misch, P.: Metasomatic granitization of batholithic dimensions, pt. 1, *Am. J. Sci.*, vol. 247, pp. 209–245, 1949.

————: Stable association wollastonite-anorthite and other calc-silicate assemblages in amphibolite facies crystalline schists of Nanga Parbat, northwest Himalayas, *Beitr. Mineral. Petrog.*, vol. 10, pp. 315–356, 1964.

Miyakawa, K.: A peculiar porphyroblastic albite schist from Nichinan-cho, Tottori Prefecture, southwest Japan, *Nagoya Univ. J. Earth Sci.*, vol. 12, pp. 1–16, 1964.

Miyashiro, A.: Regional metamorphism of the Gosaisyo-Takanuki district in the central Abukuma plateau, *Univ. Tokyo J. Fac. Sci.*, sec. 2, vol. 11, pp. 219–272, 1958.

————, and S. Banno: Nature of glaucophanitic metamorphism, *Am. J. Sci.*, vol. 256, pp. 97–110, 1958.

————, and Y. Seki: Mineral assemblages and subfacies of the glaucophane-schist facies, *Jap. J. Geol. Geog.*, vol. 29, pp. 199–208, 1958.

Muthuswami, T. N. and R. Gnanasekaran: The structure and phase-petrology of the metamorphic complex Devandanapatti, Madurai district, *Annamalai Univ. J.*, vol. 23, pp. 183–196, 1962.

Niggli, E.: Stilpnomelan als gesteinsbildendes Mineral in der Schweizer Alpen, *Schweiz. Mineral. Petrog. Mitt.*, vol. 36, pp. 511–514, 1956.

————: Mineral-zonen der Alpinen Metamorphose in den Schweizer Alpen, *Rept. Intern. Geol. Congr., 21st Session, Norden, 1960*, vol. 13, pp. 132–138, 1960.

Nixon, P. H., O. von Knorring, and J. M. Rooke: Kimberlites and associated rocks of Basutoland, *Am. Mineralogist*, vol. 48, pp. 1090–1132, 1963.

Packham, G. H., and K. A. W. Crook: The principle of diagenetic facies and some of its implications, *J. Geol.*, vol. 68, pp. 392–407, 1960.

Ramberg, H.: On sapphirine-bearing rocks in the vicinity of Sukkertoppen (West Greenland), *Gronlands Geol. Undersog. Bull.*, no. 1, 1948.

Reed, J. J.: Regional metamorphism in southeast Nelson, *New Zealand Geol. Surv. Bull. 60*, 1958.

Robinson, P.: Progressive metamorphism in the Otago schist, east Otago, New Zealand, *Bull. Geol. Soc. Am.*, vol. 70, p. 1662, 1959.

Scharbert, H. G.: Die Granulite des südlichen niederösterreichischen Moldanubikums, *Neues. Jahrb. Mineral. Abhandl.*, vol. 101, pp. 27–66, 1964.

Segnit, E. R.: Sapphirine-bearing rocks from MacRobertson Land, Antarctica, *Mineral. Mag.*, vol. 31, pp. 690–697, 1957.

Seki, Y.: Pumpellyite in low-grade metamorphism, *J. Petrol.*, vol. 2, pp. 407–423, 1961.

Sen, S.: Evolution of metamorphic rocks of East Nanvhum, India, *Proc. Natl. Inst. Sci. India, Pt A*, vol. 25, pp. 118–138, 1959.

Smulikowski, K.: Comments on eclogite facies in regional metamorphisms, *Rept. Intern. Geol. Congress 21st Session, Norden, 1960*, vol. 13, pp. 372–382, 1960.

Suzuki, J.: Petrological study of the crystalline schist system of Shikoku, Japan. *Hokkaido Imp. Univ., J. Fac. Sci.*, ser. 4, vol. 1, pp. 27–111, 1930.

Taliaferro, N. L.: The Franciscan-Knoxville problem, *Bull. Am. Assoc. Petrol. Geologists*, vol. 27, pp. 109–219, 1943.

Tilley, C. E.: Metamorphic zones in the southern Highlands of Scotland, *Geol. Soc. London Quart. J.*, vol. 81, pp. 100–112, 1925.

Trommsdorff, V.: Progressive Metamorphose kieseliger Karbonategestenie in den Zentralalpen, *Schweiz. Mineral. Petrog. Mitt.*, vol. 46, pp. 431–460, 1966.

Turner, F. J.: Schists from the Forbes Range and adjacent country, western Otago, *Trans. Roy. Soc. New Zealand*, vol. 64, pp. 161–174, 1934.

———: Contribution to the interpretation of mineral facies in metamorphic rocks, *Am. J. Sci.*, vol. 29, pp. 409–421, 1935.

———: Progressive regional metamorphism in southern New Zealand, *Geol. Mag.*, vol. 75, pp. 160–174, 1938.

———: Mineralogical and structural evolution of the metamorphic rocks, *Geol. Soc. Am. Mem. 30*, 1948.

———, and J. Verhoogen: "Igneous and Metamorphic Petrology," McGraw-Hill, New York, 1960.

Vance, J. A.: Prehnite-pumpellyite facies of metamorphism on Orcas Island, San Juan Islands, northwestern Washington, *Geol. Soc. Am., Cordilleran Section Program 1966*, pp. 73–74, 1966.

Verhoogen, J.: Les Pipes de kimberlite du Katanga, *Ann. Serv. Mines*, Bruxelles, vol. 9 (1938), pp. 3–46, 1940.

Wellman, H. W.: Talc-magnesite and quartz-magnesite rock, Cobb-Takaka district, New Zealand, *New Zealand J. Sci. Technol.*, vol. 24, no. 3B, pp. 103B–127B, 1942.

Wenk, E.: Über Diskontinuitäten in Plagioclasserien metamorphen Ursprungs, *Schweiz Mineral. Petrog. Mitt.*, vol. 38, pp. 494–498, 1958.

———: Plagioklas als Indexmineral in den Zentralalpen, *Schweiz, Mineral. Petrog. Mitt.*, vol. 42, pp. 139–152, 1962.

White, W. S., and M. P. Billings: Geology of the Woodsville Quadrangle, Vermont-New Hampshire, *Bull. Geol. Soc. Am.*, vol. 62, pp. 647–696, 1951.

Williamson, D. H.: Petrology of chloritoid and staurolite rocks north of Stonehaven, Kincardineshire, *Geol. Mag.*, vol. 90, pp. 353–361, 1953.

Winkler, H. G. F.: "Petrogenesis of Metamorphic Rocks," Springer, New York, 1965.

Wiseman, J. D. H.: The central and southwest Highland epidorites, *Geol. Soc. London Quart. J.*, vol. 90, pp. 354–417, 1934.

Wynne-Edwards, H. R., and P. W. Hay: Coexisting cordierite and garnet in regionally metamorphosed rocks from the Westport area, Ontario, *Can. Mineralogist*, vol. 7, pp. 453–478, 1963.

Yen, T. P.: Glaucophane schist of Taiwan, *Geol. Soc. China Proc.*, no. 9, pp. 70–73, 1966.

Yoder, H. S., and C. E. Tilley: Origin of basaltic magmas, *J. Petrol.*, vol. 3, pp. 342–532, 1962.

Zen, E-an: Metamorphism of lower Paleozoic rocks in the vicinity of the Taconic range in West-Central Vermont, *Am. Mineralogist*, vol. 45, pp. 129–175, 1960.

Temperature-pressure-time
Regimes of
Regional Metamorphism

RESUME OF SIGNIFICANT DATA
AND PRELIMINARY INFERENCES

From the material presented in the preceding chapters, a number of significant facts emerge—generalizations, none without exception—that relate to field and mineralogical aspects of regional metamorphism:

1. Great areal extent of metamorphic terranes.

2. Location in belts of orogenic activity (commonly broadly contemporaneous with metamorphism), and in Precambrian shields where relation to orogeny may be less obvious.

3. Interplay of episodes of metamorphic crystallization and episodes of deformation and folding during periods of orogeny measured in millions of years.

4. Progressive character of metamorphism, as revealed by mapped zonal sequences of increasing grade, based on index mineral assemblages and/or degree of textural development.

349

5. Repetition of closely similar (though never precisely identical) zonal patterns (facies series) in different regions.

6. Common association of syntectonic "granitic" migmatites with zones of maximum metamorphic grade; though with rather rare exceptions, as in the Otago-Westland terrane, New Zealand.

7. By contrast with 6, complete lack of obvious relation between regional metamorphism and large-scale development of the most voluminous of the primary magmas—basalt.

8. Existence of mineral facies of regional metamorphism; simplicity of individual mineral assemblages (in rock specimens), and of the total facies paragenesis (in metamorphic zones); gradational nature of field transitions between contemporaneous facies.

Simultaneously with our review of the data of regional metamorphism, we have developed a number of assumptions, inferences, and propositions in order to interpret the data against a background of experience and theory in chemistry, physics, and geology:

1. A common metamorphic mineral assemblage can be treated, in first approximation, as a heterogeneous system in equilibrium under a limited range of metamorphic pressure P and temperature T.

2. A metamorphic facies is an association of phase assemblages, each of different chemical composition, having a common stability range of P and T.

3. Metamorphic pressures and temperatures are maintained long enough, at least many thousands of years, for divariant equilibrium to become established in each mineral assemblage without significant overstepping of curves of univariant equilibrium. Nonhydrostatic pressure, especially at relatively low temperatures, tends to initiate cataclasis and flow, to raise free energies of strained crystals, and thus to accelerate chemical reactions leading to equilibrium.

4. Preservation of high-temperature, high-pressure assemblages during postmetamorphic unloading is attributed largely to impermeability of the relatively anhydrous high-grade rocks to water. Another factor is the thermodynamically predictable greater overstepping necessary to initiate "backward" hydration reactions as contrasted with "forward" reactions of dehydration.

5. A series of metamorphic zones expresses a P-T gradient within a surface of the earth's crust: the surface mapped. There is the possibility that different points on some such gradients also represent a gradient in time.

6. The P-T gradients of metamorphism can be calibrated against the data of laboratory experiment and thermodynamic prediction. This requires simplifying assumptions, some departure from which in nature can be expected, or may even prove to be the general rule:

(a) For hydrous systems, $P_{H_2O} = P_f = P_l$.

(b) For carbonate-bearing systems in hydrous environments, $P_f = P_l$; P_{CO_2} can fluctuate between all values up to P_l.

(c) The main thermodynamic role of nonhydrostatic pressure is to increase the value of P beyond P_l. This increment, loosely termed *tectonic overpressure*, depends on rheologic properties (largely unknown) of rocks under long-sustained stress at high P and T. It is thought to be significant only at relatively low temperature and high pressure—conditions found by experiment to increase the strength of rocks beyond values measured at room temperature and pressure.

It is now proposed to reexamine collectively the mineral facies of regional metamorphism, with special emphasis on their mutual relations in space and in time. The degree of coherence and internal consistency of the whole picture that emerges will provide some measure of the validity of both the geological data and the inferences and propositions that form the provisional basis of their interpretation. There will be obvious imperfections; and these will raise questions still not satisfactorily answered. They will furnish the starting point for further inquiry and criticism directed toward future improvement of the metamorphic model presented here.

PHYSICAL SIGNIFICANCE OF FACIES OF REGIONAL METAMORPHISM

Facies in Relation to Depth and Grade of Metamorphism

The complete gamut of metamorphic facies may be pictured in terms of two geologic variables: depth and grade. Both can be estimated from purely geological observations; so each is independent of the physical variables (notably P and T) with which it is usually correlated by inference.

In some areas of regional metamorphism, especially where the grade is relatively low, the depth of maximum burial at the time of metamorphism may be estimated within reasonable limits from stratigraphic, structural, and physiographic data. More often it is difficult to place significant limits on absolute depth; but it may still be possible to assign a measureable interval of depth to the total span of several facies or subfacies. Elsewhere, as in many Precambrian terranes, all that can be said—and this is a guess—is that metamorphism was "deepseated."

Petrographic and field criteria are used to estimate the relative grades attained in zones of progressive metamorphism. In regions where the parent rocks retain their initial character outside the first isograd, there can be no doubt as to the direction of rising metamorphic grade. In such instances increasing grade can be correlated empirically with a sequence of mineralogical and textural changes. One such change (whatever may be its physical significance) is progressive dehydration of pelitic and semipelitic rocks. Common textural changes are development of foliation and lamination (at least in the outer zones) and coarsening of grain. These criteria may be used qualitatively as indicators of increasing grade even where the sequence of zones does not extend back into a zone of little-metamorphosed parent rock. In such cases the lower-grade assemblages may match the higher-grade assemblages of a sequence elsewhere, in which the direction of increasing grade can be determined without ambiguity. In fact, there are few, if any, well-mapped sequences of metamorphic zones in which there is any doubt as to the direction of grade increase. What may be somewhat ambiguous, however, is whether the metamorphic assemblages at any point in the mapped sequence were "frozen-in" during a metamorphic episode in which grade of metamorphism was rising or falling with respect to time. In the northern Adirondacks, for example, the mapped sequence amphibolite → hornblende-pyroxene-granulite → two-pyroxene granulite is one of increasing grade (with respect to space). But is the hornblende-granulite assemblage the product of progressive metamorphism of amphibolite, or of retrogressive metamorphism of two-pyroxene granulite? Metamorphic grade, whatever its physical significance, has no unique connotation with regard to time.

Figure 8-1 is a schematic generalized plot of metamorphic facies against rectangular coordinates representing depth and grade. Of course no numerical values can be assigned to either variable; and there is no implication that the scale of either variable would be uniform along the length of the corresponding coordinate. It follows that the relative sizes and shapes of the facies fields are meaningless. What is significant is their mutual relationships with respect to depth and grade. To construct such a diagram, an arbitrary position is first assigned to any convenient facies. The sites to be assigned to other facies then automatically follow on the basis of observed transitions, always with emphasis on depth and grade. Suppose, for example, that we start with the amphibolite facies. It passes with decreasing grade into the greenschist, with increasing grade into the granulite facies. Since the depth relations between the three facies are not known, the corresponding boundaries are shown as vertical lines. There is also a transition with decreasing depth into the hornblende-hornfels facies. The rarer transitions from the amphibolite to the glaucophane-lawsonite-schist and the eclogite facies can only be correlated with increasing depth, and the former with falling grade as well. If all the observed interfacies transitions are similarly treated, there emerges inescapably the unique picture shown in Fig. 8-1.

Figure 8-1 brings out a very simple and significant generalization. The critical mineral assemblages of metamorphic facies reflect the influence

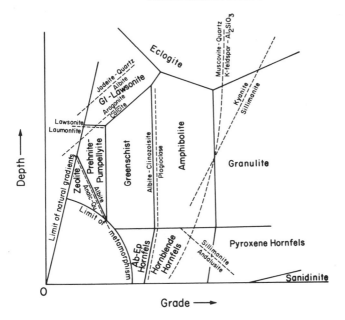

Fig. 8-1. Schematic diagram showing mutual relations of metamorphic facies with respect to depth and grade of metamorphism as inferred from purely geologic data. Broken lines represent limits of geologic provenance of chemically equivalent phases of phase assemblages.

of two factors, respectively correlated with depth and with grade. These factors, moreover, must be at least partially independent.[1] Otherwise facies plotted on Fig. 8-1 would fall in a linear series.

Facies in Relation to Temperature and Pressure

The physical variable most obviously related to depth is load pressure P_l; in most geological situations increasing depth also implies rise in temperature. Metamorphic grade, though based on petrographic criteria, has traditionally been correlated with temperature; and in contact aureoles at least, the relation of grade to temperature can scarcely be doubted. So on the basis of the geological relations of facies illustrated in Fig. 8-1, it is reasonable to examine the simple proposition that the nature of mineral assemblages in metamorphic rocks of given composition has been determined mainly by temperature and pressure of metamorphism. To test this proposition, we have drawn on Fig. 8-1 (broken lines) the limits of

---

[1] Contrast this conclusion with Grubenmann's simple correlation of what we now term facies with depth.

provenance of some critical chemically equivalent phases and phase pairs:

Andalusite–Kyanite–Sillimanite

Muscovite-quartz–K-feldspar–Al_2SiO_5

Analcite-quartz–Albite–Jadeite-quartz

Laumontite–Lawsonite

Albite-clinozoisite–Plagioclase (An_{30})

Aragonite–Calcite

Some of these lines correspond to interfacies boundaries or to standard isograds, and so can be located objectively.

Figure 8-2 shows the experimentally established or thermodynamically predicted curves of univariant equilibrium for reactions involving the same phases (cf. Chap. 4). The relative positions of corresponding boundaries in the two figures are strikingly similar. From this similarity may be drawn three significant conclusions:

1. The proposition that metamorphic phase assemblages are controlled essentially by P and T is valid.

2. Each such assemblage approximates a system in *stable* divariant or univariant equilibrium.

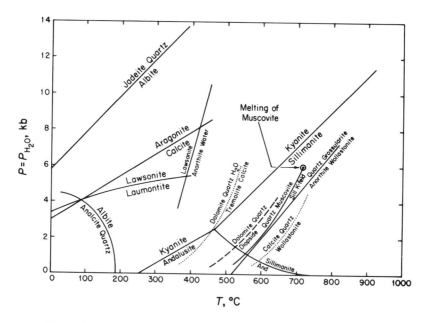

Fig. 8-2. Curves of univariant equilibrium for critical metamorphic phases and phase-assemblages, taken from Figs. 4-1, 4-3, 4-8, 4-14, 4-16, 4-21, 4-22, and 4-24. For carbonate reactions shown as broken curves, $P_{CO_2} = P$; $P_{H_2O} = 0$. For those shown as dotted curves, $P = (P_{H_2O} + P_{CO_2})$; $P_{H_2O} = P_{CO_2}$.

3. In regional metamorphism of hydrous rocks, P_{H_2O} approximates P_l; for this is the experimental condition or the thermodynamic assumption upon which the curves of Fig. 8-2 have been established.

We are now justified in attempting to evaluate quantitatively the pressure-temperature gradients of regional metamorphism in terms of the data of laboratory experiment and thermodynamic prediction; in so doing we accept the general, though not universal, validity of the propositions just stated. There is nothing new in this approach; it has been developed and used over the past half-century. It has already been employed in this book in the closing section of Chap. 6. Some of its aspects, nevertheless, have been seriously questioned from time to time (e.g., Yoder, 1952). It seems to this writer, however, that the collective picture of metamorphic facies viewed in relation to geologic environment overwhelmingly justifies calibration of the physical conditions of metamorphism in terms of a model such as that proposed above. He finds himself today in a position analogous to that of Bowen (1928, pp. 20, 21) some forty years ago, who realized that the strongest vindication of his interpretation of magmatic evolution in the light of experiment came from "the ordinary, everyday facts about rocks"—their simple predictable paragenesis and their mutual relations in the field.

ESTIMATED *P-T* GRADIENTS OF REGIONAL METAMORPHISM

The Concept of Facies Series

The Barrovian pattern of metamorphic zones, by virtue of priority in the literature, was long accepted as "normal." And indeed the zonal sequences subsequently mapped in many areas, such as Norway, New Zealand, northeastern United States, proved to be similar, though not identical to, those described by Barrow in the southeastern part of the Dalradian terrane. Presently, however, it was realized that the sequence of mineral assemblages in progressive metamorphism could be strikingly different from that in Barrow's zones. This was found to be the case along the northern border of the Dalradian terrane (Aberdeenshire and Banff-shire); and to emphasize the difference in metamorphic pattern, Read (1952) designated this the *Buchan* type, to distinguish it from the *Barrovian* type of metamorphism. At the conclusion of one of our earlier works (Fyfe, Turner, and Verhoogen, 1958, p. 237, 238) we attempted to show the relative positions of hypothetical gradients corresponding to these two zonal patterns on a $P_{H_2O}-T$ diagram.

Intensive study of regional metamorphism in Japan during the past two decades has shown that the respective patterns of zoning in the Ryoke and the Sanbagawa belts differ from both the "normal" Barrovian and the "abnormal" Buchan types. This led to Miyashiro's concept of *facies series*, expressed thus (Miyashiro, 1961, p. 277, 278):

> Even in a single metamorphic terrain, the variation in temperature would be expressed usually by a series of metamorphic facies. Such a series will be called a *metamorphic facies series* or simply a *facies series*. Thus, from the viewpoint of external conditions, each metamorphic terrain is characterized by a certain facies series.
>
> A metamorphic facies can be represented by a curve or a group of curves in a pressure-temperature diagram. According to the location of the curve or curves, the facies series *may be classified into various types* [Italics, mine].

This is a valuable concept, for it implies the unique character of every natural metamorphic gradient. It disposes of the tendency which most of us have shared, to endow the Barrovian sequence with the label of "normal." This writer, however, does not favor classification of facies series into standard types as proposed by Miyashiro. Classification of facies series has the same disadvantage that we have seen in earlier standardization and classification of subfacies: it obscures the unique character of each metamorphic situation.

Miyashiro (1961) recognized five types of facies series:

1. Andalusite-sillimanite type (Ryoke belt, Abukuma plateau, Japan)
2. Low-pressure intermediate type (= Read's Buchan type)
3. Kyanite-sillimanite type (= Barrovian type of Scotland)
4. High-pressure intermediate type [similar to kyanite-sillimanite type, but with glaucophane too (never jadeite-quartz) in some assemblages]
5. Jadeite-glaucophane type (Sanbagawa belt, Kanto Mountains, Japan)

Possible gradients for types 1, 3, and 5 were plotted by Miyashiro (1961, p. 285) on a *P-T* diagram (Fig. 8-3). The numerical values assigned to P and T are based on data relating to the transitions Kyanite $\rightleftharpoons$ Andalusite $\rightleftharpoons$ Sillimanite and Jadeite-quartz $\rightleftharpoons$ Albite. Since most critical reactions in all three facies series depend on P_{H_2O}, Miyashiro's gradients can be interpreted only if some assumption is made regarding the relative values of P_{H_2O} and P_t. In the belief that at water pressures of 3 to 4 kb the stability fields of Al_2SiO_5 polymorphs must be very limited (by hydration to pyrophyllite below 600°C and by incipient rock melting at only slightly higher temperatures), Miyashiro (1961, p. 286) concluded that "the prevailing water pressure is generally much lower than rock pressure during metamorphism." The temperature of the pyrophyllite breakdown is now known to be much lower than the value assumed by Miyashiro (probably 430°C at 3 to 4 kb). But the relation of high-grade metamorphism to rock fusion raises a real difficulty to which we shall refer later.

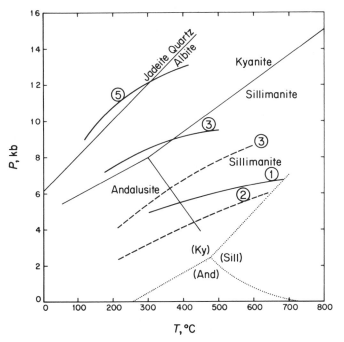

Fig. 8-3. Facies series of regional metamorphism in relation to P and T. Full lines as shown by *A. Miyashiro*. (1) Andalusite-sillimanite type. (3) Kyanite-sillimanite type. (5) Jadeite-glaucophane type. Boundaries of stability fields of critical phases as drawn by Miyashiro also shown as full lines. Corresponding boundaries tentatively accepted in this book, shown dotted. Broken curves (2) [between (1) and (3)] and (3) are for facies series as shown by *Fyfe, Turner, and Verhoogen* (1958) for $P_l = P_{H_2O}$.

Most geologists would find the relative positions of Miyashiro's curves acceptable. But recent drastic revision of the phase diagram for Al_2SiO_5 polymorphs necessitates substantial lowering of pressures on gradients 1 and 3. This adjustment must be applied also, though to a lesser degree, to corresponding hypothetical gradients proposed earlier by Fyfe, Turner and Verhoogen (1958), assuming $P_{H_2O} = P_l$ (broken curves, Fig. 8-3).[1]

---

[1] Many petrologists would probably prefer to place the Al_2SiO_5 triple point at about 500 °C, 4 kb (cf. Newton, 1966). But this would in no way invalidate the conclusion just stated. Now discredited is the triple point at 600 °C, 6.5 kb, used by some writers (e.g., Winkler, 1967, p. 180) as a principal reference point for calibrating facies series.

Some *P-T* Limits of Individual Facies Series

Glaucophane-schist paragenesis of northern California. The paragenesis of the glaucophane-lawsonite-schist facies, (cf. pp. 292–293) must be in the top left corner of Fig. 8-2. It follows that the gradient from surface conditions to those of metamorphism must be steep. Moreover, preservation of aragonite in California glaucophane schists implies postmetamorphic unloading of the dry rock down a correspondingly steep gradient, probably 10 to 12°C/km (Brown, Fyfe, and Turner, 1962). This is the main factor determining the slope of gradients 1*a* and 1*b* in Fig. 8-4. The regional paragenesis recorded by Ghent (1965) from the northern Coast Ranges, California, is represented by curve 1*a*. Characteristic assemblages contain lawsonite, aragonite, glaucophanic amphiboles, pumpellyite, and stilpnomelane in various combinations. The quartz-jadeite field is bypassed, but transitional greenschist assemblages containing aragonite are recorded. The appearance of lawsonite in advance of aragonite on curve 1*a* is consistent with the occurrence of lawsonite in calcite marbles in parts of New Zealand. The typical association in California is aragonite-lawsonite. The greenschist transition is fixed arbitrarily at a temperature 100° below that of the metastable equilibrium Lawsonite $\rightleftharpoons$ Anorthite-sillimanite-water. Any gradient entering the stability field of jadeite-quartz must be steeper than 1*a*. One such is shown as 1*b*; but even on this, the common jadeite-quartz metagraywackes of California could not form at pressures below about 8 kb. Assemblages with omphacite and garnet, transitional to the eclogite facies, are provisionally assigned to the high-temperature ends of gradients such as 1*c*. This family of curves is consistent with the great (but not precisely known) depth of the Franciscan geosyncline, and the wide prevalence of zeolitic assemblages in its less metamorphosed members.

Glaucophane-lawsonite-schist facies series, Sanbagawa belt, Japan. The zonal sequences described by Iwasaki (1963) and Banno (1964) in the Sanbagawa belt of Japan start, at the low-grade end, with the glaucophane-lawsonite-schist facies. Transitions with rising grade through the greenschist to the amphibolite facies, and locally to the amphibolite-eclogite boundary, imply flat gradients in Fig. 8-4. Since glaucophane-schist conditions can be reached only by steep gradients, the complete gradient must be curved somewhat as shown in curves 1*d* and 1*e* (Fig. 8-4). Here is an interesting implication of a heat source at depth; but the nature of the source is still unknown.

Low-grade facies series, eastern Otago, New Zealand. The facies series Zeolite → Prehnite-pumpellyite-metagraywacke → Greenschist, as represented in the southeastern half of the Otago schist belt of southern New Zealand (cf. pp. 265–277), is believed to span a very large interval of

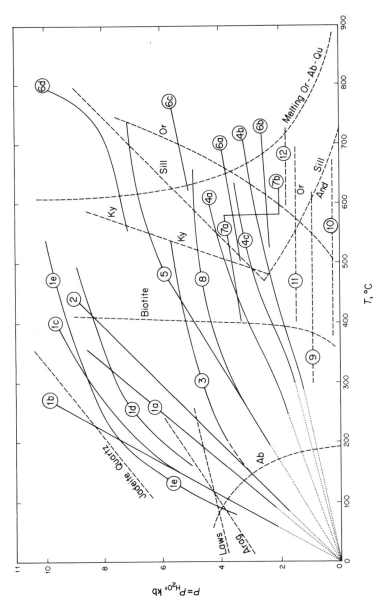

Fig. 8-4. Some estimated *P-T* gradients of individual facies series. (1) Glaucophane-schist parageneses of northern California (*a* to *c*) and Japan (*d, e*). (2) Eastern Otago schist belt, New Zealand. (3) Alpine schist belt New Zealand. (4) New Hampshire and Vermont, eastern United States. (5) Southeastern Dalradian (Barrow's zones), Scotland. (6) Amphibolite-granulite facies series: (*a*) north-western Adirondacks; (*b*) Broken Hill, Australia; (*c*) Saxony; (*d*) Danube (lower Austria). (7) Nanga Parbat massif and vicinity, Himalayas. (8) Lepontine Alps. The four horizontal dashed gradients are taken from Fig. 6-35: (9) Bosost, Pyrenees; (10) Comrie, Scotland; (11) Sierra Nevada, California; (12) Lochnagar, Scotland.

stratigraphic depth. Metamorphism has been dated radiometrically (Aronson, 1965, p. 412) as Cretaceous—100 to 120 million years. It has affected mixed sedimentary and volcanic rocks of Upper Paleozoic and Triassic age; and metamorphic grade appears to be directly related to stratigraphic depth in the column. The corresponding P-T gradient (2) in Fig. 8-4 passes through interfacies boundaries at the following points.

(a) Zeolite → Prehnite-pumpellyite-metagraywacke transition, Taringatura Hills (Triassic), not less than 6 km, possibly 10 km; corresponding conditions estimated as $P_l = 3$ kb, $T > 100°C$.

(b) Full development of prehnite-pumpellyite-metagraywacke facies in Chl. 2 subzone of Otago schists (Carboniferous or earlier), at least 20 km, possibly 30 km (Mutch, 1957, pp. 508, 509). Corresponding load pressures can scarcely have been less than 5 to 7 kb. Temperatures at this point must have been high enough to bypass the field of the glaucophane-lawsonite-schist facies; but local presence of lawsonite-calcite marble further northwest suggests that the intervening margin was small.

The fully developed greenschist assemblages (e.g., quartz-muscovite-chlorite-albite-epidote) of Chl. 4 subzone in the southeast Otago chlorite zone must itself span a considerable depth interval; for its areal extent is very great in a terrane where the topographic relief is 2 km. At the high-temperature end of the gradient, almandine and biotite begin to appear simultaneously in quartz-muscovite-chlorite-albite-epidote schists. Elsewhere (p. 307) it has been suggested that this indicates pressures intermediate between those at which almandine is first seen in glaucophane-schist terranes, on the one hand, and in the Barrovian zones, on the other.

Greenschist-amphibolite facies series, Southern Alps, New Zealand. Curve 3 in Fig. 8-4 has been drawn to illustrate a possible P-T gradient for metamorphism south of Mt. Cook in the Southern Alps of New Zealand. The metamorphic event is the same as that responsible for the facies series just described for the Otago schist belt further south and east. But the zonal patterns are different; and to explain this we must appeal to different P-T regimes of metamorphism. Curve 3 is based on Grindley's (1963, fig. 2) zonal and structural map of the Alpine region between Mt. Cook and the Haast River (cf. Figs. 1-13 and 1-14), and on petrographic and structural data recorded by Lillie and Gunn (1964) for a part of the same region. Incipient metamorphism (greenschist facies) first becomes pronounced at the outer boundary of the Chl. 2 subzone. Typical chlorite zone assemblages continue across an outcrop width (normal to the zonal trend) of 6 to 10 km. Following are a biotite zone (1 km) and an almandine-oligoclase zone (10 km) terminating on the west against the Alpine Fault. These figures provide *maximum possible* depth limits. If, as is likely, the isogradic surfaces are somewhat inclined to the vertical, the corresponding depth interval must be even smaller. An estimate of the maximum possible total interval of load pressure represented in the complete section from the Chl. 2 isograd to the Alpine Fault is perhaps 2 kb. But since the isograd pattern was imprinted after folding, the interval is probably even less than this. Probably significant is the virtual absence (except for rare occurrences of kyanite) of Al_2SiO_5 polymorphs, even in schists of maximum grade. Evidently temperatures corresponding to the first appearance of kyanite or sillimanite elsewhere were not attained on the Alpine P-T gradient of New Zealand. The total cover for Chl. 2 metamorphism in Alpine schists some 250 km north has been estimated as > 15 km (Reed, 1958, pp. 54, 55), that is, minimum $P = 4$ kb.

Greenschist-amphibolite facies series, Lepontine region, western and cental Alps, Switzerland. On the basis of isograds established by Niggli (1960) for pelitic schists, by Wenk (1962) for plagioclase marbles, and by Trommsdorff (1966) for magnesian marbles, it is possible to reconstruct in greater detail than usual the P-T gradient of regional metamorphism in the Pennine zone of the Alps along a section extending 100 km east of the Simplon (Fig. 7-29). The mineral assemblages reflect the final post-tectonic phase of Alpine metamorphism: the Lepontine metamorphism of Wenk (1962) and others.

Curve 8 (Fig. 8-4) represents a possible P_l-T gradient along a north-south line in the middle of the region shown in Fig. 7-29. The *minimum* thickness of the overlying nappe pile in the high-grade zones has been estimated at about 13 km.[1] Since the thickness thins along the northern margin, the pressure gradient along curve 8 is shown as 3 to 5 kb. This is consistent with widespread occurrence of kyanite, and, at lower grades, stilpnomelane. Assuming that in the pelitic members P_{H_2O} approximated P_l, there are several points of temperature calibration on curve 8:

1. First appearance of kyanite, must be above $450°C$ (maximum limit of stability of pyrophyllite)

2. First appearance of staurolite, and disappearance of chloritoid, is lower than $500°C$ (cf. Fig. 4-4)

3. Inversion of kyanite to sillimanite, about $600°C$

4. Breakdown of muscovite-quartz to K-feldspar and sillimanite, is just attained at maximum grade (about $680°C$)

The sequence of Ca–Mg silicates in siliceous dolomitic limestones, as given by Trommsdorff in the east-central sector of the map is

1. Appearance of tremolite just within the kyanite isograd ($> 450°C$)

2. Appearance of diopside close to the sillimanite isograd ($> 600°C$)

These temperatures are consistent with the condition $[P_l = P_f = (P_{CO_2} + P_{H_2O}); P_{H_2O} = P_{CO_2}]$ for the marble members. Appearance of talc in the early stages, and forsterite-diopside at higher grades, in the western

---

[1] Personal communication, Prof. E. Wenk.

section can be explained only by assuming low values of P_{CO_2} and correspondingly high P_{H_2O} in this area.

Greenschist-amphibolite facies series, Vermont-New Hampshire. In east-central Vermont (e.g., White and Billings, 1951; Lyons, 1955) a fully developed chlorite-zone paragenesis is replaced, as the grade of metamorphism rises, by successive pelitic assemblages whose respective index minerals are biotite, almandine, staurolite, and kyanite. It has been suggested earlier that appearance of almandine *after* oligoclase gives a hint of relatively low pressures. The persistence of staurolite and muscovite-quartz in all staurolite-bearing assemblages shows that maximum temperatures were still far short of the muscovite-quartz breakdown. The total outcrop width of the combined zones of biotite, almandine and staurolite in some places is less than 4 km; the corresponding pressure interval cannot be more than 1 kb. Gradient 4*a* (Fig. 8-4) conforms to these limitations and is shown as crossing the kyanite-sillimanite boundary; for in this section of Vermont there are restricted sillimanite zones peripheral to domed centers of granite intrusion.

In other areas on the Vermont-New Hampshire border (Billings, 1937) the Al_2SiO_5 polymorph with staurolite, almandine, muscovite and quartz is sillimanite or even (locally) andalusite (curve 4*c*). In southwest New Hampshire (Heald, 1950) the pattern is different again. Here staurolite and kyanite are lacking. There is a broad sillimanite-muscovite-quartz zone followed by a high-grade zone of sillimanite-orthoclase quartz. The corresponding gradient is shown as curve 4*b*.

Barrovian facies series, southeast Highlands, Scotland. Two widely differing *P-T* gradients have recently been proposed for regional metamorphism in Barrow's classic section of the southern Dalradian in Scotland. These are reproduced in Fig. 8-5. Curve *EF* was drawn by McNamara (1965) on the basis of speculations regarding (1) relative depths of isogradic surfaces and (2) temperatures implied by survival of anatase with respect to the Anatase $\rightleftharpoons$ Rutile inversion, and by segregation of quartz veins. More complex is Chinner's (1966, p. 172) attempt to establish a *P-T* regime, in time as well as in place, for the whole terrane of Dalradian metamorphism. He defines his model thus:

> One might therefore interpret the general distribution of metamorphic rocks in north-eastern Scotland as resulting from a two-stage process: the development of kyanite and andalusite zones by general pressure-temperature distribution corresponding to a geothermal gradient similar to [*ABC*, Fig. 8-5],[1] followed by local temperature rise bringing what are now the areas characterized by sillimanite and gneiss into the fields of sillimanite stability, partial melting, muscovite-quartz reaction, or all three.

[1] Lettering changed to correspond to Fig. 8-5.

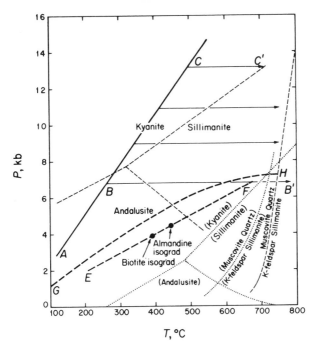

Fig. 8-5. Proposed *P-T* gradients of Dalradian metamorphism. *ABB'*, *ACC'*, and phase boundaries shown as broken lines. (*After G. A. Chinner.*) *EF* (*after M. McNamara*), *GH*, and phase boundaries shown dotted, as preferred by this writer.

The local rise in temperature postulated in the final episode is shown by arrows *BB'*, *CC'*, etc. Thus *ABB'* and *ACC'* are *P-T* gradients in time. *ACC'* corresponds to the southern border of the Dalradian terrane, the area of Barrow's zones. Numerical values of *P* and *T* in Chinner's analysis are based on the Al_2SiO_5 phase boundaries shown in Fig. 8-5 as broken lines. These are now thought to be grossly in error. The revised phase diagram shown with dotted boundaries necessitates drastic revision of Chinner's gradients. A provisional gradient for Barrow's zones that seems compatible with all available data has been drawn in Fig. 8-4 as curve 5 (*GH*, Fig. 8-5).

Amphibolite-granulite facies series, northwestern Adirondacks. By general concensus, the partially or completely anhydrous state of the granulite-facies paragenesis places it at the high-temperature extreme of the facies series of regional metamorphism. Another condition that is generally assumed is high pressure in a deep-seated crustal environment. Evidence for high pressure as a universal condition, nevertheless, is by no means conclusive. It is difficult to estimate on geologic grounds the depth of metamorphism of Precambrian terranes, the typical locale of the granulite facies. The composition range of granulite garnets has some analogies with that of eclogite garnets (e.g., Mg and Ca are both relatively high in garnets of both facies). More significant, perhaps, is the relatively high content of Al in *some* orthopyroxenes of granulites. By contrast the prevalence of cordierite, with or without garnet, in many granulite terranes can be interpreted as evidence that the field of the granulite facies extends to comparatively low pressures, thereby implying a transition to the pyroxene-hornfels facies.

The stratigraphy, structure and petrochemistry of the amphibolite-granulite transition of a part of the northwestern Adirondacks have been studied in unusual detail by Engel and Engel (1962, and works cited therein). These writers (Engel and Engel, 1962, p. 39) estimate the depth of metamorphism as at least 8 to 10 km, and possibly as much as 15 to 20 km. The corresponding pressure limits would be 3 to 6 kb. They also list mineralogical evidence, notably the chemical compositions of solid-solution series (magnesian dolomites, ferrous sphalerites) and coexisting phase pairs (K-feldspar-plagioclase, magnetite-ilmenite), which collectively indicates a temperature range of 500—525°C in the amphibolite facies, to 600—625°C in the facies transitional to granulites. The maximum temperatures deduced by Buddington and Lindsley (1964) for the transitional zone are of the same order: 560 to 625°C; and that for the highest-grade zone (E) in the Adirondacks was placed at 635 to 665°C (Buddington, 1963).

The temperature ranges estimated for Adirondack granulites are surprisingly low when compared with the experimentally determined stability limits of muscovite-quartz. In the Adirondacks, as elsewhere, this pair is eliminated in favor of K-feldspar-sillimanite at or before the amphibolite-granulite transition. A temperature of only 620°C implies values of P_{H_2O} no greater than 3 kb, though this may be raised to 4 kb if account is taken of the relatively high sodium content of the K-feldspar of granulites. Pressures of 3 to 4 kb, however, are well within the limits inferred by Engel and Engel on geologic grounds.

In Figure 8-4 curve 6a has been drawn to represent the Adirondack transition. Curve 6b has been drawn at lower pressure to illustrate the amphibolite-granulite transition in the Broken Hill region of Australia (cf. pp. 325–328) and similar areas where the granulite assemblages usually contain cordierite. To include the kyanite granulites (which lack cordierite) of yet other regions, the field of the granulite facies must be extended to much higher pressures and temperatures, presumably transitional to conditions of the eclogite facies. Gradients drawn in this region must necessarily be based largely on guesswork. They must enter the field of large-scale rock fusion (Fig. 8-4, curve 6d).

Nevertheless, and even allowing a generous margin of error for the data of laboratory experiment, it is inevitable that among the products of dehydration of muscovite-biotite-quartz-feldspar assemblages at pressures exceeding about 4 kb will be a "granitic" silicate-melt phase. Since such melts under high water pressures themselves contain 10 to 15 percent by weight dissolved water, they can form in only limited quantity from high-grade quartzo-feldspathic mica schists, containing at the most 5 percent H_2O. The melt phase may become segregated as pegmatitic veins, or completely squeezed from the system. The anhydrous residue of quartz, feldspars, kyanite or sillimanite, and garnet or cordierite, cools unchanged as a white granulite. Under the same conditions, pyroxene or hornblende-pyroxene granulites presumably crystallize without even incipient fusion.

This whole question, and the related problem of genesis of "granitic" magma and of migmatites by anatexis during the culmination of high-grade regional metamorphism, has been discussed clearly and in greater detail by Winkler (1965, pp. 115-125; 176-208).

Compound gradients. The common practice of drawing a gradient of metamorphism as a smooth curve or even as a nearly straight line implies smooth transition between the respective P-T conditions of all facies and subfacies in the corresponding series. It is now generally recognized, however, that zonal sequences in most large areas of regional metamorphism have developed over spans of time measured in millions of years. It is possible, therefore (indeed, to this writer it seems likely), that in some zonal sequences, one of the higher-grade isograds may mark a sharp break in time, and hence also in the P-T gradient of the facies series. Such a series would have a compound character, and the P-T gradient could be represented as two smooth sectors with an abrupt change of slope where they join.

It is possible to interpret in this way some otherwise anomalous features of the metamorphic zones described by Misch (1949, 1964) from the Nanga Parbat region of the Himalayas (cf. pp. 318–319). The sequence of pelitic assemblages along a section into the granite-gneiss massif of Nanga Parbat has been identified by Misch as being of the "Barrovian type." At the border of the massif, kyanite gives way to sillimanite. The typical pelitic assemblages in the massif itself contain quartz-K-feldspar-sillimanite. The anomaly raised by Misch is the widespread occurrence, in the sillimanite zone, of calcareous assemblages containing anorthite-wollastonite instead of grossularite-quartz. At pressures below 5 kb (Fig. 8-2) an interval of over 100°C separates the respective stability fields of kyanite and of wollastonite-anorthite. There must be a corresponding sharp break in the P-T gradient of the Nanga Parbat facies; for it is impossible to explain this particular anomaly by invoking differences in

P_l and P_{H_2O}. Such a break would be consistent with a model of metamorphism in two episodes separated by a substantial break in time and simultaneous reduction in pressure: (1) regional metamorphism of the "Barrovian" type (gradient 7*a*, Fig. 8-4); (2) contact metamorphism connected with uprise of granitic magma and metasomatism in the massif itself (gradient 7*b*, Fig. 8-4). This model is presented for consideration as a possible alternative to that of Misch, who views the gneiss massif as a product of granitization: the culmination of a single metamorphic episode.

A GENERAL *P-T* DIAGRAM FOR METAMORPHIC FACIES

A glance at Fig. 8-4 shows the futility of attempting to force the individually unique gradients of regional metamorphism into a few standardized facies series. It has been used, in conjunction with Fig. 8-2 and the collective data of metamorphism, as far as they can be grasped by this writer, to construct a tentative diagram (Fig. 8-6) illustrating the possible relation of generally accepted facies to pressure and temperature. This is a rather roughly calibrated version of Fig. 8-1. Many similar diagrams have been drawn up by other writers; and it is not proposed to criticize these individually. Each reader must follow his own preference. He is reminded, however, that all such generalized schemes are tentative

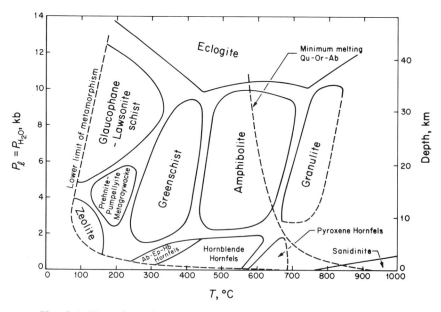

Fig. 8-6. Tentative scheme of metamorphic facies in relation to P_l ($= P_{H_2O}$) and T. All boundaries gradational.

and no two are likely to be identical. And again this writer would emphasize his personal prejudice against diagrams on which interfacies boundaries are drawn as straight lines parallel to coordinates of P and T, and against those that assign common metamorphic phenomena to environments of unrealistically high pressure or low temperature.

Attention, nevertheless, is drawn to a detailed scheme presented by an experienced student of field and petrographic aspects of metamorphism, A. Hietanen (1967), whose stimulating essay on facies series has appeared since the above was written. This contains condensed information regarding several individual facies series not discussed in this book, especially those developed in the vicinity of the Idaho batholith, United States, and the classic granulite region of Saxony. Dr. Hietanen's picture of metamorphism in relation to P and T, while not unlike that presented in Fig. 8-6, differs from this in a number of respects. Facies series are standardized, following Miyashiro, and their number increased to eight. Curiously, no two of the corresponding gradients on a P-T field intersect. The experimental data selected for calibrating the facies fields and series in terms of P and T, differ naturally enough from those preferred by this writer. The high pressure value assigned to the crucial kyanite-andalusite-sillimanite triple point is reflected in correspondingly higher pressure ranges for what are here considered facies and facies series of low pressure.

No facies diagram is adequate unless it takes account of possible relations of P_{H_2O} to P_f to P_l. Rather than introduce a three-dimensional diagram in which P_{H_2O} and P_l can be treated independently, the assumption has here been made that $P_{H_2O} = P_l$. This is admittedly an approximation. Moreover, it can be applied only to the critical mineral assemblages that are products of metamorphic dehydration-hydration reactions. Equilibria including carbonate phases may be widely distributed over Fig. 8-6. For example, calcite-diopside-forsterite, while typical of the pyroxene-hornfels facies in systems where P_{CO_2} has been maintained at a high level in relation to P_l, is found, too, in the hornblende-hornfels, the amphibolite, and the granulite facies. Such assemblages cannot be used to delineate facies. But when a facies has once been recognized on the basis of other phase assemblages, the carbonate paragenesis can give valuable information about local relative values of P_{CO_2} and P_{H_2O} during metamorphism.

REGIONAL METAMORPHISM IN RELATION TO OROGENY, PLUTONISM, AND TIME

Statement of a Complex Problem

At the conclusion of an earlier discussion it was stated (Turner and Verhoogen, 1960, p. 669) that

Large-scale crustal deformation (alpine folding), batholithic intrusion, and regional metamorphism are geographically associated, broadly synchronous, but partially independent manifestations of thermal (and mechanical?) disturbances in the mantle, not in the crust.

Viewed in the light of this statement, the *P-T* gradients inferred from any individual facies series, or the *P-T* regime deduced from the zonal distribution of facies in a metamorphic terrane, give some indication regarding the magnitude of a correlated thermal disturbance in the deep crust and the underlying mantle. To relate the thermal aspect of metamorphism to geographically associated orogeny and plutonism (intrusion of granite batholiths, development of migmatite complexes), it is necessary to explore the possible relations of all three, not only in space, but also in time.

A decade ago we closed a discussion of metamorphic facies (Fyfe, Turner, and Verhoogen, 1958, pp. 237-239) by setting up some hypothetical gradients of regional metamorphism with the purpose of raising some essential questions still requiring an answer:

In regional metamorphism the temperature distribution and the pressure-temperature relationship are determined partly by depth, partly by the rate of supply of heat [from the focus of thermal disturbance in the depths], and partly by the rate and nature of the metamorphic reactions themselves . . . .

. . . It is conceivable that the temperature at a given depth might fluctuate in time; . . . Transition from one facies to the next might be effected at constant pressure. The gradients shown for regional metamorphism of the Buchan and Barrovian types are drawn arbitrarily in Figure 108 [Fig. 8-3, dashed curves 2, 3].

In spite of their highly speculative nature Figures 107 and 108 [and the same may be said of Figs. 8-1 and 8-6 in this book] illustrate the kind of relations that must exist between facies. If they emphasize the imperfection of present knowledge they also serve to show where additional field, petrographic and experimental data are most needed. Relations in the right-hand portion of the diagrams, where fields of several facies impinge on the field of granitic magmas, raise questions such as these: What are the general relations of granulites to granites? . . . What is the significance of the cordierite and hornblende granulites? Is the broad transition field between granulites and pyroxene hornfelses (at pressures between 4 and 7 kilobars in Figure 107) commonly attained in nature? Along the low temperature border . . . the tentative disposition of facies boundaries raises yet other questions: Is low-grade regional metamorphism commonly the result of deep burial alone? Should not progressive regional metamorphism in some cases lead to metamorphic zones characterized by glaucophane schists, greenschists and amphibolites in order of increasing grade?

To some of these questions, especially those relating to low-grade metamorphism, tentative answers have now been supplied. *P-T* gradients, corresponding to the facies series Zeolite → Prehnite-pumpellyite-meta-graywacke → Glaucophane-lawsonite-schist as drawn in Fig. 8-6, lie well within what are generally considered to be normal geothermal gradients. Metamorphism of this kind today is generally termed *burial metamorphism*. The predicted facies series Glaucophane-lawsonite-schist → Greenschist → Amphibolite has indeed been discovered by Japanese geologists (gradient 1*d*, Fig. 8-4). And the prehnite-pumpellyite paragenesis and even assemblages of the glaucophane-lawsonite-schist facies have now been described in regionally undeformed rocks. So there is no longer any question as to whether deformation involving extensive rock flow (as exemplified in schistose rocks) is an essential feature of all low-grade metamorphism.

In the region of high temperature and pressure the picture is more obscure. Some of the old questions remain unanswered. But on the whole the mutual relations of metamorphic crystallization, large-scale deformation, and emplacement of large bodies of granitic rock have become clarified. This we owe especially to two relatively new lines of approach, both involving detailed field work amplified by use of newer techniques in the laboratory. One is radiometric dating of critical stages in crystallization of metamorphic minerals and of granitic rocks. The other is study of metamorphic textures with a view to relating episodes of crystallization to episodes of deformation (folding) as revealed by statistical analysis of tectonite fabrics.

Time Relations between Metamorphic Crystallization, Deformation, and Granite Plutonism

Criteria of deformational history. The strain history of a deformed rock mass is recorded in successive generations of *s*-surfaces (bedding, foliation, etc.) and the geometry of their fold patterns. It is usually possible to recognize in any large domain, or even in a single outcrop, several episodes of folding. These are conventionally designated F_1, F_2, and so on. Within any large domain, there are usually smaller domains that are homogeneous with respect to geometry and style of small-scale folds. In such a domain it is possible to determine the geometry, especially the mean attitude of fold axes B, of folds of the same generation (say F_2) as developed in preexisting *s*-surfaces. Thus bedding S is found to be folded about an axis B_{S_1}; and a foliation S_2 is synchronously folded about an axis B_{S_2}, whose attitude usually is inclined to that of B_{S_1}. If at the same time a new cleavage S_3 has developed parallel to the axial planes of folds in S_2, the axis of these folds may be designated more precisely at $B_{S_2}^{S_3}$. The strain history of any domain whose fabric is homogeneous may be worked out by statistical treatment of many measured attitudes of linear and planar fabric elements: lineations, fold axes, segments of *s*-surfaces, optical directions and cleavage or twin planes in crystals, and so on. This is the method of fabric analysis (*Gefügekunde*), first developed by Sander (1930, 1948, 1950). It has been described in English, with some modifications, additions, and illustrative examples, in books by Turner and Weiss (1963) and Ramsay (1967). The nomenclature employed here is that of Turner and Weiss.

The history of deformation in most metamorphic regions that have been studied in this way (among them the Alps, the Highlands of Scotland, the Otago and Alpine schist zones of New Zealand) typically commences with large-scale recumbent folding of bedding and of whole stratigraphic units, culminating in overthrusting and nappe development. This is followed by one or more episodes of folding on a smaller scale, each affecting any of the *s*-surfaces—notably foliations and segregation laminae—that may have formed during previous episodes. The latest manifestation is likely to be a strain-slip cleavage or a generation of small-scale kinks in plane-foliated rocks. Correlated microscopic phenomena are lamellar twinning in calcite and dolomite, kinking of mica crystals, and appearance of swarms of "deformation lamellae" in quartz.

Crystallization in relation to episodes of deformation. From the first, as he developed his philosophy and method of fabric analyses, Sander (e.g., 1950, pp. 295-306) related the crystallization of the constituent minerals of deformed rocks to periods of deformation recorded in recognizable *s*-surfaces and folds. With reference to a particular episode of deformation, he classed crystallization as pre-, syn- (para-) or post-tectonic. The principal criteria employed are textural. Clearly, a crystal of mica that has been bent into partial alignment with a strain-slip cleavage S_3 is pretectonic with respect to that particular structure. Conversely, an albite porphyroblast that crosses and encloses microfolds in S_2 is posttectonic in relation to S_2. By far the most general situation is one in which tabular and prismatic crystals tend to be aligned in the various *s*-surfaces and lineations but themselves lack any evidence of strain. And in such rocks, unstrained and more or less equant grains of quartz, calcite, or feldspar show no obvious relation to any *s*-surface. Here there are two possibilities: the grain fabric may have developed simultaneously with, or subsequently to, the last major episode of deformation.

In the various attempts that have been made during the past two decades to correlate changing *P-T* conditions with the successive episodes of folding, perhaps too much weight has been assigned to textural details as the principal criterion of a period of crystallization. Although important in relation to history of textural development, the mutual relations between grain boundaries are less significant with respect to our present problem. Considering the whole assemblage of phases seen in a microsection as a system in equilibrium, we must ask "At what point in the tectonic history of the rock was that assemblage as a whole frozen in as we now see it?" It is to this point in time that we may assign the *P-T* regime inferred from mineralogical criteria. The porphyroblasts of kyanite and staurolite, the large "cross biotites" cutting the principal foliation *S*, the crystals of quartz, micas, and feldspars aligned in *S*, and the grains of similar and other minerals enclosed in the porphyroblast, are considered as a unit. This unit reflects the *P-T* conditions appropriate to the whole assemblage. The texture shows that these have outlasted the episode of deformation responsible for *S*; but judging from the rapidity of experimental annealing and grain growth, the interval of time so expressed may be insignificant.

Throughout this book we have paid little attention to disequilibrium in metamorphic phase assemblages. Departures from equilibrium obvious enough to be recognized beneath the microscope nevertheless are common. And the partial development of a new assemblage (evidence of a *P-T* change in time) can usually be related texturally to some stage in the strain history of the rock. Particularly instructive are recognizably retrogressive changes on the microscopic scale. Local chloritization of biotite and garnet on cleavage surfaces place the development of these in a regime of waning temperature, postdating the metamorphic event expressed by the main assemblage. Such changes, accompanied by decrease in grain size and development of new platelets of chlorite and muscovite, may ultimately produce a rock of phyllitic aspect—a phyllonite (Knopf, 1931)—whose fabric is dominated by the latest *s*-surface and whose essential mineralogy is that of a low-grade facies. But relict, partially destroyed grains of staurolite and garnet may still survive as evidence of a preceding episode of higher temperature. Then there are regions such as the western Alps (Bearth, 1962) and eastern India (Roy, 1966) where retrogressive changes are most obvious on the macroscopic scale.

Most valuable on a large scale is the relation, or lack of it, between isograd patterns and structural trends of major stratigraphic units. It has been found repeatedly, especially where high topographic relief facilitates observation on a large scale, that the pattern of isograds and isogradic surfaces is simpler than that of the large-scale structures. The two generally appear to be totally independent; and the *P-T* regime expressed by the zones of progressive metamorphism must have been imprinted late in the tectonic history; later, at any rate, than the initial period of large-scale folding and nappe development.

Emplacement of granitic plutons and migmatite complexes. The time relations between emplacement or development of granitic plutons and migmatite complexes, and various episodes of deformation recorded in adjacent metamorphic rocks, are established mainly on the basis of field observations. The Newer Granite plutons of the Dalradian terrane have long been recognized as posttectonic. Their crosscutting contacts have no relation to even the late-generation fold patterns in the country rock. They are also late with respect to crystallization; for they have generated their own aureoles, superimposed upon the local mineral paragenesis of regional metamorphism. Moreover, their distribution is not obviously related to the broad pattern of Barrow's zones. The Older Granite complexes, on the other hand, include gneissic rocks that have been affected at least by the later episodes of deformation. Contacts with metamorphic rocks tend to be gradational and structurally conformable. Local contact aureoles have not been recognized. Finally there is a tendency for the Older Granite complexes to be located in zones of high-grade regional metamorphism.

More recently, age relations between granite plutonism and regional metamorphism have been determined radiometrically. Here there is still some uncertainty as to the nature of the respective dated events in the metamorphic and in the plutonic cycles. We must still question the significance of age differences of a few million years between dates determined for granite and metamorphic rock, or even for low-grade versus high-grade zones of metamorphism.

Dalradian metamorphism as an illustrative example. Regional metamorphism in the Highlands of Scotland has been studied intensively in three essential independent aspects: the nature and zonal relations of mineral assemblages in at least two facies series (*Barrovian* and *Buchan* types); structural development as revealed by statistical analysis of *s*-surfaces, lineations, and folds; radiometric dating of events relating to metamorphism and to crystallization of associated granites. Deformation involved several successive episodes of folding. Metamorphic crystallization is visualized as a prolonged process, reaching a climax in the high-grade zones, somewhere in the middle of the deformational history. A model presented by Johnson (1963) postulates the following sequence of events:

1. First episode of folding F_1, giving large-scale recumbent folds and nappes. Pelitic sediments were converted to fine-grained phyllites.

2. Growth of garnet porphyroblasts in a period of crystallization (M_1) posttectonic with respect to F_1.

3. Second episode of folding F_2, on a smaller scale, with development of a new axial-plane cleavage. Commencement of main episode of crystallization (M_2), with growth of garnet, biotite, and amphibole.

4. Continuation and culmination of M_2 crystallization, which outlasted the F_2 folding episode. This also is the "culmination of metamorphism," with growth and coarsening of garnet, kyanite, staurolite, and oligoclase. Synchronous migmatization and growth of sillimanite in areas of Older Granite. (If the Older Granite bodies are considered to be intrusive plutons, this would be the period of intrusion.)

5. Renewed small-scale folding F_3 with development of late strainslip cleavage. Local and incipient retrogressive metamorphism: chloritization of garnet, fracture of porphyroblasts.

6. Renewed minor folding F_4.

7. Intrusion of Newer Granite plutons.

Some of these events have been radiometrically dated. Potassium/argon dates of Dalradian metamorphic rocks range from 380 to 490 million years, with a strong frequency maximum at 435 million years. This age spread has been variously interpreted.

(a) Harper (1964) postulates a culmination of metamorphism at a date close to 490 million years, as determined in rocks in the upper tectonic levels. Younger dates determined in rocks from deeper levels are attributed to partial loss of argon during relatively slow cooling.

(b) P. E. Brown et al. (1965) prefer a model postulating overprinting of two successive phases of crystallization (M_3 upon M_2 in Johnson's scheme). They assign to the culmination of metamorphism, with development of Older Granite migmatites following F_2 folding, an age (pre-Arenig) of about 500 million years. The metamorphic mineral systems are thought to have become closed to argon at 420 to 430 million years, subsequent to F_3 folding.

The last event in the Caledonian orogenic cycle was intrusion of the Newer Granite plutons at 400 to 410 million years (late Silurian or early Devonian).

Other examples briefly reviewed. Regional metamorphism in the Pennine zone of the western Alps comprises a sequence of episodes collectively spanning the Tertiary Alpine orogeny. In the southern part of this region, Bearth (1962, 1966) correlates metamorphism with two stages of deformation as follows:

1. The first episode was large-scale recumbent folding and building of nappes.

2. The second episode was one of lateral compression of the nappe pile. Culmination of metamorphism is correlated with this episode. But there were also two stages of metamorphic crystallization:

(a) Regional development of a facies series from glaucophane-lawsonite-schist on the west to eclogite ("type 1") on the east (cf. pp. 296–297). The difference between the two parageneses, i.e., the existence of the facies series itself, is attributed to marked differences in P_{H_2O} and P_{CO_2}.

(b) Overprinting of greenschist facies assemblages upon those of stage (a), with rising temperature and more uniform P_{H_2O} during the culmination of metamorphism.

In the northern sector (Lepontine region) described by Wenk (1962), a third and later episode of crystallization obliterated the effects of the earlier episodes. This produced a greenschist-amphibolite facies series (Lepontine zones of Wenk). A possible P-T gradient is shown as curve 8 in Fig. 8-4.

Large-scale recumbent folding, followed by episodes of folding on a smaller scale with contemporaneous culmination of metamorphic crystallization is now generally recognized in the Otago and Alpine schist zones of New Zealand. Grindley (1963) has proposed the following model of mid-Cretaceous (Rangitata) orogeny as manifested in the Alpine sector between Mt. Cook and the Haast River:

1. Large-scale recumbent folding (F_1 episode), with development of schistosity, foliation, and mineral assemblages of the chlorite zone.

2. Post-F_1 crystallization of garnet and biotite porphyroblasts (M_1 episode).

3. Smaller-scale folding F_2 about plunging axes, with development of new cleavages and lineations.

4. Post-F_2 culmination of metamorphic crystallization (M_2) with growth of biotite and garnet porphyroblasts. The isograd pattern was established at this stage. It is relatively simple and transgresses the complex patterns of F_1 and F_2 folding. Metamorphic crystallization has been dated radiometrically by Sr/Rb measurements (Aronson, 1965) as 100 to 120 million years.

5. Postmetamorphic folding, faulting, and uplift of the Alps. Movement began on the Alpine Fault and reached a culmination (at least 200 km right-lateral displacement) in a separate Tertiary (Kaikoura) orogeny.

Although no granites are associated with the Alpine schists or the Otago schists to the south and southeast, the 100 to 120 million year period of metamorphism coincides with intense and widespread plutonic activity elsewhere in the South Island of New Zealand (cf. Fig. 8-7). This, for example, seems to be the period of extensive batholithic intrusion (granite-granodiorite) in the Fiordland area southwest of the Otago schists. Here regional metamorphism of a completely different style, mainly high-grade amphibolite facies, was closely connected with plutonic activity. All these incidents are manifestations of a single orogeny: the Rangitata orogeny of New Zealand geologists.

The stimulating attempts of Johnson, Zwart, Grindley, Roy (1966) and others to reconstruct a detailed course of metamorphic crystallization, possibly spanning millions of years, and to correlate it with some prolonged sequence of structural events, have at least succeeded in eliminating the classic concept of metamorphism as a simple event that can be pinpointed on the geologic time scale. This writer still views with caution the implication that mineral phases of low-grade metamorphic assemblages commonly survive as unstable relics in high-grade assemblages of later origin. The reverse situation where unstable high-grade relics survive in assemblages of lower grade is, of course, well known. Indeed it supplies the only sure evidence of retrogressive metamorphism.

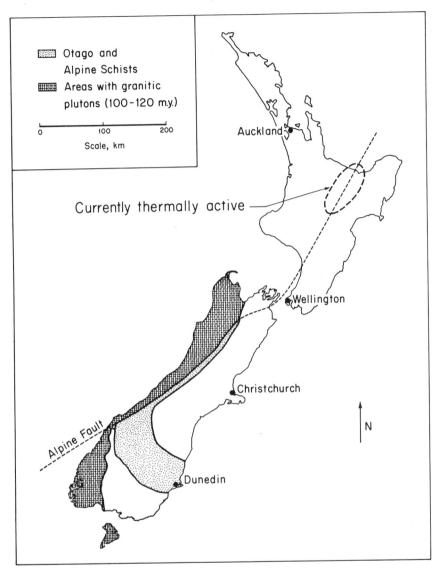

Fig. 8-7. Geographic relation of Alpine and Otago schist zones to areas of contemporaneous plutonic activity, southern New Zealand.

LOCATION AND NATURE OF HEAT SOURCES

General Implications of Isograd Patterns

The most satisfactory evidence regarding the vexed problem of heat sources in regional metamorphism is that inherent in the mapped patterns of isograds and (in all too few instances) isogradic surfaces. Before turning to natural patterns we may predict the configuration of one or more isogradic surfaces on the basis of two extremely simple models. The two isogradic surfaces shown in each case correspond to univariant equilibrium curves on a $(P_l = P_{H_2O})$-T diagram for reactions.

(1)   Hypothetical first appearance of biotite

(2)   Muscovite + Quartz $\rightleftharpoons$ K-feldspar + Al_2SiO_5 + H_2O

(3)   Kyanite $\rightleftharpoons$ Sillimanite

Case 1. Assume a uniform heat source of infinite lateral extent at some constant depth below the metamorphic terrane (cf. ideal burial metamorphism). Isogradic surfaces will be horizontal (Fig. 8-8a), since gradients of increasing pressure and temperature will both be normal to the surface. It is assumed that the geothermal gradient induced by heat flow from the underlying source increases from 15°C/km at the surface to 60°C/km at 30 km—an extreme value implying partial fusion at this depth. Figure 8-8a shows the corresponding geothermal gradient. It crosses the kyanite-inversion curve of Fig. 8-2 at K, the muscovite-breakdown curve at M. These mark corresponding isograds in the order in which they appear in the Barrovian zones. Note the impossibly high temperatures implied for the base of the crust if the Barrovian sequence were attributed merely to burial.

Case 2. Assume a uniform vertical cylindrical heat source terminating at 5 km below the surface, in a region where the normal geothermal gradient a long distance from the source is 15°C/km. Assume further that temperatures within the source are maintained at 800°C for a period of 10 million years. The pattern of isotherms and isobars developed within adjacent rocks at the end of 10 million years would have a distribution such as that shown in Fig. 8-8b (depending on the amount of heat absorbed in endothermic metamorphic reactions). On this model isogradic surfaces near the heat source have a reversed dip. The angle of dip depends upon the lateral temperature gradient with respect to distance from the source, and the P-T slope of the corresponding reaction curve.

Isograd Patterns Related to Centers of Granite Plutonism

The southeast Dalradian terrane is one of many in which there appears to be some relation between the pattern of isograds and the field distribution of more or less contemporary granite-migmatite complexes (Older Granites). The same relation has been demonstrated in the central Pyrenees (Zwart, 1963), the Lepontine zone of the central Alps (Wenk, 1962), and in Vermont, New Hampshire, and other New England states. In every

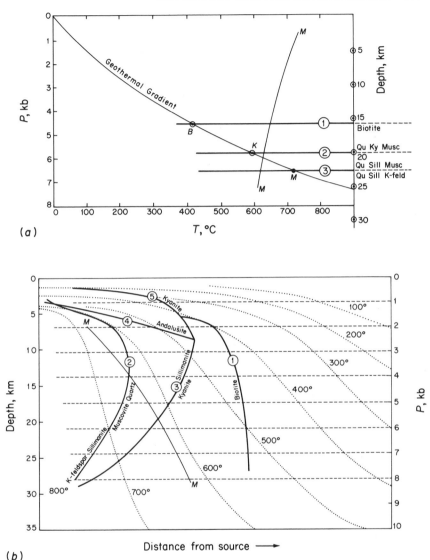

Fig. 8-8. Hypothetical distribution of isogradic surfaces in depth according to two simplified models (see text). (*a*) Uniform heat source at constant depth; (*b*) vertical heat source maintained at 800 °C.

case, the granite complexes are located in areas of maximum metamorphic grade—a fact repeatedly emphasized by Read (e.g., 1957) in his classic series of essays on granites, granitization, and metamorphism. In certain areas (e.g., New Hampshire and the Pyrenees), the high-grade sillimanite zones concentrically border individual structural domes in most of which intrusive granitic bodies are concentrated. Two interpretations have been placed on these patterns of regional metamorphism.

First, it is possible that intrusive granite plutons are the immediate source of heat for metamorphism, just as in a contact aureole. This was Barrow's original view regarding Dalradian metamorphism, as implied by the title of his classic paper of 1893: "On an intrusion of muscovite-biotite gneiss in the southeast Highlands of Scotland, and its accompanying metamorphism." In another early classic, Barrell (1921, p. 266) stated that in the New England region of the eastern United States, "regional metamorphism is intimately related to batholithic intrusion," and that metamorphic recrystallisation is "largely and directly related to batholithic heat and emanations." The same interpretation has been reiterated more recently (e.g., Billings, 1937, pp. 557, 558; White and Billings, 1951, p. 693) for metamorphism related to granite-injected structural domes in New Hampshire.

This simple explanation fails to account for what is probably the most significant feature of regional metamorphism. This is the enormous total quantity of heat necessary to drive to completion the whole series of endothermic dehydration and decarbonation reactions involved in progressive metamorphism of an initially cool sedimentary mass (cf. Turner and Verhoogen, 1960, p. 666). To this writer, therefore, a second alternative (though far short of a complete explanation) is preferable. It has been hinted or directly invoked by individual workers in the specific regions mentioned above (e.g., Lyons, 1955, pp. 105, 139; Zwart, 1963, pp. 152-154). According to this second model, the granites and migmatites are the culminating "products" of high-grade metamorphism. It is immaterial, with regard to the present problem, whether metamorphism culminates in partial fusion, or whether the granitic bodies are formed by metasomatism (granitization) without participation of a silicate-melt phase—a magma. The intrusive character of the granitic bodies is compatible with either mode of origin, if one accepts (as this writer does not), the idea that a mica schist, in becoming converted to granitic gneiss, can thereby be rendered mobile without partial fusion. All high-grade facies series have P-T gradients that impinge on or enter the field of incipient fusion of granitic rocks. The most likely origin of the central granitic gneiss massifs seems to be by partial or complete fusion at ultrametamorphic temperatures.

Under the stimulus of Read's earlier discourses on granitization in relation to metamorphism, it was fashionable twenty years ago to appeal to alkali metasomatism at high temperature as the essential factor in the genesis of migmatite complexes. Today the fashion is to invoke differential fusion of pelitic and semipelitic metasediments, with segregation of the melt phase, the final product being a laminated or veined migmatite (cf.

Turner and Verhoogen, 1960, pp. 383, 387-388, 669-672). This is of course by no means a new theory. It is as old as the concept of metamorphism itself and is inherent in Charles Lyell's model of plutonism as set out in the passage cited on page 46.

What is most debated today is the role of metasomatism in the fusion process. Some of the most detailed geochemical studies on a regional scale support a model in which an essential role is assigned to large-scale diffusion and concentration of alkalis and other elements [e.g., Engel and Engel, 1963 (northern Adirondacks); Brown, 1967 (northern Scotland)]. Other regional investigations, notably those of Mehnert and his colleagues (1957, 1961, 1963), have led to the opposite conclusion that regional transformation of metasedimentary schist and gneiss into granite migmatite does not necessarily involve any significant change in the whole rock mass, viewed on a large scale. Scale indeed may prove to be the crux of the problem. On a very small scale, that of an albite porphyroblast, metamorphism involves profound metasomatism. On the scale of a hand specimen, the same metamorphism may be isochemical. The system represented by a migmatite complex and its environment may comprise a few thousand cubic kilometers of rock. To evaluate possible changes in total composition of a system on so large a scale, and the possible degree of ionic exchange with whatever may lie beneath, presents a formidable task in sampling. Few, however, would now deny that the "granitic" fraction of migmatites was once largely or completely liquid, though some prefer to term them "mobilized granite" or "mobilizate." This conclusion receives strong support from the cumulative data of experiments on rock fusion at high water pressures. In particular, Winkler and his coworkers have shown that, given a sufficient supply of water from an external source, metagraywackes heated above 700°C at $P_{H_2O} = 2$ kb yield a substantial fraction of granite-granodiorite melt (Winkler and von Platten, 1960; Winkler, 1965, pp. 192-200).

But where is the ultimate heat source, and what is its nature? It is possible to locate the immediate source in a thermal "high" or "focus." Still completely unknown is the ultimate source of heat (presumably in the mantle beneath) and the vehicle (perhaps water) of its upward transport to thermal highs as now identified at the surface.

The preferred model just stated is analogous to that postulated as the basis of Fig. 8-8b. Billings (1937, p. 557) finds no relation between grade of metamorphism in northwest New Hampshire and stratigraphic depth. Isobaric metamorphism at 3 kb under conditions postulated for Fig. 8-8b would give a narrow zone of biotite and kyanite (presumably with staurolite and garnet as well) followed by a sillimanite-muscovite-quartz zone of similar width, which at curve 2 (second sillimanite isograd) passes into a broad sillimanite-orthoclase zone merging into migmatite. This is the situation as mapped by Heald (1950) in southwest New Hampshire. In the southeastern Dalradian terrane, there is geologic evidence that depth increases, as well as temperature, along present surface gradients normal to isograds. The observed isograd pattern is in every way compatible with that inferred from Fig. 8-8*b*. In fact, the distribution of isobars and isotherms shown on that diagram, simplified and hypothethical though it may be, supports the concept of regional metamorphism induced by temperature gradients controlled by a vertical zone of exceptional heat flow, probably extending to the mantle itself.

Isograd Patterns Unrelated to Granitic Plutons

Metamorphism possibly controlled by depth. There is a completely different but nevertheless rather general pattern characterized by very extensive development of low-grade rocks in areas lacking any trace of contemporaneous granites. Such are the Otago and the Alpine schists of southern New Zealand (pp. 358–361) and the Sanbagawa belt of Japan. In both regions, facies of low grade, though dominant, merge into less extensive high-grade zones (amphibolite facies), still without surface outcropping of granitic plutons. It is tempting to explain at least the lower-grade end of facies series of this kind by progressive burial down a normal *P-T* gradient. Coombs (1961, p. 214) has even gone so far as to designate low-grade changes in depth as *burial metamorphism*, as distinct from regional metamorphism with growth of schistosity in rocks of somewhat higher grade. A gradient of only 10 to 12°C/km could explain downward transition from the zeolite through the prehnite-pumpellyite-metagraywacke to the glaucophane-lawsonite-schist facies. This mode of origin is completely consistent with geologic data of some glaucophane-schist areas, among them the Coast Ranges of California. Those who are skeptical regarding the great depth (25 to 30 km) implied by pressures of the order of 8 kb (now generally recognized as appropriate for the glaucophane-lawsonite-schist facies), have invoked an increment of "tectonic overpressure" to load pressures of 5 or 6 kb developed at what they consider more likely depths (20 km or less). In the absence of reliable data regarding the fundamental strength (minimum stress necessary to initiate and maintain continuous yield—creep—over very long periods) of rocks, estimates of possible tectonic overpressure are at best a guess. It is not unlikely, however, that relatively cold rocks under high confining pressure might be able to maintain stresses of 2 or 3 kb induced by tectonic forces. Such are the limits of likely tectonic overpressure in the glaucophane-lawsonite-schist facies.

A satisfactory model of burial metamorphism must include a continuous supply of heat, sufficient to bring the lower levels of a sinking rock mass to metamorphic temperatures and to maintain the generally endothermic reactions of metamorphism. This problem has been discussed quantitatively in Fyfe, Turner, and Verhoogen (1958, p. 197) and Turner and Verhoogen (1960, pp. 667, 668). Simple calculation shows that a "normal" flow of heat from the basement is rapid enough to maintain a correspondingly "normal" gradient in a slowly sinking mass of chemically inert sediments, say, pure quartz sands. But geosynclinal prisms are composed of sediments and volcanic rocks that are far from inert. This of course is implied by the very fact of metamorphism. Most metamorphic reactions of dehydration and decarbonation are endothermic. For dehydration of brucite at $T = 400°C$ and $P_{H_2O} = 5$ kb, $\Delta H = 13$ kcal/mole $= 224$ cal/g (loss of water $= 31$ percent by weight). Progressive dehydration of slate to quartz-mica-garnet-kyanite schist (in the amphibolite facies), with concomitant loss of 5 or 6 percent combined water, by analogy with the above would require as much as 30 to 40 cal/g. So it has been argued that metamorphic temperatures in the lower levels of a subsiding geosynclinal prism must be consistently lower than normal. This condition is compatible with development of the glaucophane-lawsonite-schist facies in depth (cf. Fig. 8-4, curve 1b). But temperatures corresponding to the amphibolite and granulite facies could not be maintained at levels above 50 to 80 km by burial alone.

These difficulties notwithstanding, the writer still turns to a model of burial to explain the existence of highly deformed chlorite-zone schists over great areas in the eastern Otago schist belt of New Zealand, the Brisbane schist terrane of eastern Australia, and the pre-Andean basement of southern Chile. The uniform grade of metamorphism in such regions implies temperature variations that can scarcely exceed 50°C over areas of thousands of square kilometers. This surely suggests a pattern of isogradic surfaces approximately parallel to the present land surface. The gradient drawn for the schists of eastern Otago (Fig. 8-4, curve 2) places the maximum limit of depth for the biotite isograd at about 25 to 30 km ($P = 7$ to 8 kb). The corresponding gradient, about 15°C/km, is close to the upper limits of what are generally considered "normal" geothermal gradients. It may therefore be necessary to assume an abnormally high rate of heat flow from the underlying basement to provide the heat of metamorphic reaction.

This last obstacle, however, is not so serious as it might seem from the argument advanced above. Pelitic and carbonate-bearing sediments are not the main ingredients of geosynclinal fillings. In some geosynclines (e.g., in the Andes) the rocks are dominantly volcanic, and the initial reactions of metamorphism involve hydration and are exothermic. Once temperatures high enough to activate reaction have been reached by burial, metamorphism to assemblages of the greenschist facies should be self-perpetuating. The parent sediments of the Otago schists are graywackes

composed largely of anhydrous minerals; some are rich in volcanic fragments; argillaceous rocks are insignificant. A series of many analyses of
such rocks from the northern end of the Alpine schist belt (Reed, 1958,
table 11) shows a mean loss of only 0.6 percent water (by weight) in
passage from incipiently metamorphosed rocks of the Chl. 1 zone to the
fully developed muscovite-chlorite assemblages of Chl. 4. The corresponding
value of ΔH, the heat necessary for metamorphism, is only about 4 cal/g.
Such relatively small quantities of heat could even be supplied by the work
done on the rock system as a whole, one expression of which is universal
evidence of intense penetrative deformation.

Perhaps significant in this connection is a belt of greenschist, some
500 to 1000 m in width, bordered on both sides by graywackes and semischists in the vicinity of Mt. Cook (Alpine schist belt of New Zealand).
The metamorphic mineral assemblages in all these rocks, whatever their
stage of textural development, are those of the greenschist facies (chlorite
zone). According to Lillie and Gunn (1964), the completely reconstituted
rocks (greenschists) are localized in a zone of intense deformation. They
state (Lillie and Gunn, 1964, p. 421) that

> the concentration of schists within these belts of especially complex
> structure suggest that the schistosity and the accompanying distinct
> metamorphism result from the *movement* of the rocks.

Pertinent to the present problem is that the schistose rocks are largely
true greenschists, derived in all probability from rocks rich in basic volcanic
material. It is in just such material that reactions of metamorphism, once
set in motion, will be exothermic and self-perpetuating.

Somewhat different, perhaps, is the situation regarding the Sanbagawa
schists of Japan. There is no obvious relation here between metamorphism
and granite intrusion. Banno (1964, p. 307) attributes the P-T environment
of metamorphism to deep burial; in support of this he cites a tendency for
the isogradic surfaces, especially as revealed in three dimensions by deep
drilling, to lie subparallel to the main stratigraphic horizons (Banno, 1964,
p. 291). But, in places at least, both surfaces dip steeply at angles between
60 and 90°. Moreover, both bedding and isogradic surfaces are "overturned"; i.e., lower-grade horizons dip beneath horizons of higher grade.
Banno apparently attributes this situation, as shown in the vicinity of the
Bessi mine (Fig. 1-17), to postmetamorphic dislocation. An alternative
possibility is that posttectonic metamorphism of the overturned beds was
imprinted under the influence of horizontal heat flow from a lateral source
in the direction of the Median Line, some 5 km distant.

Metamorphism not obviously related to depth. The model of metamorphism controlled by depth, as proposed above for the east Otago schist

belt, cannot easily be applied to their northwestward extension in the Alpine schist zone. Here the isogradic surfaces probably dip steeply. The metamorphic grade rises westward across an outcrop width of 15 to 20 km, along a continuous belt nearly 200 km long. On the west the schist zone terminates abruptly, at maximum metamorphic grade (oligoclase-almandine zone), against the Alpine Fault. This is an immense transcurrent dislocation, on which postmetamorphic right-lateral displacement may have been 200 km. Isograds in the metamorphic zone to the east trend roughly parallel to the Fault. It seems not unreasonable to postulate a heat source for Cretaceous metamorphism in the Alpine schist zone, coinciding with the present site of the Alpine Fault. K/A dates determined on high-grade metamorphic biotites are anomalously low: around 10 million years. And this is a region where Oligocene sediments locally overlie the schist basement. The inference is that this was a region of excessive heat flow even in late Tertiary times. Today a line projecting the trend of the Fault 300 km northeast coincides with the axis of the geothermal and active volcanic belt of the North Island of New Zealand (Fig. 8-7).

This is a speculative note on which to conclude a discussion of heat sources in regional metamorphism. This writer is not prepared to extend his suggestion to cover other regions with which he is not personally familiar. It is perhaps permissible to note that the grade of metamorphism in the Sanbagawa belt of Japan rises toward another major linear crustal structure, the Median Line. More significant is the fact that there are some patterns of regional metamorphism that cannot readily be related either to centers of granite plutonism or the P-T gradients controlled by depth alone.

POSTSCRIPT

Study of mineralogical aspects of regional metamorphism in the field and in the laboratory, augmented by experimental data relating to chemical and physical behavior of minerals and mineral aggregates at high pressure and temperature, has progressed to a point that to some will appear not unsatisfactory. Sufficiently well known are the general nature, composition, and variety of common types of metamorphic rocks. Those who wish to may classify them, even with some confidence that their classifications have genetic implications and thereby are invested with an aura of "goodness." The gross compositions of most metamorphic mineral phases have also become well known; detailed variations are currently being explored by modern laboratory techniques. The facies concept has been developed to a point where it is likely to be modified only in detail; and recognition of facies series inevitably has led to the conclusion that every natural series, however it may resemble others in some respects, has its own unique character. It is now even possible to construct, within reasonable limits, the P-T regimes of metamorphism for particular regions, their relation to episodes of deformation, and their great duration in time.

Most significant, perhaps, are the major, still-unanswered, questions that have emerged with ever-increasing clarity from the cumulative data of metamorphic petrology. The closing remarks of a previous book (Turner and Verhoogen, 1960, pp. 671, 672) are still appropriate. We see even more clearly than ever the necessity to invoke concentration of heat in the deep crust and the underlying mantle from sources and by means unknown. "The fundamental driving force behind all kinds of regional metamorphism, as well as the related processes of orogeny, igneous intrusion, and volcanism, must itself depend upon temperature gradients—horizontally, vertically and in time—within the mantle and the immediately overlying portions of the earth's crust." To pursue the matter further is the problem of the geophysicist; but it is the petrologist who has posed the question and who has supplied quantitative geologic and mineralogical data that must contribute significantly to any ultimate solution. The present writer, late in his day as a geologist, may perhaps be excused for repeating to geophysicists the words attributed to one of the most eminent of their number late in a day of prolonged discussion with engineers: "A good problem; a difficult problem; I'm glad it's your problem."

REFERENCES

Aronson, J. L.: Reconnaissance rubidium-strontrum geochronology of New Zealand plutonic and metamorphic rocks, *New Zealand J. Geol. Geophys.*, vol. 8, pp. 401–423, 1965.

Banno, S.: Petrologic studies on the Sanbagawa crystalline schists in the Bessi-Ino district, central Sikoku, Japan, *Univ. Tokyo Fac. Sci. J.*, Sec. 2, vol. 15, pp. 203–319, 1964.

Barrell, J.: Relations of subjacent igneous invasion to regional metamorphism, *Am. J. Sci.*, vol. 1, pp. 1–19, 174–186, 245–267, 1921.

Bearth, P.: Versuch einer Gliederung alpinmetamorpher Serien der Westalpen, *Schweiz. Mineral. Petrog. Mitt.*, vol. 42, pp. 127–137, 1962.

————: Zur mineralfaziellen Stellung der Glaucophangesteine der Westalpen, *Schweiz. Mineral. Petrog. Mitt.*, vol. 46, pp. 13–24, 1966.

Billings, M.P.: Regional metamorphism in the Littleton-Moosilauke area, New Hampshire, *Bull. Geol. Soc. Am.*, vol. 48, pp. 463–566, 1937.

Binns, R. A.: Zones of progressive regional metamorphism in the Willyama complex, Broken Hill district, New South Wales, *J. Geol. Soc. Australia*, vol. 11, pp. 283–330, 1964.

Bowen, N. L.: The Evolution of the Igneous Rocks, Princeton, Princeton, N.J., 1928.

Brown, P. E.: Major element composition of the Loch Coire migmatite complex, Sutherland Scotland, *Contrib. Mineral. Petrol.*, vol. 14, pp. 1–26, 1967.

————, J. A. Miller, N. J. Soper, and D. York: Potassium-argon age pattern of the British Caledonides, *Proc. Yorkshire Geol. Soc.*, vol. 35, pp. 103–138, 1965.

Buddington, A. F.: Isograds and the role of H_2O in metamorphic facies of orthogneisses of the northwest Adirondack area, New York, *Bull. Geol. Soc. Am.*, vol. 74, pp. 1155–1182, 1963.

————, and D. H. Lindsley: Iron-titanium oxide minerals and synthetic equivalents, *J. Petrol.*, vol. 5, pp. 310–357, 1964.

Chinner, G. A.: The distribution of temperature and pressure during Dalradian metamorphism, *Geol. Soc. London Quart. J.*, vol. 486, pp. 159–186, 1966.

Coombs, D. S.: Some recent work on the lower grades of metamorphism, *Australian J. Sci.*, vol. 24, pp. 203–215, 1961.

Engel, A. E. J., and C. E. Engel: Progressive metamorphism of amphibolite, northwest Adirondack mountains, New York, *Bull. Geol. Soc. Am.*, A. F. Buddington vol., pp. 37–82, 1962.

————, and ————: Metasomatic origin of large parts of the Adirondack phacoliths, *Bull. Geol. Soc. Am.*, vol. 74, pp. 349–354, 1963.

Fyfe, W. S., F. J. Turner, and J. Verhoogen: Metamorphic reactions and metamorphic facies, *Geol. Soc. Am. Mem. 73*, 1958.

Ghent, E. D.: Glaucophane-schist facies metamorphism in the Black Butte area, California, *Am. J. Sci.*, vol. 263, pp. 385–400, 1965.

Grindley, G. W.: Structure of the Alpine schists of south Westland, Southern Alps, New Zealand, *New Zealand J. Geol. Geophys.*, vol. 6, pp. 872–930, 1963.

Harper, C. T.: Potassium-argon ages of slates and their geological significance, *Nature*, vol. 203, pp. 468–470, 1964.

Heald, M. T.: Structure and petrology of the Lovell Mountain quadrangle, New Hampshire, *Bull. Geol. Soc. Am.*, vol. 61, pp. 43–89, 1950.

Hietanen, A.: On the facies series in various types of metamorphism, *J. Geol.*, vol. 75, pp. 187–214, 1967.

Johnson, M. R. W.: Some time relations of movement and metamorphism in the Scottish Highlands, *Geol. Mijnbouw*, vol. 42, pp. 121–142, 1963.

Knopf, E. B.: Retrogressive metamorphism and phyllonitization, *Am. J. Sci.*, vol. 21, pp. 1–27, 1931.

Lillie, A. R., and B. M. Gunn: Steeply plunging folds in the Sealy Range, Southern Alps, *New Zealand J. Geol. Geophys.*, vol. 7, pp. 403–423, 1964.

Lyons, J. B.: Geology of the Hanover quadrangle, New Hampshire-Vermont, *Bull. Geol. Soc. Am.*, vol. 66, pp. 105–146, 1955.

McNamara, M. J.: The lower greenschist facies in the Scottish Highlands, *Geol. Foren. Stockholm Forh.*, vol. 87, pp. 347–389, 1965.

Mehnert, K. R.: Neue Ergebnisse zur Geochemie der Metamorphose, *Geol. Rundschau*, vol. 51, pp. 384–394, 1961.

————: Petrographie und Abfolge der Granitisation um Schwarzwald, IV. *Neues Jahrb. Mineral. Abhandl.*, vol. 99, pp. 161–199, 1963.

————, and A. Willgallis: Zum Alkalihaushalt der Granitisation un Schwarzwald, *Neues Jahrb. Mineral. Abhandl.*, vol. 91, pp. 104–130, 1957.

Misch, P.: Metasomatic granitization of batholithic dimensions, pt. 1, *Am. J. Sci.*, vol. 247, pp. 209–245, 1949.

————: Stable association wollastonite-anorthite and other calc-silicate assemblages in amphibolite facies crystalline schists of Nanga Parbat, northwest Himalayas, *Beitr. Mineral. Petrog.*, vol. 10, pp. 315-356, 1964.

Miyashiro, A.: Evolution of metamorphic belts, *J. Petrol.*, vol. 2, pp. 277–311, 1962.

Mutch, A. R.: Facies and thickness of the upper Paleozoic and Triassic sediments of Southland, *Trans. Roy. Soc. New Zealand*, vol. 84, pp. 499–511, 1957.

Newton, R. C.: Kyanite-andalusite equilibrium at $700°$–$800°C$, *Science*, vol. 153, pp. 170–172, 1966.

Niggli, E.: Mineral-zonen der Alpinen Metamorphose in den Schweizer Alpen. *Rept. Intern. Geol. Congr. 21st Session, Norden*, vol. 13, pp. 132–138, 1960.

Ramsay, J. G.: "Folding and Fracturing of Rocks," McGraw-Hill, New York, 1967.

Read, H. H.: "The Granite Controversy," Interscience, New York, 1957.

Reed, J. J.: Regional metamorphism in southeast Nelson, *New Zealand Geol. Surv. Bull.*, no. 60, 1958.

Roy, A. B.: Interrelation of metamorphism and deformation in central Singhbhum, eastern India, *Geol. Mijnbouw*, vol. 45, pp. 365–374, 1966.

Sander, B.: "Einführung in die Gefügekunde der Geologischen Körper," Springer, Vienna. Part 1, 1948; Part II, 1950.

Trommsdorff, V.: Progressive Metamorphose kieseliger Karbonategestenie in den Zentralalpen, *Schweiz. Mineral. Petrog. Mitt.*, vol. 46, pp. 431–460, 1966.

Turner, F. J., and J. Verhoogen: "Igneous and Metamorphic Petrology," McGraw-Hill, New York, 1960.

————, and L. E. Weiss: "Structural Analysis of Metamorphic Tectonites," McGraw-Hill, New York, 1963.

Wenk, E.: Plagioklas als Indexmineral in den Zentralalpen, *Schweiz. Mineral. Petrog. Mitt.*, vol. 42, pp. 139–152, 1962.

White, W. S., and M. P. Billings: Geology of the Woodsville Quadrangle, Vermont-New Hampshire, *Bull. Geol. Soc. Am.*, vol. 62, pp. 647–696, 1951.

Winkler, H. G. F.: "Petrogenesis of Metamorphic Rocks," Springer, New York, 1965.

————: "Die Genese der Metamorphen Gesteine," 2d ed., Springer, Berlin, 1967.

————, and H. von Platten: Experimentelle Gesteinsmetamorphose—V, *Geochim. Cosmochim. Acta*, vol. 24, pp. 250–259, 1960.

Yoder, H. S.: The MgO-Al_2O_3-SiO_2-H_2O system and the related metamorphic facies, *Am. J. Sci.*, Bowen vol., pp. 569–627, 1952.

Zwart, H. J.: Some examples of the relations between deformation and metamorphism from the central Pyrenees, *Geol. Mijnbouw*, vol. 42, pp. 143–154, 1963.

AUTHOR INDEX

SUBJECT INDEX